THE ELEMENTS OF STATISTICS

PRENTICE-HALL MATHEMATICS SERIES

Albert A. Bennett, Editor

THE ELEMENTS

OF

STATISTICS

BY

ELMER B. MODE

Professor of Mathematics
Boston University

New York
PRENTICE-HALL, INC.

First Printing.............................July 1941
Second Printing ....April 1942
Third Printing ....October 1945
Fourth Printing..........................July 1946
Fifth Printing ....July 1947
Sixth Printing........................August 1948
Seventh Printing.....................September 1948
Eighth Printing ....April 1949

"The time has come," the Walrus said,
  "To talk of many things:
Of shoes—and ships—and sealing-wax—
  Of cabbages—and kings—"

PREFACE

It has been said that the peculiar characteristic which sets man apart from the other animals is his capacity for capitalizing the achievements of his ancestors. Surely statistics offers a striking example of man's attempt to employ the records of the past in solving the problems of the present and in plotting the course of the future.

Much of the field of elementary or descriptive statistics has been pretty well organized, so that the general route of progress for the beginner can be mapped out with little difficulty. Yet this route, plainly marked as it is, may be traversed with such facile mathematical skill—and nothing else—as to cause the novice to lose some of the most valuable lessons in simple critical analysis which statistics can teach. There is a peculiar logic associated with the study of statistics. Some call it common sense; others prefer a more exact characterization. In any case, it is difficult to dissociate the purely mathematical aspects from those which are not exactly mathematical but which do require a good brand of clear thinking. It is hoped that this book, dealing as it does with the elementary phases of statistics, will develop on the part of the reader an appropriate attitude of critical reasonableness toward the subject. There is no reason why sound mathematical conclusions should not be accompanied by a healthy appreciation of what such conclusions do *not* assert.

A large amount of important work can be done without extensive preparation in mathematics. Most persons who study elementary statistics are motivated by the fact that it has a direct bearing on a related field of interest: business, economics, sociology, biology, psychology, education, and others. They want to acquire "sufficient statistical terminology and technique" to enable them to read intelligently and somewhat critically the statistical content of the literature in these fields. If called upon to perform a simple statistical analysis, they wish to be able to handle the fundamental procedures.

The present book favors no particular field of interest. The subjects enumerated above are well represented. There is an unusual abundance and a wide variety of exercises, *none* of which have been borrowed from other textbooks. They have been carefully selected and devised with a view to their practicality as well as their adaptability to general assignments.

Practical computation forms an essential part of statistical work, and should not be ignored. After considerable experience with its problems, the author has found that three or four class hours spent with the simpler rules of approximate computation and the required use of the slide rule (and, where possible, the computing machine) lead to much saving of time later on and to a grateful appreciation on the part of the student. An intelligent appraisal of limits of accuracy, accompanied by the elimination of useless calculations, is a legitimate and an important aim in the teaching of statistics.

The arrangement of material allows much flexibility in the choice of topics. Many sections and some chapters may be eliminated, if so desired, without affecting the continuity of the book. These are marked with an asterisk (*) in the Table of Contents. Proofs are generally included, but may be omitted if the occasion warrants. In particular, the writer has aimed to describe the full purport of each distinctive mathematical concept.

Other features which seem worthy of special mention are the use of graph paper of various sorts (for example, logarithmic and probability papers), the early introduction of the notion of probability, brief discussions of limitations in procedures and results, the recurrent use of graphical methods, and the later chapters leading to an introduction to sampling theory.

The method of numbering sections, pages, tables, figures, and exercises should stimulate the use of cross references. A list of references appropriate to an introductory study of this kind will be found at the end of the book. This list also contains the names of some sources for standard statistical supplies.

The Mathematical Tables which appear as a supplement on the inside back cover should prove convenient and adequate. It is hoped that their uniform arrangement will aid in removing that prejudicial state of mind which many students have toward inverse interpolation.

It has seemed wise to place answers to many of the exercises in a separate pamphlet, a copy of which is available, to teachers, from the publishers.

The author is indebted to Professor R. A. Fisher and to Messrs. Oliver & Boyd, of Edinburgh, for permission to reprint Table III from their book *Statistical Methods for Research Workers*, 7th Edition (1938).

The author's thanks are due to his kind colleague, Professor Albert Morris, for helpful comments made after reading the manuscript, and especially to Professor Albert A. Bennett, whose constructive criticisms and invaluable suggestions have added greatly to the interest of the book. For any errors which may have crept into the text, the author assumes full responsibility.

ELMER B. MODE

CONTENTS

❖❖〕|||||||||||❑|||||||||||❑|||||||||||❑|||||||||||❑|||||||||||❑|||||||||||❑|||||||||||❑|||||||||||❑|||||||||||❑|||||||||||❑|||||||||||❑|||||||||||❑❖❖

CONTENTS

THE ELEMENTS OF STATISTICS

CHAPTER

I

INTRODUCTION

❖⫿▬▬▬⫿▬▬▬⫿▬▬▬⫿▬▬▬⫿▬▬▬⫿▬▬▬⫿▬▬▬⫿▬▬▬⫿▬▬▬⫿▬▬▬⫿▬▬▬❖

"In 1786, I found that in Germany they were engaged in a species
of political inquiry, to which they had given the name of Statistics
. . . an inquiry for the purpose of ascertaining the political strength
of a country, or questions respecting matters of state."

SIR JOHN SINCLAIR, *The Statistical Account
of Scotland*, Vol. 21 (1791–1799).

1. The origin of statistics. It is curious that the modern
science of statistics traces its origin to two quite dissimilar
human interests, political states and games of chance. In
the mid-seventeenth century, the gambler Chevalier de
Méré proposed to Blaise Pascal the famous "Problem of the
Points," which may be described as follows: Two men are
playing a game of chance. The one first gaining a certain
number of points wins the stake. They are forced to quit
before the game is completed. Given the number of points
each has won, how should the stake be divided? This problem offered a real challenge to the wits of the two astute
French mathematicians, Pascal and Fermat. A lengthy cor-
respondence between the two men led to solutions, not only
of the problems proposed, but of more general ones. The
methods employed by Pascal may be said to represent the
beginnings of the mathematics of probability, about which
modern statistical theory centers today.

In the mid-eighteenth century, *statistics* itself was born as

1

a word describing the study of "the political arrangement of
the modern states of the known world." The description of
states was at first verbal, but the increasing proportion of
numerical data in the descriptions gradually gave the new
word the quantitative connotation which is associated with
it now. From the rather restricted study of data pertaining
to a state, statistics branched out into other fields of investigation.

Between 1835 and 1870, the Belgian astronomer Quetelet
was applying the theory of probability to anthropological
measurements. His conclusions may be summarized and
extended by stating that the same general laws of variation
governing gambler's luck may be discovered in the statures
of soldiers, the intelligence quotients of children, the batting
averages of baseball players, the speeds of molecules of a gas,
and innumerable other aggregates of observations. During
the last half of the nineteenth century, the power of general
methods based on probability concepts became more clearly
perceived. As a result, applications have been made to
many diverse fields of inquiry. An appreciation of the importance of the statistical method in man's attempt to come
to grips with a marvelously complex physical and social
world is a serious and legitimate aim of any educated person.

2. The meaning of statistics. The layman frequently
conceives of statistics as a mass of figures or a collection of
data such as we might find in the publications of the United
States Census Bureau, among the records of a school principal, or in the files of a large hospital. The often repeated
phrase "Statistics show ..." is likely to imply that a given
mass of figures contains salient and unalterable characteristics which can easily be discerned among the mass by any
person of normal intelligence. That the word *statistics* may
apply to certain aggregates of figures is not to be denied, but
that important facts contained therein are easily detected is
by no means always true.

A second meaning of statistics is simply the plural of
"statistic," where a "statistic" is a certain kind of measure
used to evaluate a selected property of the collection of items

under investigation. The average weight of a football squad, for example, may be found by adding the weights of the individual players and dividing by their number. The average thus obtained is a *statistic*.

A third meaning of *statistics* is of prime concern to us in this book. It is the science of assembling, analyzing, characterizing, and interpreting collections of data. In this sense, statistics is a field of study, a doctrine concerned with mathematical characterizations of aggregates of items.

3. Applications. Statistics, as a science, is fundamentally a branch of applied mathematics, just as mechanics is mathematics applied to problems connected with bodies subjected to forces. In statistics, the applications may be made to almost any aggregate of observations or measurements. For this reason it is useful in business, economics, sociology, biology, psychology, education, physics, chemistry, astronomy, and related fields.

An aggregate of individuals is called a *population*. The individual may be animate, as in the case of a living bacterium or a twelve-year-old boy; or it may be inanimate, as in the case of a molecule of hydrogen, the wage of a coal miner, or the distance of a shot from its target. Statistical items, whether they are observations, measurements, estimates, or actual living individuals, are all subject to the same method of analysis and, in many cases, to the same general laws of distribution. For this reason, the science of statistics may be studied fruitfully from a broad general standpoint, and then applications may be made to any particular field of interest. This fact will become increasingly apparent as we progress from chapter to chapter in this book.

A relatively small collection of individuals, subjected to immediate, direct measurement, is designated a *sample*. This sample may be conceived to be selected from a larger, perhaps infinite, aggregate or population. A batch of 1,000 United States Army recruits constitutes a sample of individuals imagined to be selected at random from a much larger aggregate or population, say from 1,000,000 recruits, or from an infinite number of them. The number of bacteria in a quart of stagnant water is, for all intents and purposes, practically infinite, but our analysis of a drop of water on a microscope slide may involve only a relatively small number of them.   What conclusions can we draw from a sample of individuals concerning the larger population from which the sample is drawn?   Take a specific case: If we know the distribution of shoe sizes among 1,000 army recruits, what conclusions can we safely draw concerning the distribution of shoe sizes for 1,000,000?   The answer to this question is important to the man responsible for supplying the army.   This type of problem is basic in statistics and is one to which notable contributions have been made in recent years.   Before we can answer such a question in a given case, we must subject the sample aggregate to a preliminary analysis.   This analysis is usually important in itself, aside from its possible relation to a theoretically larger population.

4.   Empirical statistics.   We may, for convenience, divide statistical analysis into two broad categories, which we shall designate as *empirical* and *theoretical*.   The former is generally moderate in difficulty; the latter demands a somewhat higher order of mathematical technique and critical judgment.

Suppose that we are confronted with a set of measurements or observations actually obtained from life.   Such a set usually represents a complex of data from which it is possible to extract an almost unlimited amount of information.   For example, the weekly wages of a group of steel workers may yield information of the following kinds: the total wage received by the group, the highest wage, the lowest wage, the most frequent wage, the range of wages, the average wage, the number of wages below $25, the number above $60, the number between $30 and $40, and so on.   The task of the statistician is to select a few procedures and measures by means of which the significant aspects of the given data may be thrown into high relief.   These aspects may be obtained by means of *classification*, *graphing*, and *averaging*.   Because we are concerned only with an effective characterization of the given data themselves as they come to us through observation, and not with any estimates or conclusions involving theoretically related populations, we shall distinguish this type of statistical analysis by means of the word *empirical*. This analysis, confined exclusively to the experimental data before us, deals with methods of recording or tabulating the constituent items, with their visual presentation, with the properties of various kinds of measures, with devices for computing them, and, in fact, with all means of giving a summary description of the data themselves.

5. Theoretical statistics. The second type of statistical investigation relates the given data to a hypothetical population from which the data are assumed to have been selected in a random manner. We may seek information about the given items in the light of the properties of the population as a whole, or we may seek to derive the properties of the population from the limited information contained within the sample. It is clear that in any case we must make certain assumptions and interpret our results in the light of them. Theoretical analysis of this type is based upon the mathematical theory of probability. It has important applications, for instance, in industry, medicine, and the social sciences.

6. Some nonmathematical aspects. Although statistics is fundamentally a mathematical study, there are certain phases of it which may be termed nonmathematical, and which are, in many respects, prerequisite to successful statistical analysis. It is useless to perform elaborate calculations and to derive conclusions from data of questioned reliability and ambiguous meaning.

(i) *Sources.* Data may arise from books, reports, tables, and so forth, or from the results of original investigation, such as interviews, questionnaires, direct observations, actual measurements, and the like. How accurate are the printed sources, and do they measure the precise thing we seek? Did the author collect his data with evident bias? Were the records transcribed accurately? Were the interviews and questionnaires designed to elicit unbiased replies? Were the observations made on an unrepresentative sample?

A check of samples by census tracts in a study of the size of families

in a certain area revealed that the samples had indicated larger house-
holds than were actually true of the district. . . . It was then discovered that the enumerators failed to revisit all the families not at
home when they called. Obviously the larger the family, the
greater the likelihood of someone being home when the enumerator
called.[1]

(ii) *Definitions.* The nature of the attributes studied in
a statistical investigation may profoundly influence the magnitudes involved and the conclusions drawn; for this reason
it is essential that basic terms be clearly understood. It is
often necessary to make precise definitions, or to describe in
detail the method of measurement. If we have records of
human head lengths, we may wish to know the exact points
on the head between which the length is taken and the kind
of instrument used for measurement. If we are conducting a
housing survey and wish accurate information on the number of rooms per dwelling, how shall we define a room? Does
the term *room* include Mrs. Gotrox's spacious reception hall,
Professor Wise's closet study, Mrs. Smith's unfinished attic,
or Mr. Lowe's basement workshop? Much controversy may
arise from questions of definition and interpretation.

(iii) *Purposes.* The nature and extent of a statistical
study are determined largely by the purpose in view. Frequently, the objective is a single concise result displayed in a
manner readily understood by "the man on the street." In
such cases, finely drawn distinctions, precise mathematical
results, and distracting details may be sacrificed to a simple,
graphic representation which catches the eye and impresses
the mind. Other investigations may aim to establish a
thesis—or to destroy one—by means of a comprehensive
analysis of all relevant factors. Such studies often require
elaborate technical equipment on the part of the reader as
well as the writer.

7. Misuses of statistics. Statistics, properly taught,
should train the student to read with some degree of dis-
crimination various books and articles containing the results

---

[1] Jerome B. Cohen, "The Misuse of Statistics," *Journal of the American Statistical Association*, December, 1938. See also Clyde V. Kiser, "Pitfalls in Sampling
for Population Study," in the same *Journal*, Vol. XXIX, page 251.

of statistical inquiry.   A person of average intelligence may, with moderate instruction, be made aware, at least, of the abuses of the statistical method and of the pitfalls into which impressive figures may lead the layman.   Before any systematic discussion of methodology is even begun, it is possible to detect certain types of misleading statements and erroneous conclusions which only too frequently emanate from books, newspapers and periodicals, the platform, and the radio.   Let us give a few samples of them; they may help us to detect more subtle errors later.

A New York newspaper in an optimistic editorial "cited statistics on retail sales to prove that conditions were really better than people imagined.   Figures showed retail sales in April of 1938 to be higher than sales in April, 1937.   The editorial neglected to mention, however, that the Easter holiday in 1937 fell at the end of March and that Easter shopping was therefore concentrated in the middle two weeks of March, whereas in 1938 Easter occurred in the middle of April, resulting, therefore, in a concentration of Easter shopping in the first two weeks in April."[2]

An unpublished report recently sent to the author attempts to prove that the physical condition of the American people is deteriorating.   Among the surprising statements made is the following: "In 1900 there was one hospital bed for 240 persons in our country.   Today the ratio is better than 1 to 120.   Illness is increasing steadily."   Obviously, the increase in the number of beds is due to the growing realization on the part of the public of the advantages of expert hospital care and to the enlarged demand for such care.   We might add that there is a greater social consciousness of the necessity to provide adequate facilities for our sick and a resulting increase in public and private expenditures for that purpose.   The statistics cited hardly reflect the physical condition of the American people.

The air battle of Britain in 1940 was accompanied by a discussion of the method of comparing British and German airplane losses.   It was claimed that the majority of German

---

[2] See the first reference in footnote 1.

losses were bombers—larger, more expensive machines than fighting planes—that were manned by crews of three or four, whereas the British losses involved fighting planes largely, less expensive to build, and handled by a crew of one. The sheer comparison of numbers of planes lost on each side obviously concealed a substantial amount of significant information.

The frequent misuse of statistics will be further illustrated in the exercises at the end of this chapter.

8. Bibliography. In a book employing a minimum amount of mathematical equipment, it is obviously impossible to establish rigorously, or even informally, some of the theorems and formulas which are needed. Neither is it feasible to include much interesting and important material concerned with topics of current importance or of special interest in a restricted field. It is hoped that the list of references compiled at the end of this book will prove helpful. These will be referred to by number throughout the book. Other references to special topics will appear occasionally in the text itself.

I—Exercises

What is misleading or fallacious in the statements 1–10? Many have been taken from published reports.

1. In this city 1,463 men and 228 women drivers were in motor car accidents during 1937. Women are obviously safer drivers than men. *more men than women drive*

2. There is no excuse for the United States' going to war with a country like Japan, 10,000 miles away. *Japan attacked us*

3. A school principal told a certain teacher that her class was below the average for the school. He said that he wanted no classes below the average.

4. In 1932 more than 7,000,000 persons were admitted to hospitals in the United States. In ten years the total would equal half the population. *now!!*

5. Under treatment A, 15 out of 20 patients recovered; under treatment B, only 12 out of 20 recovered. Treatment A is thus shown to be superior to B.

6. (For Democrats only) During the 1936 presidential campaign, the Republican National Committee circulated the information that food costs had jumped 40 per cent in the three years since 1933.[3] *Value of Dollar deflated*

7. (For Republicans only) During the 1936 presidential campaign, the New Deal orators pointed to economic progress under President Roosevelt by comparing 1936 figures with those of early 1933.[4] *Depression in 1933*

8. By winning six games out of eight, Mr. and Mrs. Jones clearly demonstrated their superiority as bridge players over Mr. and Mrs. Brown. *Luck of the cards*

9. The climate of Toonerville is particularly agreeable, for the average year-round temperature is 70° F.

10. The town of Wellville publishes annually the median bacteria count of the milk sold by dairies within the town. The published count for Dairy *A* was 2,000, for Dairy *B*, 4,000. Dairy *A* tells its prospective customers that its milk is twice as pure as that of its competitor, Dairy *B*.

*   *   *

11. The United States Bureau of the Census lists six classes of unemployed persons. One class consists of those out of work, able to work, and looking for work. Suggest at least three additional classes of unemployed persons.

12. For purposes of census enumeration in the United States, a "farm," in terms of area, has been defined as three or more acres of land upon which agricultural operations are conducted under one management. Places of less than three acres have also been accepted if they had $250 worth of products. Criticize this definition.

---

[3] See the first reference in footnote 1.
[4] See the first reference in footnote 1.

CHAPTER

II

COMPUTATION

❖⊐||||||||||⊏⊐||||||||||⊏⊐||||||||||⊏⊐||||||||||⊏⊐||||||||||⊏⊐||||||||||⊏⊐||||||||||⊏⊐||||||||||⊏⊐||||||||||⊏⊐||||||||||⊏⊐||||||||||❖

> "Seeing there is nothing (right well beloved students in the Mathe-
> matickes) that is so troublesome to Mathematicall practice, nor that
> doth more molest and hinder Calculators than the Multiplications,
> Divisions, square and cubical Extractions of great numbers, which,
> besides the tedious expense of time, are for the most part subject to
> many slippery errors . . . and having thought upon many things to
> this purpose, I found at length some excellent briefe rules."
>
> JOHN NAPIER, *Mirifici Logarithmorum*
> *Canonis Descriptio* (1614).

1. Introduction. A story has been told of a certain popular lecture on geology. At its close, the speaker addressed
the following question to his audience: "And now, my friends,
how old do you think this good earth of ours is?" A youth
in the audience promptly arose and answered, "Two billion
and four years." "Why do you say two billion and four
years?" asked the lecturer. The youth promptly replied,
"Because I heard you give this lecture four years ago."

This little tale may well illustrate the damage to common
sense which an exaggerated desire for mathematical exacti-
tude may cause. Statistics, perhaps more than any other
branch of applied mathematics, demands not only arithmetical precision but also a liberal admixture of good judgment.

The study of statistics involves the handling of large quantities of numbers, and, in particular, it involves computation
with them. The labor need not be arduous if one makes free

use of the tables and instruments available as aids in computation, and if one develops an appreciation of the limits of accuracy of the measurements involved. Without going into the theory justifying many rules of computation, it will be the purpose of this chapter to discuss briefly important procedures useful in the computational work of statistics.

2. Exact numbers. It is necessary to distinguish between two sources of numbers, those which are directly or indirectly the result of counting, and those which are directly or indirectly the result of measuring, estimating, and so forth. If we count carefully the number of pupils in a classroom or the number of dollars in a purse, we are able to obtain precise answers, such as 46 students or $7.68. No fractions of pupils or of cents are possible. If, for some generous reason, we wish to give $7.68 to each of 46 students, we are able to compute the exact number of dollars and cents required. $46 \times 7.68 = 353.28$, and the exact amount is $353.28. In dealing with numbers such as those described, errors can be avoided by the exercise of ordinary care. Numbers which belong to the type described will hereafter be called *exact numbers*.

3. Approximate numbers. Suppose that a surveyor measures the length of a line with a steel tape and records his

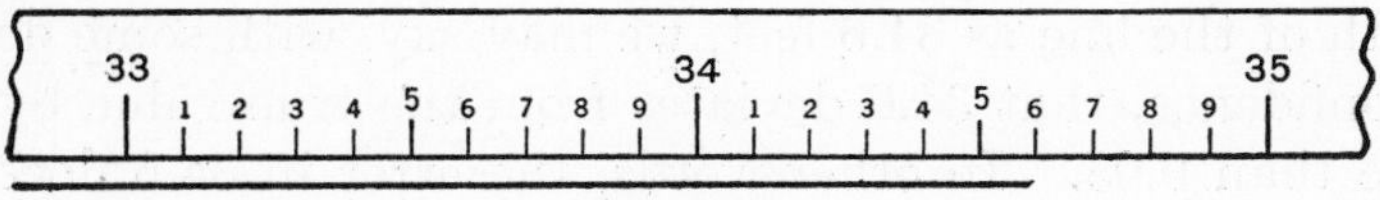

FIG. II-1

result as 34.6 feet. This implies, ordinarily, that the true length of the line is between 34.55 and 34.65 feet. Assuming accuracy of the tape and of the work of the surveyor, we can say that, if the line were really a little shorter than 34.55 feet, its length would have been recorded as 34.5 feet; and, if the line were actually somewhat longer than 34.65 feet, its length would have been recorded as 34.7 feet. The measurement 34.6 feet is approximate and has a maximum possible error of ± 0.05 feet. Thus, the number (of feet) 34.6 is intrinsically of a different character from the number (of dollars) 7.68 mentioned in the preceding section. The former is only an approximate value, and may be termed a number of three *significant digits*. Each of the digits 3, 4, and 6 has significance not only by virtue of its character and position, but also by the fact that it expresses definite information about the length of the line. In particular, the last digit, 6, carries with it (in the absence of different information) the implication that the measurement was made to the nearest tenth. The number 7.68 is an absolutely correct value. It is really composed of an infinite number of significant digits and might be written as 7.68000 · · · or as 7.67999 · · · . Numbers which are only approximations will hereafter be called *approximate numbers*. They may arise in two ways: (i) as the result of observation or measurement, or (ii) as convenient estimates for numbers which are theoretically exact. Numbers such as π, $\sqrt{2}$, and log 72,348, lead to approximate numbers of the latter kind. Thus, we say that $\pi = 3.1416$ approximately. The number 3.1416 differs from the true value by less than 0.00001. A closer approximation would be 3.14159.

The term *error* is employed in approximate computation, not in the sense of a mistake, but in the sense of a deviation from a true value. Thus, when the surveyor records the length of the line as 34.6 feet, we may say, with some degree of confidence, that 34.6 deviates from the true value by not more than 0.05. In other words, the error in 34.6 does not exceed 0.05. Again, when we write $\pi = 3.1416$, we recognize that this value differs from a more accurate value, $\pi = 3.141593$, by about 0.000007, and hence has an error of about 0.000007.

4. Significant digits. Suppose that with a certain measuring instrument we obtain the dimensions of a given rectangle. Let the length found be 41.234 inches and the width 9.432 inches. Suppose, also, that with the same apparatus we find the diameter of a certain steel wire to be 0.027 inches. The number of significant digits in the preceding numbers are 5, 4, and 2, respectively. If there is doubt concerning this statement with regard to 0.027 inches, imagine that *one thousandth of an inch* had been taken as the unit of measurement instead of *one inch*. Then the last value would have been recorded as 27 *thousandths inches*. Thus, recording in a unit 1,000 times as large does not affect the significance of the result. The zeros in 0.027 are therefore not counted as significant, for they merely aid in indicating the position of the decimal point.

On the other hand, if the weight of a truckload of stone is set down as 13,500 pounds, it is not known whether this is a number of 3, 4, or 5 significant digits. If the weighing apparatus is precise to the nearest *pound*, 13,500 possesses 5 significant digits; if, however, the apparatus weighs only to the nearest *hundredweight*, then 13,500 has but 3 significant digits. The ambiguity in the latter case may be removed by writing the weight as 135 *hundredweight*, 13,5oo *pounds*, or as 135×10^2 *pounds*. The use of powers of 10 is desirable when the magnitudes are very large or very small.

With these preliminary remarks, we are ready to give a formal definition of the phrase "number of significant digits."

DEFINITION. *The number of significant digits in a decimally expressed approximate number whose error is numerically not greater than 5 in a given decimal place, to be called the "decimal place of error," is the number of digits obtained by counting from left to right, beginning with the first non-zero digit and ending with the digit just preceding the decimal place of error.*

For example, the maximum numerical error in the diameter of the wire recorded as 0.027 is 0.0005, hence the number of digits counted from left to right beginning with 2 and ending with 7 is two. Or suppose the truckload of stone to be weighed to the nearest hundred pounds. The weight 13,500 has an error not exceeding 50 pounds. The number of (significant) digits counted from left to right, beginning with 1 and ending with 5, is three. As a further example, suppose that the length of the side of a lot of land is measured to the nearest hundredth of a foot and is found to be 106.00 feet. Since the error does not exceed 0.005 feet, the number

106.00 has five significant digits. Terminating zeros at the right of the decimal point should be written only when they are significant.

5. Pseudo zeros. In the approximate number 13,500 just considered, it is evident that the zeros are not true zeros at all, but merely marks made to aid in indicating the position of the decimal point. x's might have done as well, perhaps better, since they often stand for "unknowns." Thus, $13,5xx$ would not suggest false information, which 13,500 might. Such ambiguous zeros may be termed *pseudo zeros*.[1] As a further example, consider the statement, "He left a fortune of $2,000,000." Probably all six zeros are pseudo zeros; the number 2,000,000 represents, apparently, a rough estimate. It is probably a number of one significant digit.

6. Precision, accuracy, and error. In the interest of good usage, we should differentiate, at this point, between *precision* and *accuracy*. *Precision* is a concept appropriate to addition and subtraction. We speak of numbers as being precise to a given unit (for example, thousandths of an inch, hundredweight, tenths of a second, and dollars), which, in many cases, means precise to a given decimal place. We add or subtract numbers which are precise to the same unit; hence in the addition or subtraction of decimally expressed numbers, we add only numbers of equal precision, that is, numbers expressed to the same decimal place. This will be illustrated in the next section.

Accuracy is a concept suited to multiplication and division, for it is intimately connected with the notion of relative error. The *relative error* is defined as the error divided by the true value. When the true value is unknown, a sufficiently good approximation to the relative error may usually be obtained by dividing the error by the approximate value. Since the relative error is a quotient, its magnitude will depend mainly upon the number of significant digits in the divisor, and for this reason the notion of the accuracy of a number is connected, not only with its relative error, but

---

[1] Luise Lange, "Zeros and Pseudo Zeros," *American Mathematical Monthly*, February, 1928.

also with the number of its significant digits. Thus, we speak of a number as being accurate to five significant digits, to three parts in one thousand, to within four per cent, and so on. For example, the number 41.234 is precise to three decimal places and accurate to five significant digits.

7. The addition and subtraction of approximate numbers. In adding the following approximate numbers:

$$13.456$$
$$9.30$$
$$8.423$$
$$913.2$$
$$8.21$$

it would be incorrect to add them as they now stand and to write 952.589 as the sum, for such an addition means that the blank spaces in the columns added have been replaced by zeros when they are actually x's, or unknowns:

$$13.456$$
$$9.30x$$
$$8.423$$
$$913.2xx$$
$$\underline{8.21x}$$
$$952.589$$

Clearly, the sum of a column of digits containing x's is inaccurate. At this point, the discussion in the first paragraph of the previous section becomes useful, and we may state at once the following rule:

The sum or the remainder obtained from the addition or the subtraction of approximate numbers should have no greater precision than that of the least precise number involved in these operations.

For example, to find the sum of the numbers above, we "round off" each number to the tenths decimal place, since the least precise number is the fourth one, 913.2. Thus, we have the following results.

$$13.5$$
$$9.3$$
$$8.4$$
$$913.2$$
$$8.2$$
$$952.6$$

Hence, we may write:

Formal answer: 952.6.

Reliable answer: 953.

The possibility of the accumulation of errors due to the "rounding off" process makes the digit in the tenths place of the answer unreliable. In particular, the sum obtained from a long column of numbers may be erroneous in the last two digits of the formal answer for the same reason. (See Exercise 30.) Some mathematicians prefer to save all digits in the formal answer despite the fact that they are "semi-reliable."

In "rounding off" a number to a specified decimal place, it is standard practice to round off to the nearest number. Thus, 3.147 rounded off to the second decimal place becomes 3.15. The number 7,184,730 rounded off to the nearest ten thousand becomes 7,180,000, or better, 718×10^4. If there are two "nearest" numbers, a good rule is to select the even one. Thus, 0.0345 rounds off to 0.034, and 8.150 rounds off to 8.2.

Subtraction, in these respects, is similar to addition. It should also be noted that the remainder may have fewer significant figures than either the minuend or the subtrahend. Thus,

$$61.4383 - 61.422 = 0.016.$$

In statistics, we are frequently required to add long columns of approximate numbers and to perform simple subtractions. The observance of the simple rules just illustrated and those which are to follow will save much time and effort.

When the arithmetic mean of a small number of items (say, less than 30) is computed, the number of significant figures to be saved is ordinarily the same as that in most of the individual items.   Thus, we write the mean of 11.2, 12.4, 9.5, and 10.4 as:

$$\frac{11.2 + 12.4 + 9.5 + 10.4}{4} = 10.9.$$

When the number of items is large, the precision of the mean may exceed somewhat the common precision of the separate items.   In fact, the arithmetic mean of N items of common accuracy can be shown to be roughly $\sqrt{N}$ times as accurate as the items themselves.

8.   The multiplication and division of approximate numbers.   Consider the ordinary method of multiplying the two approximate numbers 41.234 and 9.43 as illustrated below.

$$
\begin{array}{r}
41.234 \\
9.43 \\
\hline
123702 \\
164936 \\
371106 \\
\hline
388.83662
\end{array}
$$

The multiplication proceeds from right to left in the multiplier, 9.43.   The multiplicand, 41.234, is multiplied by the digits 3, 4, and 9 in that order (right to left) to obtain the *partial products* 123702, 164936, and 371106, respectively. Since the factors involved are *approximate* numbers, this method can be shown to be unnecessarily long and the product, 388.83662, to be unreliable in the last five digits. Of the two factors multiplied, the *larger* relative error occurs in the multiplier, since it has the *smaller* number of significant digits, and this larger relative error dominates the relative error of the product.   On the basis of such considerations, thus briefly sketched, we state the following working rule.   This rule is susceptible to formal justification, but that will not be given here.

The product or the quotient obtained from the multiplication ★
or the division of approximate numbers should contain no more
significant digits than occur in the least accurate factor.

Thus, if the approximate numbers 41.234 and 9.43 are to be multiplied, the product should contain but three signifi-

cant digits, the number found in 9.43.   Instead of multiplying by 9.43 from "right to left," as just shown, a much more
satisfactory method is obtained by multiplying from "left to
right," with 9 as the first multiplier used, instead of 3, to
obtain the first partial product.   Since we are to save but
three significant digits in the final product, it is considered
good practice to save an extra digit, that is, four digits, in the
first partial product.   [See (a) below.]   These four digits

41.234	41.234	41.234
9.43	9.43	9.43
3711	3711	3711
	165	165
		12
(a)	(b)	(c)

will be obtained if we delete the last two digits, 34, in the
multiplicand, 41.234, before multiplying by 9.   We multiply
mentally the deleted 3 by 9 and "carry" 3 to obtain the first
partial product, 3711.   (3 is carried, since $9 \times 3 = 27$ and
27 is nearer 30 than 20.)

To obtain the next partial product, we delete the next digit,
2, in the multiplicand, and multiply by 4 to obtain the second
partial product, 165.   [See (b).]   Again we multiply (mentally) the deleted 2 by 4 and "carry" 1.   ($2 \times 4 = 8$, and 8
is nearer 10 than 0.)   The first digit obtained in each partial
product is placed in the same vertical column at the right.

Finally, we delete the 1 in the multiplicand and multiply
by 3.   There is nothing to "carry," since 3×1 is nearer 0
than 10.   We may now set down the complete operation.

$$
\begin{array}{r}
41.234 \\
9.43 \\
\hline
3711 \\
165 \\
12 \\
\hline
3888
\end{array}
$$

Answer: 389.

The sum of the partial products, if we disregard the decimal
point, is 3888, which is rounded off to 389.   Finally, the
position of the decimal point is found by estimating the gen-

eral magnitude of the product. The two factors are, roughly, 40 and 9, so that the product is of the same magnitude as 360. The final answer is, therefore, 389.

Division may be performed in a similar manner. The work of dividing 38.46 by 1,843.56 is shown below. The numbers are assumed to be approximate numbers. Since only 4 significant digits are to be saved in the final quotient, we employ only 4 in the divisor and divide first by 1844 to obtain 2 as the first significant digit on the left of the quotient. Then 4 is discarded, and 184 becomes the next divisor, and so on. The decimal point is placed by estimating the magnitude of the quotient.

$$
\begin{array}{r}
2086 \\
1844 \overline{\smash{)}3846} \\
3688 \\
\hline
158 \\
147 \\
\hline
11 \\
11 \\
\hline
0
\end{array}
$$

Answer: 0.02086.

9. Remarks concerning approximate computation. It should be observed that the general rule stated in the preceding section applies also when one of the numbers involved is exact. In fact, in any series of operations involving only multiplication and division, the number of significant digits in the least accurate factor determines the number of significant digits in the final answer.

The reader should bear in mind that the rules of Sections 7 and 8 are only *general* rules and are intended only to lead to simple workable procedures and reasonably accurate results. In other words, these rules are valid *most* of the time, and lead to no serious errors in the type of work to which we are about to apply them. For more detailed information about the limits of error or the precision of results, one must consult larger works on the subject. The subject of approximations, probable error, and the like cannot be discussed in its entirety within the limits of this book, let alone a single chapter.

10. Pencil computation. When appropriate tables and calculating instruments are not available, one must resort to pencil and paper in performing many of the computations of statistics. If, in these "pencil" computations, one follows intelligently the few simple rules of the preceding sections, a very considerable amount of labor may be saved.

11. Computing instruments. The addition of a column of figures can be quickly performed on any of the standard computing machines which are designed to be operated either manually or electrically. Such instruments may also be used for subtraction, multiplication, and division. A half hour's practice will enable one to use a standard computing machine for the more frequent operations of addition and multiplication.

For the purposes of this book, a slide rule will be the most useful single instrument. With its aid, multiplication, division, raising to a power, and finding a square root can be swiftly done with an accuracy appropriate to most of the problems encountered on these pages. The theory and use of the slide rule will be discussed presently.

Machines which expedite the mechanical operations required in extensive statistical tabulations are available for purchase or hire from a number of well-known business corporations. (See Ref. 2, Chap. II.)

12. Logarithms. Certain phases of statistical work require logarithms, both in theory and in practice. For most of the work of elementary statistics, a four-place logarithm table is adequate. The student should review briefly the theory of logarithms and the use of logarithm tables. In particular, he should recall the following fundamental definition.

DEFINITION. *The logarithm, x, of a number, N, is the index of the power to which a positive number, b, ($b \neq 1$) called the "base," must be raised in order to equal N.*

This definition asserts, briefly, that $\log_b N = x$ if and only if $b^x = N$. From this definition and the theory of exponents of elementary algebra, the following four theorems or laws of logarithms may be readily deduced:

THEOREM 1. *The logarithm of the product of two numbers equals the sum of their logarithms, that is,*

$$log_b NM = log_b N + log_b M.$$

THEOREM 2. *The logarithm of the quotient of two numbers equals the logarithm of the dividend minus the logarithm of the divisor, that is,*

$$log_b \frac{N}{M} = log_b N - log_b M.$$

THEOREM 3. *The logarithm of the **k**th power of a number equals the logarithm of the number multiplied by **k**.*

$$log_b N^k = k \, log_b N.$$

THEOREM 4. *The logarithm of the **k**th root of a number (**k** being a positive integer) equals the logarithm of the number divided by **k**.*

$$log_b N^{\frac{1}{k}} = \frac{1}{k} \, log_b N.$$

In the practical work of computation with logarithms, the preceding four theorems are used extensively. The base b employed is 10, except in certain kinds of theoretical work where the base e has certain natural advantages. The letter e is a symbol for a determinate, irrational number 2.71828 · · · which has a nonterminating decimal representation, just as the Greek letter π is a symbol for the irrational number whose decimal expansion is given by 3.14159 · · · ·

A logarithm is conveniently conceived as having two parts, an integral portion called the *characteristic* and a positive "decimal fraction" called the *mantissa*. When the base 10 is used, the characteristic of the logarithm of a number is found by inspection of the number itself. The mantissa may be found in Table A of the Supplementary Tables. A table of logarithms whose base is 10 is really a table of mantissas.

One property of the logarithm of a number requires special mention here. As a positive number, N, increases, its logarithm to the base 10 does also, but the increase in the logarithm is not proportional to the increase in the number. This fact is best appreciated by examining the three columns of numbers shown.   The mantissas of the logarithms of the integers from 1 to 10 are obtained from an ordinary four-place logarithm table.

Number	Logarithm	Difference
1	0.0000	
		0.3010
2	0.3010	
		0.1761
3	0.4771	
		0.1250
4	0.6021	
		0.0969
5	0.6990	
		0.0792
6	0.7782	
		0.0669
7	0.8451	
		0.0580
8	0.9031	
		0.0511
9	0.9542	
		0.0458
10	1.0000	

The differences in the third column are obtained by subtracting each logarithm from the one below it.   Of foremost importance here is the fact that these differences become smaller and smaller as we proceed down the column.   Thus, the logarithms themselves increase with the numbers but not at the same rate.   The logarithms above, laid off to scale, have the following appearance:

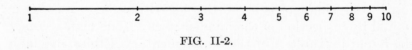

FIG. II-2.

The distance between the mark for a given number and that for 1 represents the logarithm of the number.

13.   The slide rule.   Perhaps the most useful single computational device in elementary statistics is the slide rule.

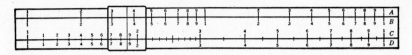

FIG. II-3. A SLIDE RULE (CLOSED).

This instrument may be described briefly as a mechanical logarithm table. Its chief use in statistics is in multiplication and division, but it may be employed for finding powers, roots, logarithms, and trigonometric functions, and for other operations according to the type of rule available. The most common type of slide rule is illustrated in simplified form in Figure II-3, and the following discussion refers to this type. When the slide rule is in the "closed" position (Figure II-3), it will be observed that the two lower scales, marked C and D, are identical throughout and are of the type shown in Figure II-2. In addition, each division from 1 to 2, 2 to 3, and so on is further subdivided to correspond to the subdivisions of the numbers from 100 to 200, 200 to 300, and so forth, in any standard logarithm table. Scale C is free to slide along scale D. In the "open" position shown in Figure II-4, the 1 of sliding scale C is set on 173 of the fixed

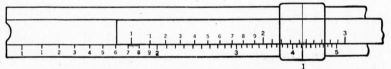

FIG. II-4. A SLIDE RULE (OPEN).

scale D. Thus, the distance on scale D from 1 to 173 represents the mantissa of log 173. The sliding indicator I in Figure II-4 is set on 244 of scale C. Thus, the distance on scale C from 1 to 244 represents the mantissa of log 244. Since scales C and D are identical, it follows that the distance from 1 on scale D to the indicator I is the sum of the two distances just described and represents the sum of the mantissas of log 173 and log 244, and this total distance corresponds to 422 on scale D, which is the number under indicator

I. It follows, then, from Theorem 1 of Section II-12 and the rule of Section II-8, that the product of two numbers of three significant digits each, whose first three significant digits are 173 and 244, is a number of three significant digits whose first three significant digits are 422. Thus the product of 1.73 and 24.4 is, by the slide rule, 42.2. The position of the decimal point is determined by making the usual estimate of the answer.

In multiplying 0.0721 by 62.7, it will be observed (Figure II-5) that when the 1 of scale *C* is set on 721 of scale *D*, the

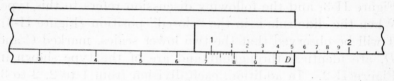

FIG. II-5.

number 627 on scale *C* lies beyond the range of scale *D*. This will always happen when the product of the first significant digits on the left of the two factors multiplied is 10 or more. Thus, the first significant digit in 0.0721 is 7, and the first in 62.7 is 6, and $7 \times 6 = 42$. However, in the preceding product of 1.73 by 24.4, $1 \times 2 = 2$, and of course 2 is less than 10. In the product of 4.25 and 2.81, the product of 2 and 4 is less than 10 but the complete product is more than 10, and again a setting for the product carries us beyond the range of scale *D*. Whenever the first significant digit of a product increases beyond 9, the characteristic of the logarithm of the product increases by 1. To take care of such an increase, a duplicate scale *D* might be adjoined at its right to the one given. Then, for example, in finding the product of 0.0721×62.7 mentioned above, the number 721 would lie above the duplicate scale *D*, and the first three significant digits of the product would be read from this duplicate scale. However, this reading is readily seen to be exactly the same as that given when the extreme right-hand 1 of scale *C* is set on 721 instead of the usual left-hand 1.

Referring to Figure II-6, we see then that the product is 4.52.

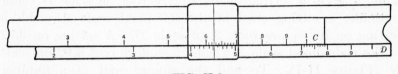

FIG. II-6.

The rule for making a setting for a product is, then, very simple. *When the left-hand 1 of scale C does not work, use the right-hand 1.* The left-hand 1 *never* works when the product of the first significant digits exceeds 9, when the product of the first two significant digits exceeds 999 (as in 3.41 × .00375, where 34 × 37 = 1,258), when the product of the first three significant digits exceeds 99,999 (as in 31.4 × 32,800, where 314 × 328 = 103 × 10^3), and so on.

Figure II-4 is not merely a setting for finding the product of 1.73 by 24.4, but it may be regarded also as a setting for finding the quotient, 42.2 divided by 24.4. The answer 1.73 is found under the 1 of scale C. Thus, in dividing one number (42.2) by another (24.4), we set (1) the indicator over the dividend on scale D, (2) the divisor on scale C under the indicator, and (3) read the quotient (1.73) under either the left-hand 1 or the right-hand 1 of scale C, as the case may be.

The square root and the square of a number may be computed by means of scale D used in conjunction with the two identical upper scales A (Figure II-7). It will be observed that each scale A is exactly the same as scale D ex-

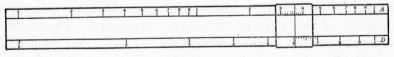

FIG. II-7.

cept that its length has been reduced by one half. Thus, any setting of the indicator on scale D yields a setting on scale A which represents double the logarithm indicated on D; and by Theorem 3 of Section 12 the number under the indicator on A is, therefore, the square of the number under the indicator on D. Conversely, a setting on a number of scale A gives a setting on its square root on scale D. For example, a setting on 4 of the left-hand scale A yields a setting on its square root, 2, of scale D. A setting on 36.2 of the right-hand scale A yields its square root 6.02 on scale D (Figure II-7). To find the square root of a number greater than 1, we use the left-hand scale A if the number of digits to the left of the decimal point is odd, and the right-hand scale if the number is even. To find the square root of a number less than 1, we use the left-hand scale A if the number of zeros to the right of the decimal point is odd; otherwise, we use the right-hand scale. The position of the decimal point in the answer may be fixed, as usual, by making an estimate of the answer, as described in the next section. To square a number, we merely set on this number on scale D and read off the answer on A. In finding squares and square roots, readings can be made on the slide rule to three digits, but the third digit is not always reliable. However, in most of the work of elementary statistics requiring square roots, two-figure accuracy will be sufficient.

It should be mentioned that formal rules exist for calculating the position of the decimal point in a number obtained from any of the usual slide-rule operations. Engineers and others often employ them.

Further details concerning multiplication, its inverse, division, and other operations on the slide rule can be obtained from the instruction book published by the maker of any reputable slide rule. A ten-inch slide rule of standard make is good for at least three-digit accuracy, and this is adequate for most of the work of elementary statistics. The theory is simple, and an hour's practice should make one proficient in multiplication and division. Many other kinds of computation are possible but are hardly necessary for our work.

14. Computation tables. Tables of powers, roots, and reciprocals will frequently save the computer considerable time and increase the accuracy of his work. Inasmuch as squares, cubes, square roots, and reciprocals are required often in statistical work, they may be found in Tables B, C, and D of the Supplementary Tables. In finding roots from such tables, it is often necessary to make a rough estimate of the answer in order to find the root properly. In this connection we should recall that the pencil method of finding the square root of a number requires the marking off by pairs, in either direction from the decimal point, of the digits composing the number. For example, the number 341.16785 is marked thus: 3'41'.16'78'5. The first digit on the left of the square root of 341.16785 is 1, the first approximation to $\sqrt{3}$. The final square root will then have the form:

$$1x \cdot xxxxxx,$$

where the x's are to be determined. In finding cube roots, we mark off the digits in triples.

Barlow's Tables (Ref. 26) constitute one of the most complete tabulations of squares, cubes, square roots, cube roots, and reciprocals. They should be used freely, for in practical statistics powers and roots, particularly of the second order, are frequently required.

Glover's Tables (Ref. 29) contain extensive tabulations of roots, powers, and reciprocals, and have a wealth of other material valuable to the statistician. *Crelle's Tables* (Ref. 27) give the products of all possible pairs of integers from 1 to 1,000.

Some of the later work of this book will require the use of special tables of statistical values. These will therefore be discussed at the proper time.

II—Exercises

1. Of the numbers appearing in the statements below, which are exact and which are approximate?

    (*a*)   The shortest man in the group was 5.4 ft. tall. *app.*

    (*b*)   The maximum temperature for July was 93.8°. *app.*

    (*c*)   The committee studied the records of 2,984 students. *exact*

    (*d*)   His cows produced milk with an average fat content of 5.65 per cent.

    (*e*)   Mr. Brown's income for the year was $4,198.68. *exact*

    (*f*)   The fullback weighed 197 lbs., 9 oz. *app.*

(g) The lowest interest rate bid for the town's $100,000 note was 1.93 per cent. *exact*

(h) The average per cent of sugar in 42,997 beets was found to be 15.22.

(i) $\sqrt{5} = 2.23607.$ *app*

(j) Log $\pi = 0.49715.$ *app*

2. How many significant digits are there in each of the approximate numbers (printed in italics) in the statements below?

4 (a) The number of inhabitants per square mile in New Jersey in 1930 was *537.8*.

5 (b) Siam exported *11,369* metric tons of rubber during 1933–1934.

1 (c) The weight of the earth has been estimated to be *6 × 10²⁴* kilograms.

4 (d) In 1934 the world produced *4,647* million bushels of wheat.

5 (e) The square root of 0.0065 is *0.080623*.

4 (f) The wholesale purchasing power of the dollar in 1932 was *$1.543*, as compared with $1.00 for 1926.

1 (g) The number of police department employees in Boston, Mass., per 1,000 inhabitants was *3.0* in 1934.

3 (h) The gravitational constant has been estimated to be *0.0000000666*.

4 (i) As of January 1, 1935, the average farm value of a horse was *$76.18*.

3 (j) The area of the Cathedral of St. John the Divine in New York City is *121,000* square feet.

5 (k) The total tree capital of Norway is estimated at *11,388,-000,000* cubic feet.

4 (l) Colorado harvested *1,506* thousands of tons of sugar beets in 1934.

7 (m) The diameter of the earth through the poles is *7,899.988* miles.

3. Underline, in the numbers appearing in the following statements, the zeros which are probably not significant:

(a) 42,000 pounds of fish were landed at T wharf.

(b) The atomic weight of silver is 107.880.

(c) The speed of light is 300,000 kilometers per second.

(d) The line measured 20.07 feet.

(e) His blood count dropped from 12,600 to 7,400.

(f) The length of the race track at the Olympic games was 100 meters.

(g) The lot of land was 162.00 feet deep.

4. Express with a proper number of significant digits the sum of the numbers given in each of the following:

(a)

City	Estimated Population in 1934
Buffalo..........................	601,696
Pittsburgh.......................	685,800
Minneapolis.....................	489,400
New Orleans....................	487,000

(b) Dividend payments made by steam roads:

Year	No. of Dollars
1932..........................	186,700,000
1933..........................	136,248,358
1934..........................	171,575,000

(c) Certain college endowments:

University of Cincinnati.........	$ 9,058,433
Brown University..............	10,360,000
California Inst. of Tech.........	8,000,000
Amherst College...............	14,535,000
New York University..........	9,085,269

5. The frontages, in feet, of six adjacent lots on a certain village street were stated to be as follows: 38.97, 147.8, 94.61, 232, 103.04, 56.9. Find their total frontage.

6. Find $(.246)^2 + (.246)^4 + (.246)^6$, where

$$(.246)^2 = .0605;$$
$$(.246)^4 = .00366;$$
$$(.246)^6 = .000222.$$

7. Find the sum of the following approximate numbers:

19.37
1.46
48.0
0.93
205.7

8. According to the *World Almanac* for 1940 (page 612), the imports and exports of the United States for the year 1790 were $23,000,-000 and $20,205,156, respectively. The excess of imports is given as $2,794,844. Comment on the precision of this result.

9. The area of Egypt is 386,000 square miles; the area of Ethiopia, 347,490 square miles. How many more square miles has Egypt than Ethiopia? (From published data.)

10. In 1926 the United States Mints held $78,540,565 in gold coinage; in 1927, they held $125,645,000. Find the increase. (From published data.)

11. In 1915–1916, the average spot price per pound for cotton at Galveston was 12.06 cents; in 1916–1917, it was 19.06 cents. What was the change in the average price? (From published data.)

12. Find $5,194 \times 10^7 - 4.16 \times 10^{10}$.

13. Find $16.3 \times 10^{-5} - 0.98 \times 10^{-4}$.

*   *   *

[In Exercises 14–26, carry out the necessary operations according to at least one of these methods: (1) common-sense "pencil" computation; (2) the slide rule; (3) a computing machine. It is suggested that at least two methods be used for each exercise as a check.]

14. In calculating a certain weighted index of factory employment, the relative $R = 134.5$ and the weight $W = 162.4$ were multiplied to give the product $RW = 21,842.80$. Comment on the accuracy of this result. How would you write the product RW?

15. A shipment consisted of 416 boxes of soap, each box averaging 37.4 pounds in weight. Find the total weight of the shipment.

16. An airliner flew 436 miles with 13 passengers. What was the number of passenger-miles flown?

17. The area of Texas is 265,896 square miles, and its population density was 21.9 per square mile in 1930. Estimate its population for that year.

18. If the number of molecules in a cubic centimeter is 6.06×10^{23}, how many are there in a rectangular box whose dimensions are exactly $12 \times 14 \times 18$ centimeters?

19. In 1929 there were 97,806 thousands of acres of corn harvested, with an average yield per acre of 25.9 bushels. In 1930 the corresponding figures were 101,083 and 20.4. Compute the difference in total production for the two years.

20. From January 1 to June 30, 1935, 42,005 airline trips were scheduled, of which 39,441 were started. What per cent were not started?

21. The gross debt of the United States June 30, 1935, was $28,-700,892,624, and the per capita debt was reported as $225.71. Compute the population upon which the last-named figure was based.

22. On December 31, 1933, 50,170,000 people were served by the manufactured-gas industry through 95,700 miles of main. What is the average number of miles of main for each person served?

23. On April 15, 1914, the average net price for the first 1,000 cubic feet of manufactured gas for household use in certain principal cities was $0.94; on December 15, 1933, it was $1.14. Compute the per cent of increase for the period.

24. In 1932 there were 26,350 deaths from automobile accidents in the United States. The population was 120,122,000. Find the death rate per 100,000 population.

25. What was the per capita wealth of Indiana in 1930 if its total wealth was $9,910,000,000 and its population 3,238,503?

26. Perform the required computation by means of a slide rule:

(a) $\dfrac{6.18 \times 4.19}{36.5}$.

(d) $\dfrac{31.4}{8.45} \times \dfrac{0.804}{78.3}$.

(b) $28.4 \times \dfrac{7,190}{52.7}$.

(e) $\dfrac{6,120,000 \times 4.30}{39,400}$.

(c) $\dfrac{687 \times 0.0192}{0.0884}$.

(f) $\dfrac{71.9 \times 0.000432}{0.0515}$.

* * *

27. Assume the numbers in the following operations to be approximate. Find the answers by means of Tables B and C in the Supplementary Tables. Express each answer with an appropriate number of significant figures. Check your answers with the slide rule.

(a) $(4.62)^3$.

(h) $\sqrt{0.0568}$.

(b) $\sqrt{2197}$.

(i) 814^2.

(c) $(19.1)^2$.

(j) $(8.14)^2$.

(d) $(0.0246)^3$.

(k) $(65.5)^3$.

(e) $\sqrt{0.913}$.

(l) $(36.7)^{1/2}$.

(f) $(0.563)^{1/2}$.

(m) $\sqrt{30,170}$.

(g) $(0.846)^4$.

(n) $(\sqrt{47.1})^3$.

28. Find to four decimal places the logarithms of the following:

(a) 317.8.   (g) 0.8884.
(b) 9,846,000.   (h) 3,407,000,000.
(c) 0.04191.   (i) 44.86.
(d) 1.23.   (j) 0.0004277.
(e) 7,846.   (k) 268.
(f) 2.497.   (l) 54.

29. What is the approximate error in each of the following?

(a) $\pi = 3.14$.   (c) $\log 84 = 1.92$.
(b) $\sqrt{2} = 1.41$.   (d) $\sqrt{3} = 1.732$.

30. In the following, perform the indicated additions in two ways: first, by adding the columns as they now stand and then rounding off the answers to the first decimal place; second, by rounding off each number to the first decimal place and then adding. How do you account for the discrepancies in the answers?

(a) 13.76   (b) 212.34
  16.17   98.62
  18.49   101.73
  15.76   68.03
  12.17   235.54
  3.18   18.96
         128.93
         67.32

III

CHARTS, DIAGRAMS, AND GRAPHS

❖❘❘❘❘❘❘❘❘❘❘❘❘❘❚❑❘❘❘❘❘❘❘❘❘❘❘❘❚❑❘❘❘❘❘❘❘❘❘❘❘❚❑❘❘❘❘❘❘❘❘❘❘❘❚❑❘❘❘❘❘❘❘❘❘❘❘❘❚❑❘❘❘❘❘❘❘❘❘❘❘❚❑❘❘❘❘❘❘❘❘❘❘❘❚❑❘❘❘❘❘❘❘❘❘❘❘❚❑❘❘❘❘❘❘❘❘❘❘❘❚❑❘❘❘❘❘❘❘❘❘❘❘❚❑❘❘❘❘❘❘❘❘❘❘❘❘❚❖

"The statistic mongers . . . have calculated to a nicety how
many quartern loaves, bars of iron, pigs of lead, sacks of wool,
Turks, Quakers, Methodists, Jews, Catholics, and Church-of-Eng-
land men are consumed or produced in the different countries of .
this wicked world."

WILLIAM M. THACKERAY, *Character Sketches.*

1. **Introduction.** It is often desirable to give a succinct
presentation of statistical data. This may be done effectively by graphical or pictorial methods which enable one to
grasp swiftly significant proportions, differences, or trends in
the data. Important quantitative items may be exhibited to
a public in such diagrammatic form that they are self-ex-
planatory. It is the purpose of this chapter to describe briefly
a few types of charts and graphs which are in common use
today.

2. **The one hundred per cent bar chart.** When the relative magnitudes of the component parts of a fixed amount
are to be emphasized, they may be represented as appropriate parts of a narrow rectangular bar. Thus, the kinds of
exports of the United States in 1933 are classified in Figure
III-1. The percentage that each item is of the total is
computed and determines the length of the corresponding
rectangle. The rectangles are then arranged according to
diminishing length from bottom to top, if the bar is vertical,

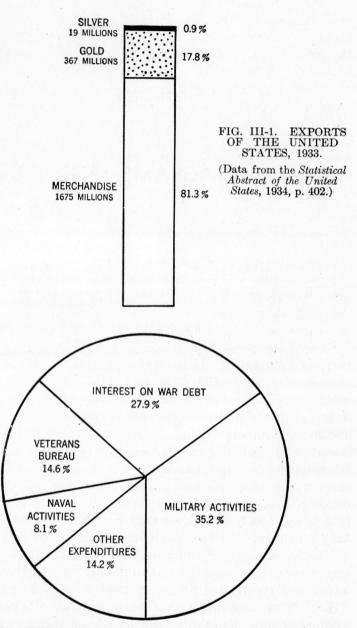

SILVER
19 MILLIONS
0.9 %

GOLD
367 MILLIONS
17.8 %

MERCHANDISE
1675 MILLIONS
81.3 %

FIG. III-1. EXPORTS OF THE UNITED STATES, 1933.

(Data from the *Statistical Abstract of the United States*, 1934, p. 402.)

INTEREST ON WAR DEBT
27.9 %

VETERANS BUREAU
14.6 %

NAVAL ACTIVITIES
8.1 %

OTHER EXPENDITURES
14.2 %

MILITARY ACTIVITIES
35.2 %

FIG. III-2. PERCENTAGE DISTRIBUTION OF COSTS OF THE WORLD WAR TO THE UNITED STATES TO JUNE, 1933. (Adapted from data in the *Statistical Abstract of the United States*, 1934, p. 198.)

or from left to right, if the bar is horizontal. A simple check on the computation is made to verify that the sum of the percentages is 100. Labels, totals, and per cents should be printed horizontally in positions in which they may be easily read. Often the different rectangles are shaded or colored. If more than three or four items are present, the vertical position usually permits clearer labeling. An advantage of the bar chart is the ease with which constituent parts are compared.

3. **The pie chart.** An effective and much used form of percentage chart represents the constituent parts as sectors of a circle, that is, as "pieces of pie." These sectors are arranged, usually, in order of magnitude. Occasionally an item *"Miscellaneous"* or *"All others"* violates the order of magnitude and is placed at the end of the circular array. Circular chart paper printed with peripheral divisions of hundredths and fractions thereof is available (Refs. 35 and 36). Without such paper, one can readily

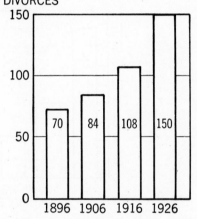

FIG. III-3. NUMBER OF DIVORCES PER 1,000 MARRIAGES IN THE UNITED STATES. (Data from the *Statistical Abstract of the United States*, 1934, p. 90.)

construct a given chart with the aid of a protractor. The title and per cent for each sector should be printed horizontally and placed within the sector if it can be read easily. Shaded or colored sectors are frequently used. The circle seems to be a particularly effective figure for suggesting the whole and its component parts. (See Figure III-2.)

4. **The vertical bar chart.** This consists of equally spaced vertical rectangles of the same width, placed upon a common horizontal base line. The heights of the rectangles are proportional to the magnitudes represented. All labels and ac-

companying numbers are placed below the base line. This type of chart may be used to compare values which are obtained from some kind of numerical tabulation or classification. It is used most frequently for magnitudes which vary with the time. (See Figure III-3.) It is sometimes used for magnitudes which are associated with a noncontinuous classification. (See Figure III-4.)

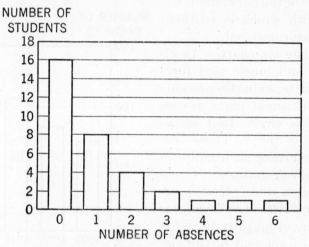

FIG. III-4.   NUMBER OF ABSENCES PER STUDENT IN A FRESHMAN CLASS IN MATHEMATICS.   (Original Data.)

5.   The horizontal bar chart. This type of chart consists of horizontal adjacent or equally spaced rectangles of the same width placed with their left-hand ends lying along a common vertical line. Most often the rectangles are arranged in order of length with the largest at the top. Such a chart may be used for comparing magnitudes at a fixed time when these have a qualitative or geographic classification. (See Figure III-5.).

6.   The pictograph. The purpose of this type of diagram is to catch the attention of the reader and to convey to him in a vivid manner certain basic facts. It aims at a "popular presentation." In general, the quantities to be compared are represented by appropriate pictures or sketches arranged in a row or column with easily read labels and

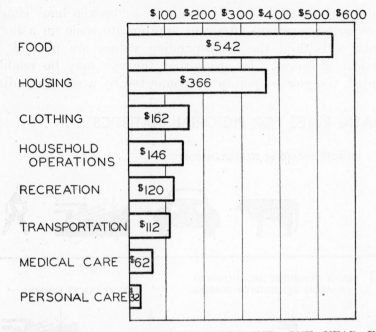

FIG. III-5. AVERAGE EXPENDITURES FOR ONE YEAR FOR FAMILIES OF HUSBAND AND WIFE ONLY IN NEW YORK CITY, 1934–1936; WAGE EARNERS AND CLERICAL WORKERS. (Adapted from Faith M. Williams, "Methods of Measuring Variations in Family Expenditures," *Journal of the American Statistical Association*, March, 1937, p. 44.)

numbers. The reader will find the attractive books of Modley (Ref. 24) and Neurath (Ref. 25) suggestive and stimulating.

A question presents itself in connection with the comparison of magnitudes by means of three-dimensional pictures. The volumes of solid objects are proportional to the third power of their linear dimensions; and hence, if strict mathematical accuracy is desired, the solid objects representing the compared magnitudes should have linear dimensions proportional to the cube roots of the magnitudes. In practice, however, this rule is frequently disregarded in favor of the nonmathematical public for which the diagrams are usually designed. The rules suggested in Figure III-6 will avoid criticisms of this kind.

7. The line graph. Perhaps the most important simple method of representing changes in value over successive

equal periods of time is by means of a "broken line" chart.
The periods are laid off to an appropriate scale on a horizontal axis, and the corresponding values are plotted as
vertical distances. In order that the eye may be readily
guided, the plotted points are connected by a series of adja-

BASIC RULES FOR PICTORIAL STATISTICS

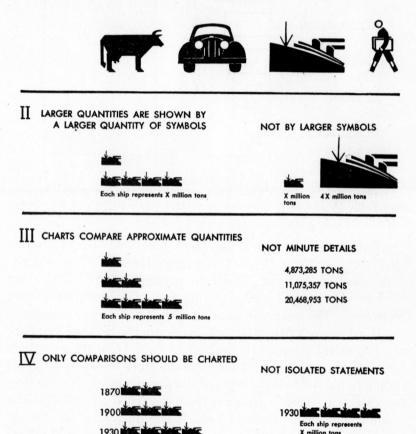

FIG. III-6. SUGGESTED RULES FOR PICTORIAL STATISTICS.
(From Rudolf Modley, *How to Use Pictorial Statistics*, Harper and Brothers,
p. 15.)

cent line segments to form a broken line. (See Figure III-7.) Such a chart enables one to grasp quickly the significant changes or trends in the variable involved.

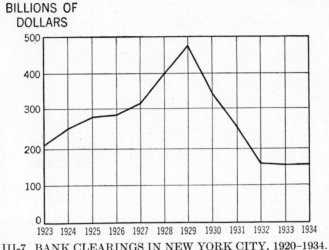

FIG. III-7. BANK CLEARINGS IN NEW YORK CITY, 1920–1934. (Data from the *World Almanac*, 1936, p. 282.)

Often two or more line graphs are constructed on the same sheet for purposes of comparison. In such cases, each broken line should be clearly identified by means of proper labels or modifications in the forms of the lines themselves. Figure III-8 illustrates these rules and also another fact which, when neglected, can produce a misleading chart. The data for Figure III-8 are given, after rounding off to three significant digits, as follows:

Year	England (Pound)	France (Franc)
1929............	486	3.92
1930............	486	3.92
1931............	453	3.92
1932............	351	3.93
1933............	424	5.03
1934............	504	6.57

The values of the pound and franc are stated in cents. It would be unwise to use the same vertical scale (in cents) for both exchange rates. The value of the franc is so small compared with that of the pound that the changes in the value of the latter would appear to be almost microscopic on a uniform scale. A fair comparison of changes, however, would be obtained by using the same number of significant digits (three) in each set of exchange rates, and using a scale based on these figures *independent* of the decimal point.

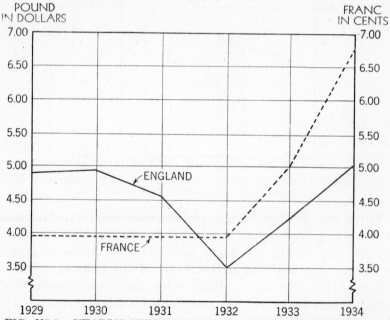

FIG. III-8. YEARLY AVERAGE FOREIGN EXCHANGE RATES FOR ENGLAND AND FRANCE, 1929–1934. (Data from the *World Almanac*, 1936, p. 283.)

Relative changes in the rates are important here, and not the absolute changes. Thus, a change of 0.05 cents in the value of the franc is comparable to that of 5 cents in the pound.

Statistically, the superimposed graphs of Figure III-8 show clearly the greater stability of the franc during the years 1930 to 1932 inclusive; they also exhibit rapid rises in value for both franc and pound from 1932 to 1934.

When two series of items involving different kinds of magnitudes are to be graphically represented on the same sheet, the vertical scale for one should be clearly indicated at the left and for the other at the right.

The line graph is also used to represent variations which are not dependent upon the time, as for example, in the case of the frequency distribution, an important use described in Chapter IV.

8. The graph of moving averages. We have just seen that some data are tabulated with respect to the time (Figures III-7 and 8). For this reason we define a *time series* as a set of values corresponding to a succession of instants or intervals of time. The line graph of a time series often exhibits periodic variations due to seasonal, climatic, or other changes. It may also give indications of a general trend upward or downward. To eliminate the effect of such seasonal changes, the method of "moving averages" is often employed. An example will best demonstrate the method. Table III-1 gives the average price in dollars per 100 pounds of milk received by producers for 36 successive months. The column headed *12-Month Average* contains the moving averages. The value $2.30 opposite the space between June and July, 1930, represents the average of the monthly prices for the year 1930, that is, the sum of the 12 prices divided by 12. The next value, $2.26, opposite the space between July and August, 1930, represents the average of the 12 prices, beginning with that for February, 1930, and so on. Each average is a measure of a complete cycle of prices for 12 months with all seasonal changes involved.

The seasonal changes as well as the moving averages are represented graphically in Figure III-9.

Inasmuch as the source of the data gives the average milk prices for the *fifteenth* of each month, the points representing the prices are placed in the *center* of each horizontal interval representing a month. On the other hand, the points representing the moving averages are placed at the end points of these intervals. Note also that the labels for the years are placed below the middle of the spaces representing these periods.

The evident downward trend in the "wavy" curve is

TABLE III–1

AVERAGE PRICE OF MILK PER 100 POUNDS RECEIVED BY PRODUCERS IN THE
UNITED STATES, 1930–1932

(Data from the *Yearbook of Agriculture*, 1936, p. 607.)

Year	Month (15th)	Price in Dollars	12-Month Average (Unweighted)
1930	Jan.	2.53	
	Feb.	2.44	
	Mar.	2.38	
	Apr.	2.35	
	May	2.28	
	June	2.22	2.30
	July	2.15	2.26
	Aug.	2.18	2.22
	Sept.	2.25	2.18
	Oct.	2.30	2.14
	Nov.	2.31	2.09
	Dec.	2.20	2.05
1931	Jan.	2.04	2.00
	Feb.	1.96	1.96
	Mar.	1.92	1.91
	Apr.	1.85	1.86
	May	1.73	1.81
	June	1.66	1.77
	July	1.62	1.73
	Aug.	1.64	1.69
	Sept.	1.70	1.65
	Oct.	1.72	1.61
	Nov.	1.73	1.58
	Dec.	1.67	1.53
1932	Jan.	1.56	1.50
	Feb.	1.49	1.46
	Mar.	1.43	1.43
	Apr.	1.39	1.39
	May	1.29	1.35
	June	1.17	1.32
	July	1.20	
	Aug.	1.21	
	Sept.	1.25	
	Oct.	1.28	
	Nov.	1.26	
	Dec.	1.26	

clearly brought out by the "smoother" graph of the 12-month averages. In Chapter XI, we shall show how to express this trend by means of a straight line. The seasonal fluctuations exhibit maximum prices in October or November and minimum prices in June, July, or August. Of course, the period for which the moving average is taken depends entirely upon the variations of the particular data in hand. In many cases, the period is a year when the data are given by months, but it may be a group of years, say five, or it may be a month if the data are given by days or by weeks. Where possible,

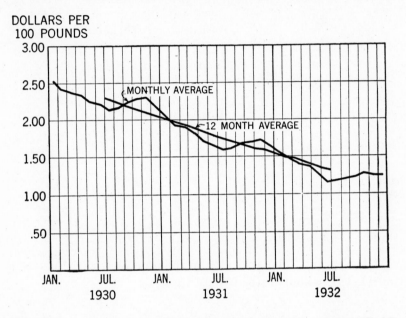

FIG. III-9. MONTHLY AVERAGE AND 12-MONTH AVERAGE OF MILK PRICES.

it is wise to use an odd number of items per group (say five years, rather than six) in order to have a middle item.

9. Ratio charts. Certain types of time series represent changes or trends in value which are not immediately discernible. For example, the population of the United States given by decades from 1790 to 1930, Table III-2, does not, at first glance, appear to follow any simple mathematical law of growth, nor does the graph (Figure III-10) tell the complete story. If, however, one computes the ratio of the population for one decade to that for the preceding decade (Table III-2), it becomes apparent that the ratios are fairly constant save for the last few decades. We seek, therefore, a form of graph which will enable us to detect, without the labor of computing ratios, values which increase or decrease so as to form, approximately, a geometric progression.

TABLE III–2

POPULATION OF THE UNITED STATES, 1790–1930

Year	Population	Ratio
1790........	3,929,214	
1800........	5,308,483	1.35
1810........	7,239,881	1.36
1820........	9,638,453	1.33
1830........	12,866,020	1.33
1840........	17,069,453	1.33
1850........	23,191,876	1.36
1860........	31,443,321	1.36
1870........	38,558,371	1.23
1880........	50,155,783	1.30
1890........	62,947,714	1.26
1900........	75,994,575	1.21
1910........	91,972,266	1.21
1920........	105,710,620	1.15
1930........	122,775,046	1.16

At this point, let us recall the theorem on logarithms (Section II–12), which states briefly that:

$$log \frac{N}{M} = log\ N - log\ M.$$

If, for a series of values, the ratio $\frac{N}{M}$ is approximately constant, then $log \frac{N}{M}$ and its. equal, $log\ N - log\ M$, are also. We employ, therefore, a form of graph paper known as *semilogarithmic* paper. (See Figure III–11.) The horizontal scale is uniform; the vertical scale is logarithmic. It will be observed that each of the three identical vertical scales is exactly of the form of that represented in Figure II–2; hence, the distance on the vertical scale corresponding to any number, N, on the horizontal scale represents $log\ N$. The graph of Figure III–11 is plotted on "3–cycle" paper, a type of paper containing three identical vertical scales. As discussed in Section II–13, an increase in the characteristic of log N leads one to the next scale or cycle above. In other words, the number of cycles necessary on logarithmic paper

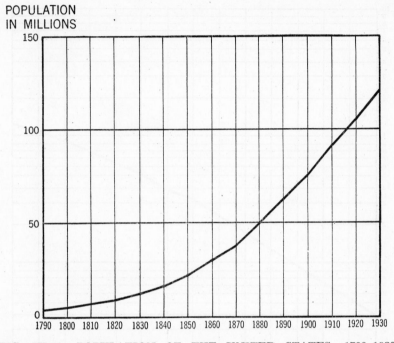

FIG. III-10. POPULATION OF THE UNITED STATES, 1790–1930.

for a given set of values will be 1 more than the difference between the greatest and the smallest characteristic of the logarithms of the values involved. The graph of Figure III–11 is plotted by laying off the population numbers (rounded off to three significant digits) on the vertical scale opposite the given year on the horizontal scale. From 1820 to 1830, the population increased from 9,638,453 to 12,866,-020, and thus the graph passes into the second cycle. From 1910 to 1920, the graph passes into the third cycle. The resulting graph is very nearly linear, save in the later decades. This fact indicates a set of fairly constant ratios, for, as previously stated, the difference between the logarithms of two successive values is practically constant. If, then, the graph rises by a constant amount for each successive period, the graph must be a straight line. (See also Section XI–14.)

Excellent examples of time series for which the successive

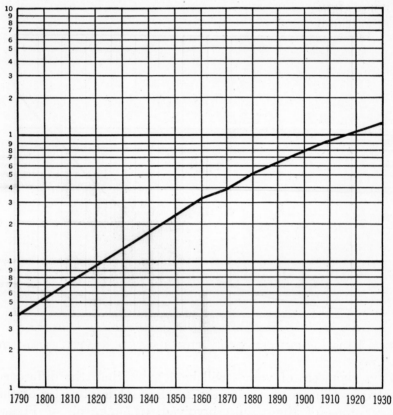

FIG. III-11. SEMILOGARITHMIC CHART FOR THE POPULATION
OF THE UNITED STATES, 1790–1930.

ratios are absolutely constant may be found in Table G of the Supplementary Tables, where the compound amounts of one dollar at given rates for a series of years are given. The corresponding graphs on semilogarithmic paper are always perfectly straight. See Exercises 32 and 33.

Logarithm paper with one, two, three, or five cycles is available. (See Refs. 35 and 36.)

10. Other graphs. The frequency polygon (Sections IV–4 and 5), the cumulative frequency diagram or ogive (Section VI–3), and the Lorenz and Pareto curves (Sections VI–4 and 5) are highly important forms of line graphs which will be discussed later. Occasionally recourse is made to "log-log" paper, in which both horizontal and vertical scales are logarithmic. (Section XI–15.) Probability paper may also be employed to advantage in studying the form of distribution of certain kinds of data. (Section X–14.)

III—Exercises

Construct a one hundred per cent bar chart for each of Exercises 1–3.

1. The approximate percentage composition of dried skim milk.

Proteins	38	Moisture	3
Lactose	50	Fat	1
Salts	8		

2. The world gold production in millions of dollars in 1934.

Africa	403	South America	9
North America	127	Far East	33

3. The chief grain crops of Kansas in 1934 in thousands of bushels.

Corn	10,576	Barley	1,988
Wheat	79,700	Rye	176
Oats	16,094		

*   *   *

Construct a pie chart for each of Exercises 4–8.

4. The popular vote for presidential electors in 1932.

Republican	15,761,841
Democrat	22,821,857
Other Parties	1,007,235

5. How the railroad dollar goes.

Labor	44.1	Depreciation	5.9
Fuel	5.8	Taxes	7.3
Materials	17.4	Rentals	3.9
Loss and Damage	1.5	Net Income	14.1

6. The membership of religious bodies in the United States in 1926.

Roman Catholic...	18,605,003	Presbyterian......	2,625,284
Baptist...........	8,440,922	Episcopalian......	1,859,086
Methodist.........	8,070,619	Disciples of Christ.	1,377,595
Jewish...........	4,081,242	All Others........	5,550,592
Lutheran..........	3,966,003		

7. A certain recommended average home budget for an income of $3,000.

Operating Expense.	$900	Advancement.....	$180
Food.............	810	Health..........	150
Wearing Apparel...	360	Amusement......	240
Thrift...........	360		

8. Immigrants admitted to the United States in 1934.

Canada..........	7873	Poland..........	1032
Italy.............	4374	Great Britain.....	1305
Mexico...........	1801	Other countries...	2567
Germany.........	4392		

*   *   *

Construct a vertical bar chart for each of Exercises 9–12.

9. The number of children under five years per 100 persons in the United States.

1880.................	13.8	1910................	11.6
1890.................	12.2	1920................	10.9
1900.................	12.1	1930................	9.3

10. The production of cigarettes by millions in the United States.

1924.............	72,709	1929............	122,392
1925.............	82,247	1930............	123,802
1926.............	92,097	1931............	117,063
1927.............	99,809	1932............	106,632
1928.............	108,706	1933............	111,763

11.   The number of students in teacher-training classes in arithmetic.   (National Council of Teachers of Mathematics, *Tenth Year-book*, Columbia University, 1935, p. 163.)

No. of Students	No. of Institutions
0– 9.............	1
10–19.............	8
20–29.............	22
30–39.............	45
40–49.............	18
50–59.............	1
60–69.............	0
70–79.............	1

12.   The sizes of shoes worn by 235 college girls.   (See Ex. IV–13.)

*   *   *

Construct a horizontal bar chart for each of Exercises 13–15.

13.   The disposition without conviction of defendants in criminal cases in 25 states (1934).

Dismissed by prosecution........	22,801
Dismissed on motion of defense...	2,139
Acquitted by court..............	2,194
Acquitted by jury...............	9,628
Never in custody................	1,670
Other dispositions..............	4,131

14.   Types of studies preferred by a group of young women.

Office work.....................	316
Miscellaneous professions........	132
Home economics.................	125
Beauty culture..................	87
Art and music..................	131
Semiprofessional fields	94
Nursing........................	89
Teaching.......................	54
Business and finance............	16
Miscellaneous..................	17

15.   Distribution of farmer bankruptcies, July 1, 1898, to June 30, 1934.   (See page 50.)

New England.........	4,905	East South Central....	8,614
Middle Atlantic........	5,444	West South Central...	8,431
East North Central....	15,714	Mountain............	8,355
West North Central....	30,190	Pacific..............	6,847
South Atlantic.........	12,348		

*   *   *

Construct a line graph for each of Exercises 16–20.

16. Average price of eggs per dozen received by United States producers in 1934 (in cents).

Jan.	17.6	July	14.1
Feb.	15.8	Aug.	17.2
Mar.	14.4	Sept.	21.9
Apr.	13.5	Oct.	23.7
May	13.3	Nov.	28.6
June	13.2	Dec.	27.0

17. Average freight rates on wheat in cents per bushel, 1910–1920.

1910	4.08	1916	5.00
1911	4.36	1917	5.50
1912	4.32	1918	9.80
1913	4.57	1919	8.31
1914	4.27	1920	11.05
1915	4.47		

18. Marriage rates per 1,000 of the population of the United States, 1887–1906.

1887	8.7	1897	8.9
1888	8.8	1898	8.8
1889	9.1	1899	9.0
1890	9.0	1900	9.3
1891	9.2	1901	9.6
1892	9.1	1902	9.8
1893	9.0	1903	10.1
1894	8.6	1904	9.9
1895	8.9	1905	10.0
1896	9.0	1906	10.5

19. The number of heads which should (theoretically) appear when five pennies are tossed 32 times.

No. Heads	No. Times Appearing
0	1
1	5
2	10
3	10
4	5
5	1

20. Sizes of shoes worn by 235 college girls. (Ex. IV–13.)

*   *   *

In Exercises 21–23, construct line graphs on the same sheet for purposes of comparison.

21. The normal precipitation and the actual precipitation in 1934 in Boston, Mass.

Month	Normal	Actual
Jan.	3.61	2.67
Feb.	3.37	4.45
Mar.	3.57	4.04
Apr.	3.34	3.21
May	3.18	1.56
June	2.89	3.11
July	3.49	1.25
Aug.	3.62	1.83
Sept.	3.14	5.67
Oct.	3.15	2.94
Nov.	3.33	1.78
Dec.	3.45	1.64

22. The number of labor disputes and the number of workers involved in 1934.

Month	No. Disputes Beginning	No. Workers Involved
Jan.	98	81,650
Feb.	94	89,562
Mar.	161	91,559
Apr.	210	185,282
May	226	145,830
June	165	56,244
July	151	180,268
Aug.	183	80,071
Sept.	150	423,915
Oct.	187	69,441
Nov.	130	37,869
Dec.	101	25,004

23.   Death rates of certain countries, 1919–1930.

Year	Rate per 1000 Population		
	U. S.	Germany	Japan
1919.........	12.9	15.6	22.8
1920.........	13.0	15.1	25.4
1921.........	11.6	13.9	22.7
1922.........	11.7	14.4	22.3
1923.........	12.2	13.9	22.8
1924.........	11.7	12.3	21.2
1925.........	11.8	11.9	20.3
1926.........	12.3	11.7	19.2
1927.........	11.4	12.0	19.8
1928.........	12.1	11.6	19.9
1929.........	11.9	12.6	20.0
1930.........	11.3	11.1	18.2

*   *   *

Construct the line graphs of the time series given in Exercises 24–28.   Compute the moving averages for the period indicated, and construct their graphs also.

24.   Average wholesale price per dozen of eggs (western firsts) at Boston, 1932–1934.   Use 12-month averages.

Year and Month		Price in Cents	Year and Month		Price in Cents	Year and Month		Price in Cents
1932	Jan.	19	1933	Jan.	24	1934	Jan.	23
	Feb.	17		Feb.	14		Feb.	21
	Mar.	14		Mar.	14		Mar.	18
	Apr.	14		Apr.	14		Apr.	17
	May	15		May	14		May	17
	June	14		June	14		June	17
	July	15		July	15		July	17
	Aug.	18		Aug.	15		Aug.	21
	Sept.	21		Sept.	18		Sept.	23
	Oct.	24		Oct.	21		Oct.	24
	Nov.	30		Nov.	24		Nov.	28
	Dec.	32		Dec.	20		Dec.	27

25.   Debits, in billions of dollars, to individual accounts reported by New York City banks, 1927–1929.   Use 12-month averages.

Year	Month	Debits	Year	Month	Debits	Year	Month	Debits
1927	Jan.	31	1928	Jan.	38	1929	Jan.	55
	Feb.	27		Feb.	33		Feb.	46
	Mar.	34		Mar.	45		Mar.	55
	Apr.	32		Apr.	42		Apr.	48
	May	31		May	45		May	50
	June	33		June	45		June	43
	July	31		July	35		July	49
	Aug.	32		Aug.	35		Aug.	49
	Sept.	33		Sept.	39		Sept.	50·
	Oct.	34		Oct.	45		Oct.	63
	Nov.	33		Nov.	45		Nov.	54
	Dec.	39		Dec.	53		Dec.	40

26. Average weekly car loadings in the United States, 1929–1932. Use 12-month averages.

Year	Month	Loadings in Millions of Tons	Year	Month	Loadings in Millions of Tons
1929	Jan.	893	1931	Jan.	718
	Feb.	942		Feb.	709
	Mar.	963		Mar.	734
	Apr.	997		Apr.	752
	May	1036		May	740
	June	1073		June	748
	July	1040		July	738
	Aug.	1120		Aug.	748
	Sept.	1136		Sept.	727
	Oct.	1170		Oct.	763
	Nov.	978		Nov.	655
	Dec.	835		Dec.	555
1930	Jan.	849	1932	Jan.	567
	Feb.	877		Feb.	561
	Mar.	879		Mar.	570
	Apr.	905		Apr.	555
	May	919		May	522
	June	930		June	492
	July	889		July	484
	Aug.	934		Aug.	516
	Sept.	931		Sept.	573
	Oct.	950		Oct.	634
	Nov.	798		Nov.	547
	Dec.	695		Dec.	497

27. Average yield per acre of wheat in the United States, 1876–1900. Use 5-year averages. (See page 54.)

Year	Bushels	Year	Bushels
1876	10.9	1889	14.0
1877	14.1	1890	12.2
1878	13.5	1891	16.5
1879	13.0	1892	14.2
1880	13.2	1893	12.4
1881	11.0	1894	13.5
1882	15.1	1895	13.9
1883	12.3	1896	12.8
1884	14.8	1897	14.0
1885	11.4	1898	15.2
1886	14.1	1899	12.5
1887	13.3	1900	12.2
1888	12.1		

28. Homicide rate in cities having a population of 100,000 or more, 1905–1930. Use 3-year averages.

Year	Rate per 100,000	Year	Rate	Year	Rate
1905	6.1	1914	8.5	1923	10.0
1906	7.2	1915	8.2	1924	10.8
1907	8.5	1916	8.5	1925	11.1
1908	8.0	1917	9.5	1926	10.5
1909	6.9	1918	8.5	1927	10.5
1910	8.0	1919	8.9	1928	10.2
1911	7.9	1920	8.4	1929	9.8
1912	7.7	1921	9.2	1930	10.3
1913	8.6	1922	9.2		

*   *   *

Construct ratio charts on semilogarithmic paper for the data given in Exercises 29–34.   What conclusions can you draw from the appearance of your graphs?

29. The amount of money kept invested by a certain man by 5-year intervals.

Year	Amount	Year	Amount
1900	$10,000	1920	$22 000
1905	12,200	1925	26,700
1910	14,800	1930	32,400
1915	18,000		

30. The number of claims paid for automobile accidents by a well-known insurance company.

Year	No. Claims	Year	No. Claims
1924	3612	1928	5775
1925	4350	1929	5979
1926	4903	1930	6536
1927	5292		

31. The earnings on loans of member banks of the Federal Reserve System.

Year	Earnings—$1,000,000	Year	Earnings—$1,000,000
1929	1563	1933	604
1930	1349	1934	540
1931	1073	1935	498
1932	851	1936	513

32. The amount on $1.00 at 2 per cent compound interest by 5-year intervals up to 40 years beginning with 5 years. Use Table G of the Supplementary Tables.

33. As in Exercise 32, for 4 per cent by 1-year intervals up to 10 years.

34. Average ages of entrance of Harvard freshmen.

Period	Age		Period	Age	
	Years	Mos.		Years	Mos.
1856–60	17	10.86	1881–85	18	11.52
1861–65	18	4.81	1886–90	19	3.63
1866–70	18	4.67	1891–95	19	1.43
1871–75	18	6.71	1896–1900	19	0.48
1876–80	18	10.10			

* * *

35. Criticize Figure III-12 below.

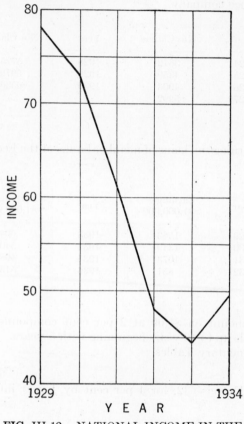

FIG. III-12.   NATIONAL INCOME IN THE
UNITED STATES.

36. Criticize the following chart. Is it misleading in any respect?

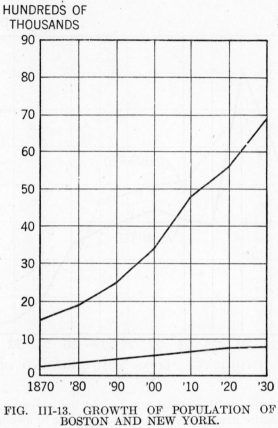

HUNDREDS OF
THOUSANDS

FIG. III-13. GROWTH OF POPULATION OF
BOSTON AND NEW YORK.

37. Criticize the following chart. Is it misleading in any respect?

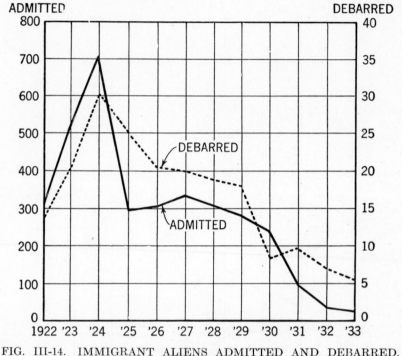

ADMITTED   DEBARRED

FIG. III-14. IMMIGRANT ALIENS ADMITTED AND DEBARRED, 1922–1933.

38. On semilogarithmic paper, a straight line ascending from left to right indicates magnitudes which are increasing at a constant rate; an ascending curve concave upward denotes magnitudes which are increasing at an increasing rate. What do the following curves indicate:

(a) An ascending curve concave downward?
(b) A descending curve concave downward?
(c) A descending curve concave upward?
(d) A descending straight line?

39. What answers would you make to the preceding question if the curves described existed on ordinary (nonlogarithmic) paper?

FREQUENCY DISTRIBUTIONS

❖❖⫶⫶⫶⫶⫶⫶⫶⫶⫶⫶⫶⫶⫶⫶⫶⫶⫶⫶⫶⫶⫶⫶⫶⫶⫶⫶⫶⫶⫶⫶⫶⫶⫶⫶⫶⫶⫶⫶❖❖

> "Figures may not lie, but statistics compiled unscientifically and analyzed incompetently are almost sure to be misleading, and when this condition is unnecessarily chronic the so-called statisticians may well be called liars."
>
> E. B. WILSON, *Bulletin of the American Mathematical Society*, vol. 18 (1912).

1. Tabulation. Statistical data often come to us in a form unsuitable for immediate interpretation. It is usually necessary to group the data into appropriate classes before their general characteristics can be detected and measured. Thus, in Table IV–1 on page 60, no trend or pattern in the bills for electricity is evident other than the obvious tendency for most of the amounts to lie between $6 and $7. However, if we tabulate the values according to a certain plan, it will be found that they are distributed according to a well-known law.

Examination of the data shows that the smallest bill is $3.27 and the largest $8.99, so that the *range* of the values is $8.99 minus $3.27, or $5.72. We may conveniently divide this range into 12 *class intervals* each of length $0.50, as indicated in Table IV–2, and assign each monthly bill to its appropriate class. For purposes of tabulation, the *limits* for the class intervals are set down in order of magnitude in one column and a tally mark is placed in the adjoining column as each amount is assigned to its proper class. When all have been assigned, the tallies are counted and the resulting *frequency* for each class is written in the third column. The

TABLE IV-1

MONTHLY BILLS FOR ELECTRIC CURRENT (*Author's Data*)

5.82	6.84	5.25	6.45	7.26	6.45
5.67	6.09	8.99	6.72	6.46	5.13
3.96	6.42	6.21	7.67	7.40	3.27
4.41	6.00	7.02	6.92	7.80	5.85
4.83	5.25	5.76	6.20	7.40	7.29
5.40	5.76	6.93	6.53	6.11	6.06
6.30	6.27	6.00	6.95	6.91	5.28
6.54	4.77	6.33	4.85	6.67	7.32
5.88	6.72	6.48	6.98	8.59	6.03
6.39	8.55	5.76	5.27	6.81	7.89
7.20	6.24	5.19	6.96	5.85	7.71

completely tabulated record, consisting of a series of class intervals and their associated frequency numbers, is called a *frequency table*. The frequency of a class is merely the

TABLE IV-2

FREQUENCY TABLE FOR MONTHLY BILLS FOR ELECTRICITY

Class Interval	Tallies	Frequency
3.00–3.49	/	1
3.50–3.99	/	1
4.00–4.49	/	1
4.50–4.99	///	3
5.00–5.49	₦/ //	7
5.50–5.99	₦/ ///	8
6.00–6.49	₦/ ₦/ ₦/ ///	18
6.50–6.99	₦/ ₦/ ///	13
7.00–7.49	₦/ //	7
7.50–7.99	////	4
8.00–8.49		0
8.50–8.99	///	3

Total Frequency   66

number in that class. Thus, the frequency of the class 6.00–6.49 is 18, which means that there were 18 bills having amounts from $6.00 to $6.49 inclusive. Likewise, there were 4 bills having amounts from $7.50 to $7.99 inclusive, and so on. When data have been classified in such a way that they may be described in terms of class frequencies, the result is called a *frequency distribution*. The *relative frequency* of a class is the fraction obtained by dividing the class frequency by the total frequency. Thus, the relative frequency of electric bills ranging from $5.50 to $5.99 inclusive is $\frac{8}{66}$, or approximately 0.121. This is equivalent to saying that 12.1 per cent of the bills lay within the interval 5.50–5.99. The frequency distribution is, perhaps, the most important initial concept in statistics, for its formation is usually the first step in many statistical investigations.

The *range* of a set of values often supplies important information. We may cite the interest of the doctor in the range of the fluctuating temperatures of his patient, of the margin speculator in the "highs" and "lows" of his stock, or of the horticulturist in the climatic extremes of a given geographic region.

As a first simple result of the tabulation of the data in Table IV–2, we may say that the distribution is somewhat symmetrical, with the largest frequencies near the center of the table and the other frequencies diminishing as we recede in opposite directions from the center. Bills from $6.00 to $6.49 are most frequent, and the average bill probably lies within or near that interval. As we proceed with our study of frequency distributions, we shall notice that the approximately symmetrical distribution, of which Tables IV–2 and 3 are simple examples, is, perhaps, the most basic type in all statistics.

2. The frequency distribution. Consider the frequency distribution of Table IV–3. The measurements of head lengths were apparently made to the nearest millimeter, so that any reading, such as 184 mm., for example, is an approximate number and represents a true length not less than 183.5 mm. and not more than 184.5 mm. (See Section II–3.) The class intervals chosen for these data were 4 mm. in width. The class limits (Column 1) are not the same as the *class boundaries* (Columns 2 and 3), for the class with limits 172–175, for example, may contain lengths as small as 171.5 (the lower boundary) and as large as 175.5 (the upper boundary). The *class mark* of each class interval (Column 4) is the mid-value and has important uses to be discussed later.   In most practical work, it is not necessary to construct a frequency table containing all the different columns, 1 to 4, which appear in Table IV–3.   Usually, either Column 1 or Column 4, together with the column of frequencies, are sufficient to

TABLE IV–3

HEAD LENGTHS IN MILLIMETERS OF 462 ENGLISH CRIMINALS, AGE 25–30
(Data from Charles Goring, *The English Convict*, H. M. S. Office,
1913, p. 54.*)

(1) Class Limits	(2) Lower Boundary	(3) Upper Boundary	(4) Class Mark (Mid-Value)	(5) Frequency
172–175	171.5	175.5	173.5	3
176–179	175.5	179.5	177.5	9
180–183	179.5	183.5	181.5	29
184–187	183.5	187.5	185.5	76
188–191	187.5	191.5	189.5	104
192–195	191.5	195.5	193.5	110
196–199	195.5	199.5	197.5	88
200–203	199.5	203.5	201.5	30
204–207	203.5	207.5	205.5	6
208–211	207.5	211.5	209.5	4
212–215	211.5	215.5	213.5	2
216–219	215.5	219.5	217.5	1
			Total	462

specify adequately the classification of the data.   It should be noted also that the width of the class interval may be obtained by subtracting any number in any of Columns 1, 2, 3, and 4 from the number just below it.   It is *not* necessarily the difference between the limits for a given class.   This difference in Table IV–3 is 3, which is not the class interval.

As an illustration of data of a slightly different kind, consider that of Table IV–4 on page 63.   There is no question of choice of class interval here, for the classification is a natural one.   Class limits, boundaries, and mid-values have no real

* By Permission of The Controller of His Britannic Majesty's Stationery Office.

meaning here, although later we may have occasion to establish artificial boundaries for such data.   [Section X–12 (v).]

Observations occurring in statistical work are often recorded with scientific care.   Thus, the head lengths of criminals were measured "to the nearest" millimeter, so that the class boundaries or end-values could be established with precision.   On the other hand, common commercial methods of describing classes contain such phrases as "under ten years of age," "up to fifty pounds," and so forth.   Inas-

TABLE IV–4

FREQUENCY DISTRIBUTION FOR NUMBERS
OF HEADS WHICH APPEARED WHEN SIX
PENNIES WERE TOSSED 128 TIMES

No. of Heads	Frequency
0.	2
1.	10
2.	28
3.	44
4.	30
5.	13
6.	1
Total	128

much as ages are usually recorded only to the whole completed year, a person aged 9 years, 11 months, for example, would be *nine years old*, although his nearest birthday is the tenth.   Occasionally, ages *are* recorded to the nearest birthday.   An express package weighing 49 pounds and 15 ounces should fall within the category "up to 50 pounds," although an inaccurate weighing machine or a careless weigher might record it as exactly 50 pounds.   When the classification "from . . . up to . . . " or a similar one is employed, as it often is for the census, taxes, and other data, it includes the lower end-value but not the upper.

A classification according to age, such as that of Table IV–5, will be understood in this book to include values exactly equal to the lower limit and up to and including values or "fractions thereof" of the upper limit. For example, the age class 10–14 of Table IV–5 means ages of exactly 10 years and up to and including 14 years and any fraction thereof, but not 15 years. Note that this means that the mid-values or class marks are 2.5, 7.5, 12.5, 17.5, and so on, and *not* 2, 7, 12, and so forth. It is perhaps unfortunate that the word *limit* as used here is different from the customary use in the field of mathematics. The class limits of ages just mentioned, 5, 9, 10, 14, and so on, are not constants approached by a certain variable. They are convenient values used to designate the extremities or approximate extremities of certain ranges.

Frequency distributions often come to us "ready made," in many different forms, and it is sometimes difficult, if not impossible, to decide what the original basis of tabulation was. A group of men might have been weighed to the nearest half-pound or to the nearest quarter-pound; a set of discount rates at the bank might have been expressed to the nearest sixteenth of a per cent or to the nearest hundredth; ages might have been given to the nearest birthday or to the last birthday. When the statistician meets such already classified distributions, he must exert good judgment in deciding the probable basis of classification. Sometimes he must trace the original data.

The *class mark* is a convenient value used to represent or typify the values within a class interval. It is usually the mid-value of the interval, but it does not always have to be. (See the last paragraph and footnote of Chapter V.) Inasmuch as the purpose of many statistical investigations is to present data in a succinct form, readily understood by the nonmathematical reader, the use of simple class limits and class marks is desirable. It is not uncommon to find that an attempt to achieve unerring precision has obscured simple but important facts and has led only to mathematical pedantry.

3. Class intervals. When a certain characteristic of a large number of individuals is recorded quantitatively, the set of values obtained belongs usually either to a *continuous* set or to a *discrete* set of numbers. Thus, the head lengths of criminals or the average daily July temperatures of a certain city belong to continuous sets, since any head length or any temperature (between reasonable limits) is possible. On the other hand, the numbers of heads appearing when six pennies are tossed or the sizes of shoes sold in a given store belong to discrete sets, since intervals or gaps exist in the range of the data, within which no values exist. Two and one-half heads cannot appear when six pennies are tossed, nor can a shoe of size 6.83 be purchased at a store.

Given data which are to be assembled into a frequency distribution, the choice of an appropriate class interval is guided by a few simple rules. In the first place, grouping is generally considered disadvantageous when the total frequency is below 50. When grouping is desirable, the number of classes should, if possible, range from about 15 to 25. Fewer than ten classes leads to inaccuracies in computation, and more than thirty classes usually leads to cumbersome operations. Integral values, unity especially, constitute frequent class intervals in the case of discrete sets. Simple fractions, such as one-half in the case of shoe sizes, are also common. In both continuous and discrete data, it is good practice, when feasible, to express the class limits in terms of integers or simple fractions. These rules follow from the desire to make all graphical representations and computations as simple and as accurate as possible.

4. Graphical representation. The frequency distribution of Table IV–3 may be pictured by means of a *histogram* (Figure IV–1). This is constructed as follows. The twelve class intervals of four millimeters each are laid off to a convenient scale on a horizontal line. The end-points of these intervals correspond to the class boundaries. The corresponding class frequencies are measured to a convenient scale on a vertical line, and a rectangle is constructed for each class. Thus, the histogram consists of a set of adjacent rectangles the bases of which equal the class width, and the altitudes of which equal the corresponding class frequencies. The total area of the histogram equals the sum of the areas of the rec-

tangles; and in the usual case where the class interval or
width is the same, this total area equals the product of the
common width by the sum of the frequencies (the heights).
If we call the class width k, and the sum of the frequencies
N, the area of the histogram will be Nk.

By joining the adjacent mid-points of the upper bases with
line segments, as indicated in Figure IV–1, a *frequency polygon* is obtained. When the polygon is continued to the
horizontal axis just outside the range of lengths, as in the
figure, the total area under the polygon will be equal to that
of the histogram. For each triangular portion of a rectangle

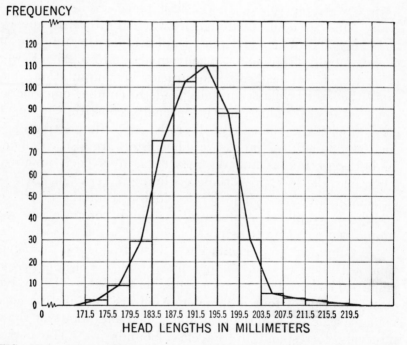

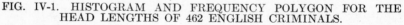

HEAD LENGTHS IN MILLIMETERS

FIG. IV-1. HISTOGRAM AND FREQUENCY POLYGON FOR THE
HEAD LENGTHS OF 462 ENGLISH CRIMINALS.

cut off by the polygon, an equivalent triangular portion above
the lower adjacent rectangle is added. Sometimes it is convenient to consider each rectangle to have a width of unity
and a height equal to the relative frequency. Such a choice

makes the area of the frequency polygon unity. Its advantages will be apparent later.

The rectangular histogram serves the purpose of suggesting to the reader the fact that each class frequency is associated, not with a single value, but with a whole range of values, represented by the width of a rectangle. The frequency polygon, with its line segments sloping upward and down-

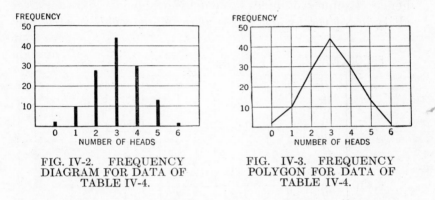

FIG. IV-2. FREQUENCY DIAGRAM FOR DATA OF TABLE IV-4.

FIG. IV-3. FREQUENCY POLYGON FOR DATA OF TABLE IV-4.

ward, gives a picture of the way in which frequency of occurrence varies over the complete gamut of values.

The distribution of Table IV–4 is discrete, and does not involve ranges of values. For this reason, many statisticians prefer to use heavy vertical lines instead of vertical rectangles in the frequency diagram. (See Figure IV–2.) There are, however, certain advantages in using a polygon representation, as in Figure IV–3. For reasons to be discussed later, one may also wish to use the histogram (Section XIII–13). Another method of emphasizing the discontinuity of the data is to use the vertical bar chart (Section III–4).

The monthly bills for electric current (Table IV–2) form a frequency distribution slightly different from the two distributions just discussed. Strictly speaking, the data are discrete inasmuch as the amounts do not involve portions of a cent. The class limits are also the class boundaries, but the upper boundary of any class is not the lower boundary of the next class, as is the case for the distribution of head lengths. Nevertheless, in constructing the histogram, one may disregard this fact and use the boundaries shown in Figure IV–4. These are more desirable for the purpose of popular presentation.

Data are often tabulated with unequal class intervals, as in Table IV–5. In constructing the histogram for such data, one must keep in mind the fact that the areas of the rectangles should be proportional to the corresponding frequencies; hence, if some rectangles have *double* the width of others, the altitudes of the former must correspond to *half* the frequen-

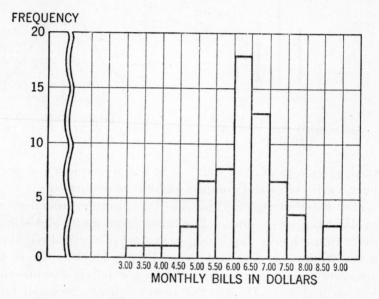

FIG. IV-4. HISTOGRAM FOR DATA OF TABLE IV-2.

cies of the larger class. Thus, in Figure IV–5, the height of the rectangle having the base 35–45 corresponds to 295.5 (half the frequency 591), but the area of this rectangle corresponds to 591.

5. Frequency polygons. The construction of a frequency polygon involves only elementary ideas, yet it is of considerable importance in obtaining a first notion of the nature of a given frequency distribution. There are several important widely different types of distributions. Figures IV–1, 3, 4,

TABLE IV–5

Deaths from Typhoid Fever, by Age, in
the United States, 1930 (*Mortality
Statistics*, 1930, U. S. Dept. of
Commerce, p. 266.)

Age	No. of Deaths
0– 4	270
5– 9	425
10–14	616
15–19	939
20–24	881
25–29	579
30–34	381
35–44	591
45–54	456
55–64	275
65–74	141
75 and over	45

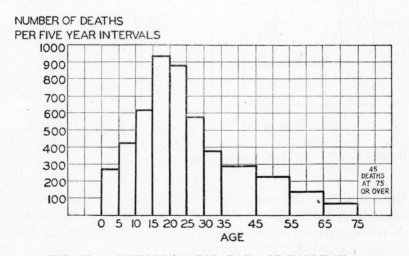

FIG. IV-5.   HISTOGRAM FOR DATA OF TABLE IV-5.

and 5 are all of the same general type, roughly symmetrical
with respect to a definite, somewhat central peak. They
illustrate the most numerous and most important class of

frequency distribution. Figure IV–6 belongs to the *J-type* of distribution, which is fairly common. (The J is here reversed.)

The relative proportions of a frequency polygon or of any graph are dependent upon the size of the horizontal unit compared with the vertical unit. Too small a horizontal unit makes the common form of frequency polygon seem

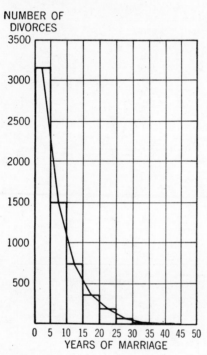

NUMBER OF DIVORCES

YEARS OF MARRIAGE

FIG. IV-6. HISTOGRAM AND FREQUENCY POLYGON FOR DATA OF TABLE IV-6.

TABLE IV–6

DISTRIBUTION OF DIVORCE CASES IN CHICAGO, 1919, BY FIVE-YEAR PERIODS OF MARRIED LIFE (Ernest R. Mowrer, *Family Disorganization*. Chicago University Press, 1927, p. 86.)

Years of Marriage	No. of Divorces
0– 4......	3164
5– 9......	1515
10–14......	743
15–19......	348
20–24......	191
25–29......	70
30–34......	25
35–39......	15
40–44......	4

narrow and tall; too large a unit makes it broad and flat. We might say for guidance that the rectangle enclosing the graph should ordinarily range from a height equal to about half the length to a height about equal to the length. A ratio of two to three is usually good. The graph itself should fairly well fill the rectangle.

In any graphical representation of statistical data, the diagram should contain the following items:

a. A label or title which completely describes the nature and source of the data. This should be printed so as to be read and understood easily.

b. The scale of measurement clearly indicated along the appropriate axes.

c. An accurately constructed figure of adequate size and proper proportions.

6. Applications. It has been remarked that many frequency distributions yield frequency polygons which are

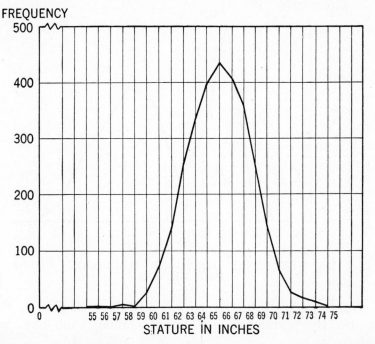

FIG. IV-7. FREQUENCY POLYGON FOR THE STATURES OF 2984 ENGLISH CRIMINALS. (Data from Charles Goring, *The English Convict,* H. M. S. Office, 1913, p. 386, slightly modified.)

characterized by a certain degree of symmetry with respect to a somewhat central peak. In particular, biological data involving measurements of length, width, weight, and so forth, are usually of this character. Sometimes this symmetry is very nearly perfect, as in the case of Figure IV–7. In other cases, the data may yield a *skew* polygon.

The class which corresponds to the maximum frequency in a distribution or to the peak of a polygon is called the *modal class.* For fairly symmetric distributions, it should be obvious that the average value will be somewhere within or near the modal class. From these facts it is often possible to derive important conclusions concerning the nature of observed data by reference to the frequency polygon alone. The following two illustrations bear on this point.

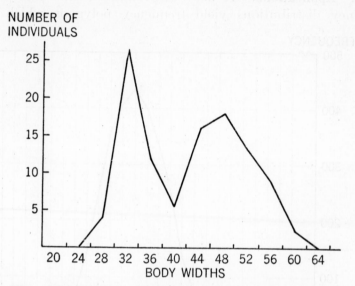

FIG. IV-8. FREQUENCY POLYGONS FOR BODY WIDTHS OF PARAMECIUM.

EXAMPLE 1. From *Genetics*, by Herbert E. Walter, 1919, p. 48 (By permission of The Macmillan Company, publishers.):

Sometimes two conspicuous modes make their appearance in a frequency polygon, as Jennings found, for example, in measuring the body width of a population of the protozoan *Paramecium*. [Figure IV-8.]

It was subsequently found that the two modes in this polygon were due to the fact that the material in question was a mixture of two closely related species, *Paramecium aurelia* and *Paramecium caudatum*, the individuals of which arranged themselves around their own mean in each instance.

Although such an explanation does not always turn out to be the right one, the biometrician is led to suspect when a two or more moded polygon appears that he is dealing with a mixture of more than one kind of material, each of which fluctuates around its own average.

EXAMPLE 2. From *Studies in Human Biology*, by Raymond Pearl, Williams and Wilkins, 1924, pp. 367-369.

Comparison of the two polygons below would lead one to

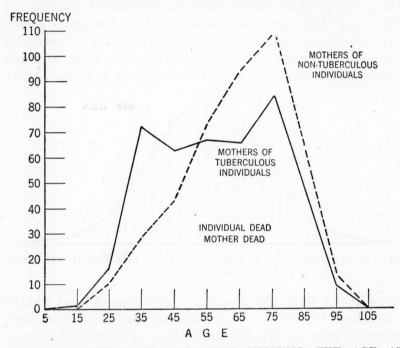

FIG. IV-9. FREQUENCY POLYGONS SHOWING THE AGE AT DEATH OF MOTHERS OF TUBERCULOUS AND NON-TUBERCULOUS INDIVIDUALS (THEMSELVES DEAD).

infer that the mothers of non-tuberculous individuals live, on an average, longer than do mothers of tuberculous individuals. This conclusion has been further justified by an analysis of the numerical data.

7. The frequency curve. Table IV–3 exhibits the head lengths of 462 criminals arranged according to class intervals of four millimeters each, and Figure IV–1 shows the corresponding histogram and frequency polygon. The head lengths range from 171.5 to 219.5 millimeters. Suppose that we had been able to record the head lengths of a group of criminals four times as numerous, and had chosen a class interval one-fourth as wide. The total frequency, N, would have changed from 462 to 1848, and the class interval, k, would have changed from four millimeters to one millimeter. Thus, the product, Nk, would have remained constant at 1848, and this represents the area of the histogram or the equivalent area under the polygon. The effect of increasing the total frequency and decreasing the class interval would have been to "smooth out" the frequency polygon and to

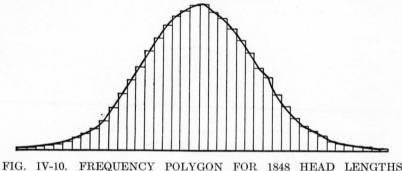

FIG. IV-10. FREQUENCY POLYGON FOR 1848 HEAD LENGTHS
(Imaginary Data).

make it look more like a curve. The range of head lengths would have been increased and the polygon would have been extended more to the left and right. The general appearance would probably have been as in Figure IV–10. An excellent example from real life of a similar distribution is shown in Figure IV–7. Note that the large total frequency, 2984, increases the number of abnormally small and abnormally large statures, and thus tends to make the polygon "tail out" more gradually to the left and to the right.

If the total frequency, N, is imagined to increase indefinitely while the class interval, k, approaches zero in such a manner that the area, Nk, under the polygon remains constant, the polygon may be considered to approach, as a limiting form, a smooth curve of the type shown in Figure IV–11. This ideal curve is called a *frequency curve*. The shape of a frequency curve will be determined by the nature of the data which it represents. Its size and relative proportions will depend upon the units or scale of measurement. The two most common types of frequency curves are the symmetric type (Figure IV–11) and the asymmetric or skew type (See Figure VIII–2). The concept of the frequency curve is of the highest importance in statistical work. The curve is interpreted as the geometric representation of the ideal law of distribution for the given data.

The generally symmetric character of a vast number of

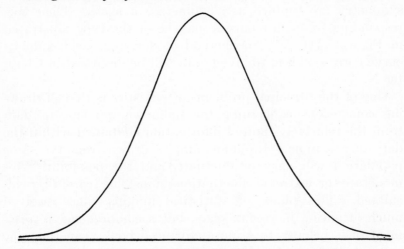

FIG. IV-11.   A NORMAL FREQUENCY CURVE.

frequency distributions arising in widely different fields of statistical inquiry is one of the most significant properties observed. This symmetry is concerned primarily with the more central values of the distribution, and not with its "tails." Good symmetry, for example, is observed in the distribution of the head lengths of English criminals. This group of criminals may be imagined to be a sample group selected from a much larger, potentially infinite group of criminals. This larger (fictitious) group is called the *population* or *universe* from which the sample is conceived to originate. The frequency curve of Figure IV–11 may represent the (infinite) universe or population of head lengths. The pattern which sample frequency distributions tend to follow is assumed to be that of the universe.

The normal frequency curve is the name given to a certain symmetric, bell-shaped curve illustrated in Figure IV–11. Such a curve, it should be noted, is asymptotic to the horizontal axis; that is, it approaches a condition of tangency to this axis as the curve recedes indefinitely to the left and right. Normal frequency curves are associated with frequency distributions which are fairly symmetric. Distributions lacking symmetry are typified as asymmetric or skew. Their corresponding frequency curves may be of the type illustrated in Figure VIII–2. The method of deriving the frequency curve corresponding to given data will be discussed in Chapter X.

One of the principal problems of statistics is that of drawing conclusions concerning the unknown universe of data from the relatively limited information contained within the data of a sample. Random samples drawn from the same population will vary or fluctuate, and the possibilities for moderate or extreme fluctuations must be carefully calculated. This phase of statistical inference has received much attention in recent years, but a comprehensive treatment of it belongs to a more advanced book than this one.

8. A system of notation. In many of the illustrations and exercises given in the preceding two chapters, each set of data involves a varying magnitude, such as the price of milk, the population of the United States, the number of divorces, and so on, together with recorded values of this magnitude. The changing magnitude is called a *variable*, and in mathematics is usually symbolized by one of the letters near the end of the alphabet, such as t, x, y, and so on. A recorded value of the variable is called a *variate*. Thus, the prices of milk in dollars (Table III–1), the populations of the United States (Table III–2), and the numbers of divorces (Table IV–6), are examples of variates. Variates are usually represented by the symbol for the variable with subscripts attached, such as t_1, x_4, y_i, and so forth. These are read as follows: t sub-one, x sub-four, y sub-i, and so on.

It is necessary at this point to introduce an important notation for variates and other quantities associated with them. The mid-values of the class intervals arising in a frequency distribution may be treated as variates. These will be denoted, in order, by x_1, x_2, x_3, . . . x_n, and their corresponding frequencies by f_1, f_2, f_3, . . . f_n. Thus, in Table IV–3, $x_1 = 173.5$, $x_2 = 177.5$, $x_3 = 181.5$, . . . $x_{12} = 217.5$, and $f_1 = 3, f_2 = 9, f_3 = 29, . . . f_{12} = 1$. Here n, the number of classes, equals 12. The total frequency will always be denoted by N. The *relative frequency* of the ith class becomes $\dfrac{f_i}{N}$. Obviously,

$$f_1 + f_2 + f_3 + \cdot \cdot \cdot + f_n = N.$$

In the data of Table IV–3, $N = 462$, and $\dfrac{f_7}{N} = \dfrac{88}{462} = 0.190$.

Inasmuch as we shall be using sums of variates throughout future work, a standard symbol, the capital Greek letter *sigma*, Σ, will be employed to denote a sum, as illustrated below:

$$\sum_{i=1}^{n} f_i = f_1 + f_2 + f_3 + \cdot \cdot \cdot + f_n.$$

The symbol on the left may be read "summation f_i, i taken from 1 to n," and means that the subscript i is a discrete variable whose values are the integers from 1 to n inclusive. These values are attached to f as subscripts, and the sum of the resulting f_i's taken. In like manner,

$$\sum_{i=1}^{10} x_i = x_1 + x_2 + x_3 + \cdot \cdot \cdot + x_{10};$$

$$\sum_{i=1}^{n} f_i u_i = f_1 u_1 + f_2 u_2 + f_3 u_3 + \cdot \cdot \cdot + f_n u_n;$$

and

$$\sum_{j=1}^{8} f_j(x_j + y_j) = f_1(x_1 + y_1) + f_2(x_2 + y_2) + \cdot \cdot \cdot + f_8(x_8 + y_8).$$

Note that the variable in the summation is indicated below the summation sign, Σ. In the last three lines, the variable subscripts are i, i, and j, respectively.

There are a few basic theorems involving summations whose proofs follow immediately from the definition of the summation symbol.

THEOREM 1. *The summation of a constant times a variable equals the constant times the summation of the variable, that is:*

$$\sum_{i=1}^{n} kx_i = k \sum_{i=1}^{n} x_i.$$

Proof:
$$\sum_{i=1}^{n} kx_i = kx_1 + kx_2 + kx_3 + \cdots + kx_n$$
$$= k(x_1 + x_2 + x_3 + \cdots + x_n)$$
$$= k \sum_{i=1}^{n} x_i.$$

THEOREM 2. *The summation of the sum (or difference) of two variables equals the sum (or difference) of their summations, that is:*

$$\sum_{i=1}^{n} (x_i \pm y_i) = \sum_{i=1}^{n} x_i \pm \sum_{i=1}^{n} y_i$$

Proof:
$$\sum_{i=1}^{n} (x_i \pm y_i) = (x_1 \pm y_1) + (x_2 \pm y_2) + \cdots + (x_n \pm y_n)$$
$$= (x_1 + x_2 + \cdots + x_n) \pm (y_1 + y_2 + \cdots + y_n)$$
$$= \sum_{i=1}^{n} x_i \pm \sum_{i=1}^{n} y_i.$$

THEOREM 3. *The summation of a constant taken from 1 to* **n** *equals* **n** *times the constant, that is:*

$$\sum_{i=1}^{n} k = nk.$$

Proof: Since the constant, k, is unaffected by the subscript,

$$\sum_{i=1}^{n} k = k + k + k + \cdots + k$$
$$= nk.$$

THEOREM 4. *The summation of the frequencies in a frequency distribution equals the total frequency, that is:*

$$\sum_{i=1}^{n} f_i = N.$$

The proof is obvious, for, by definition, $f_1 + f_2 + f_3 + \cdots + f_n = N$.

As a simple example of the use of the summation symbol, we can prove readily that the area of a histogram corresponding to a total frequency, N, and a common class interval, k, is Nk. The area of each rectangle is the product of its width, k, by its altitude, f_i. The total area is, therefore, $\sum_{i=1}^{n} kf_i$, where n represents the number of classes.

But,
$$\sum_{i=1}^{n} kf_i = k \sum_{i=1}^{n} f_i \qquad \text{by Theorem 1,}$$
$$= kN \qquad \text{by Theorem 4.}$$

9. Simple probability. Most of us are aware, in a vague way at least, of the notion of probability. Books on "How to Play Bridge" often contain the probabilities of holding certain cards or combinations; Monte Carlo's existence depends upon fundamental laws of probability in gambling; life insurance companies build their premium rates from the probabilities or expectations of life computed from mortality tables. (See Table K of the Supplementary Tables.) Just what do we mean by *probability* in mathematics? It is difficult to frame a completely adequate definition of this word, but we can state a simple one which will be useful for the purposes of this book.

If an event can happen in **N** *different ways equally well, and if* **f** *of these ways are called favorable, the probability for success is defined as the quotient* $\dfrac{f}{N}$.

For example, if a box contains seven balls alike in every respect except as to color, and if five of them are white and two are black, the probability of drawing a white ball at random from the box is $\frac{5}{7}$. In this case, $N = 7$ and $f = 5$. If a coin is tossed, the probability of getting heads is $\frac{1}{2}$. Here $N = 2$ and $f = 1$.

Obviously, mathematical probability is a number ranging from 0 to 1 inclusive. When (as here discussed) the number of alternatives is finite, a probability of 1 means certainty; a probability of 0 means impossibility. If p is the probability for the success of an event, and q is the probability for failure, then $p + q = 1$, for we are certain to have either success or failure.

Suppose we ask, "What is the probability that a criminal chosen at random from among the 462 of Table IV–3 has a head length between 183.5 and 187.5 millimeters?" Here $N = 462$ and $f = 76$. Therefore, the relative frequency, $\dfrac{f}{N}$, gives us the answer $\dfrac{76}{462}$, or about 0.16. Again, suppose that we wish to find the probability that just two heads will appear when six pennies are tossed. We could find the answer in either of two different ways, by simple mathematical analysis or by actual experiment.

Using the former method, it can easily be shown by methods to be discussed later (Section XIII–9) that the desired probability equals $\dfrac{6!}{2! \, 4!}$ $(\tfrac{1}{2})^2$ $(\tfrac{1}{2})^4$, or $\tfrac{15}{64}$. (Here $6! = 6 \cdot 5 \cdot 4 \cdot 3 \cdot 2 \cdot 1 = 720$, $4! = 4 \cdot 3 \cdot 2 \cdot 1 = 24$, and $2! = 2 \cdot 1 = 2$.) This is an *a priori* result: it has been obtained *in advance* by simple mathematical calculation based upon the definition of probability stated above. The result states that *theoretically* two heads appear 15 times in 64 tosses. Another way of putting it is to say that $\tfrac{15}{64}$ is the theoretical relative frequency in the long run with which two heads appear when six pennies are tossed together repeatedly.

Suppose that we compare this theoretical result with an actual result shown in Table IV–4. We find there that out of 128 tosses of six pennies, two heads appeared 28 times. The actual relative frequency was $\tfrac{28}{128}$, or $\tfrac{14}{64}$, which differs slightly from the theoretical frequency or probability just stated. There is no reason to expect always close agreement between corresponding actual and relative frequencies, but it can be shown that this agreement improves as the total frequency, N, increases. This important fact will be made clearer in the next two paragraphs.

To find, experimentally, the probability requested above, we should have to toss six pennies a great many times, say several thousand times, and divide the recorded number of times, f, that two heads appeared, by the total number, N, of tosses. The fraction, $\dfrac{f}{N}$, obtained would yield a reasonably approximate answer for the probability. We could increase the accuracy of our answer by increasing the number of tosses. If the tosses were made with equal "randomness," it would be found that the ratio $\dfrac{f}{N}$ would approach as a limiting value $\frac{15}{64}$. We could consider the true probability to be the limit approached by the relative frequency $\dfrac{f}{N}$ as N is conceived to increase without limit. The last statement can be written symbolically in the form $p = \lim\limits_{N\to\infty} \dfrac{f}{N}$, which is read "$p$ equals the limit of f over N as N becomes infinite." Probability defined in this manner is sometimes called *a posteriori* or empirical probability. The probabilities computed from mortality statistics are all empirical probabilities, based upon extensive records of life and death.

Suppose now that we return to the frequency distribution of head lengths. We could say that the probability, p_i, that a criminal selected from the whole universe of criminals* belonged to the class with mid-value x_i is given by the formula:

$$p_i = \lim_{N\to\infty} \frac{f_i}{N}.$$

10. Theoretical frequency distributions. The distributions which we have studied thus far have all arisen from actual observation or experiment. In particular, the data of Table IV–4 arose from an actual series of tosses. Some frequency distributions, however, are theoretical, not empirical. If we compute, as shown in Chapter XIII, the respective probabilities of obtaining 0, 1, 2, 3, 4, 5, and 6 heads when six pennies are tossed, we arrive at the results shown in Table IV–7.

---

* That is, English criminals of the type studied.

Any series of numbers proportional to the probabilities (theoretical relative frequencies) constitutes a theoretical frequency distribution. The last two columns of Table IV–7 give theoretical frequency distributions for 64 and 128 tosses. The actual distribution of Table IV–4 constitutes a sample set of tosses, and it may be compared with the ideal or

TABLE IV–7

THEORETICAL FREQUENCY DISTRIBUTIONS FOR THE NUMBER OF HEADS WHEN SIX PENNIES ARE TOSSED

No. of Heads	Probability	Theoretical Frequency	
		64 Tosses	128 Tosses
0	$\left(\dfrac{1}{2}\right)^6 = \dfrac{1}{64}$	1	2
1	$\dfrac{6!}{1!5!}\left(\dfrac{1}{2}\right)\left(\dfrac{1}{2}\right)^5 = \dfrac{6}{64}$	6	12
2	$\dfrac{6!}{2!4!}\left(\dfrac{1}{2}\right)^2\left(\dfrac{1}{2}\right)^4 = \dfrac{15}{64}$	15	30
3	$\dfrac{6!}{3!3!}\left(\dfrac{1}{2}\right)^3\left(\dfrac{1}{2}\right)^3 = \dfrac{20}{64}$	20	40
4	$\dfrac{6!}{4!2!}\left(\dfrac{1}{2}\right)^4\left(\dfrac{1}{2}\right)^2 = \dfrac{15}{64}$	15	30
5	$\dfrac{6!}{5!1!}\left(\dfrac{1}{2}\right)^5\left(\dfrac{1}{2}\right) = \dfrac{6}{64}$	6	12
6	$\left(\dfrac{1}{2}\right)^6 = \dfrac{1}{64}$	1	2
Total	1	64	128

theoretical result shown in the last column of Table IV–7. This comparison is shown in Table IV–8. Samples will deviate more or less from the theoretical form. As already stated, the degree of variation between a sample and its ideal or *norm* is studied in great detail in more advanced work on statistics. Chapters XIII and XIV give a brief introduction to this important field of study.

Special attention should be called to the fact that the approach to the study of the ideal frequency distribution and its curve may be made through the concept of the theoretical

TABLE IV–8

Comparison of Theoretical and Actual Frequencies for the Number of Heads Occurring When
Six Pennies Are Tossed 128 Times

No. of Heads	Theoretical	Actual
0	2	2
1	12	10
2	30	28
3	40	44
4	30	30
5	12	13
6	2	1
Total	128	128

frequency distribution of which Table IV–7 is an illustration.
The computed underlying probabilities are of first importance
in such an approach.

IV—Exercises

1. Toss five pennies 64 times and record the frequency distribution, together with the tallies, for the number of heads appearing on
each toss. Shake the pennies before each toss.

2. Try to cut a double pack of playing cards (104 cards) exactly
in the middle, and repeat the process until 50 cuts have been made.
Shuffle the pack between cuts. At each trial, record the number of
cards removed at each cut, and construct a frequency distribution,
with tallies, from your result.

3. The marks in Higher Mathematics received by candidates in
the British Civil Service Examination of 1937 are given in Table IV–9.
Using class intervals 0–19, 20–39, and so on, construct a frequency
table similar to that in Section IV–1.

4. Using class intervals of your own choosing, construct a frequency table like that in Section IV–1 for the heights in Table IV–10.

5. Do the preceding exercise for the weights.

6. (a) What are the class boundaries in Exercises 7, 8, 9, 10,
and 12?

(b) What are the class marks (mid-values) in Exercises 7, 8,
11, 14, and 16?

(c) Select from the frequency distributions of Exercises
7–18 those which are discrete.

TABLE IV–9 (To accompany Ex. IV-3.)

MARKS IN HIGHER MATHEMATICS RECEIVED BY CANDIDATES IN THE BRITISH
CIVIL SERVICE EXAMINATION OF 1937 (MAXIMUM MARK, 200 POINTS)

(From *Questions, Papers, and Table of Results of the Competition Held in April
1937*, Civil Service Commission, Executive Group.   By permission of the Controller of His Britannic Majesty's Stationery Office.)

168	153	115	105	73	78
185	140	128	90	95	90
150	143	85	125	93	60
135	133	128	123	13	23
168	125	100	85	90	20
155	155	133	75	53	48
118	130	100	130	70	33
165	170	120	130	90	48
153	145	120	108	90	25
140	138	115	85	98	20
143	133	138	53	88	80
160	140	73	98	83	18
145	108	123	73	40	30
130	130	150	93	75	33
125	95	135	88	25	28
135	143	48	85	68	63
160	90	123	113	43	20
115	118	70	113	78	50
138	135	103	65	65	33
140	163	90	100	50	3

*   *   *

In Exercises 7–16 and Exercise 18, construct histograms (unless
vertical line or bar charts are more appropriate) and frequency polygons for the distributions.

✕ **7.**   The precipitation in New York City for the month of March,
1878–1933:

No. of Inches	Frequency
0.00– .99...............	1
1.00–1.99..............	7
2.00–2.99..............	11
3.00–3.99..............	12
4.00–4.99..............	15
5.00–5.99..............	6
6.00–6.99..............	4

TABLE IV–10 (To accompany Exs. IV: 4, 5.)

HEIGHTS IN INCHES AND WEIGHTS IN POUNDS OF 285 BOSTON UNIVERSITY WOMEN STUDENTS

Hts.	Wts.	Hts.	Wts.	Hts.	Wts.	Hts.	Wts.	Hts.	Wts.	Hts.	Wts.	Hts.	Wts.
61	122	65	124	63	128	66	112	65	146	63	119	65	128
65	132	72	137	67	130	62	102	64	109	59	113	64	128
62	125	62	115	66	122	59	107	63	106	62	102	70	189
62	121	66	132	67	129	66	120	68	123	66	130	63	120
64	120	64	132	66	152	66	130	64	100	60	96	64	124
64	122	64	123	63	121	60	104	61	113	68	128	62	118
64	118	62	100	62	123	66	140	66	141	67	149	63	113
64	111	68	118	60	105	61	116	65	119	70	176	64	135
63	113	63	124	59	150	62	117	61	109	62	108	64	122
67	152	65	130	65	134	67	200	66	135	67	123	66	143
64	104	65	120	61	111	68	158	65	116	60	103	66	149
63	133	67	129	64	116	64	125	65	130	66	118	62	134
63	123	63	153	68	136	61	127	66	171	65	121	62	123
58	103	62	108	63	144	66	134	61	131	66	156	69	135
63	110	66	120	63	121	69	161	63	102	64	144	62	123
64	180	65	138	60	107	62	112	61	122	62	126	67	158
68	164	66	117	67	137	66	118	67	115	68	142	65	132
64	131	64	119	63	131	65	104	63	126	66	112	63	105
68	142	63	109	62	122	62	131	66	120	63	196	65	127
61	124	63	115	64	108	62	144	59	117	69	138	60	108
65	134	64	122	64	124	62	115	61	95	67	170	64	133
61	121	63	113	67	135	63	137	64	129	65	118	63	130
66	135	63	106	65	140	64	100	61	133	64	108	59	107
61	112	67	131	63	134	65	146	65	113	65	117	67	147
65	129	63	138	66	136	61	93	60	95	62	100	62	115
64	127	69	131	68	137	63	112	65	129	64	121	65	125
62	122	66	97	60	108	64	143	64	114	67	145	62	122
66	141	64	130	64	137	60	104	64	120	67	111	66	152
64	108	62	112	62	143	63	124	68	140	67	131	63	120
63	116	65	129	62	120	60	106	59	88	64	121	63	143
59	98	66	120	63	115	60	88	66	136	69	137	61	97
67	128	63	123	71	125	65	130	62	101	66	120	65	118
65	145	62	95	64	156	62	96	64	119	63	111	65	116
66	106	66	120	61	109	65	118	59	118	65	119	64	112
65	130	63	116	66	103	62	119	61	95	65	130	66	117
64	119	66	121	63	131	62	115	65	123	64	143	69	153
63	108	59	100	67	141	66	129	62	103	61	126	63	132
65	178	64	136	62	120	64	158	64	133	66	142	63	141
62	130	65	138	64	115	63	120	65	124	63	127	57	178
63	120	61	132	62	114	64	146	65	114	64	131		
63	120	64	125	64	116	66	128	61	124	67	148		

8. The maximum daily temperatures in New York City for January, 1919–1925:

Temperature	Frequency
8–12	2
13–17	4
18–22	12
23–27	16
28–32	25
33–37	34
38–42	37
43–47	34
48–52	17
53–57	3
58–62	2
Total	186

9. Call discount rates (weekly averages) at a certain bank for 100 weeks:

Rate in Per Cent	Frequency
2.00	8
2.50	7
3.00	12
3.50	10
4.00	12
4.50	15
5.00	16
5.50	8
6.00	7
6.50	3
7.00	2

10. Rates of taxation for school support in cities and towns of Massachusetts, for the year 1921–1922 (adapted from Swift, Graves, and Tiegs, *Studies in Public School Finance*, Vol. 2., University of Minnesota, Minneapolis, 1923, p. 88).

(Table on next page.)

Dollars per $1000 of Assessed Valuation	Total No. of Cities and Towns Levying
1.50	1
2.50	0
3.50	3
4.50	5
5.50	17
6.50	40
7.50	50
8.50	49
9.50	57
10.50	53
11.50	28
12.50	27
13.50	19
14.50	3
15.50	2
16.50	1
Total	355

11. The brain-weights of adult Swedish males (from Raymond Pearl, *Studies in Human Biology*, Williams and Wilkins, Baltimore, 1924, p. 47):

Grams of Brain-Weight	Observed
Under 1100	0
1100–1150	1
1150–1200	10
1200–1250	21
1250–1300	44
1300–1350	53
1350–1400	86
1400–1450	72
1450–1500	60
1500–1550	28
1550–1600	25
1600–1650	12
1650–1700	3
1700–1750	1
1750 and over	0
Total	416

12. Intelligence quotients of runaway boys (from Clairette P. Armstrong, *660 Runaway Boys*, Richard C. Badger, Gorham Press, Boston, 1932, p. 31). (Table on next page.)

I. Q.	Number
30– 39	2
40– 49	6
50– 59	60
60– 69	140
70– 79	184
80– 89	139
90– 99	78
100–109	37
110–119	14

13. Sizes of shoes worn by 235 college girls (original data):

Size	No. of Girls
$2\frac{1}{2}$	2
3	2
$3\frac{1}{2}$	15
4	21
$4\frac{1}{2}$	21
5	36
$5\frac{1}{2}$	48
6	42
$6\frac{1}{2}$	26
7	15
$7\frac{1}{2}$	5
8	1
$8\frac{1}{2}$	1

14. Wages per day of male employees in 1860 (from Wesley C. Mitchell, *A History of the Greenbacks*, University of Chicago, 1903, p. 293):

Wage Classes	Number
$0.25–0.49	118
0.50–0.74	123
0.75–0.99	599
1.00–1.24	2,186
1.25–1.49	542
1.50–1.74	609
1.75–1.99	184
2.00–2.24	628
2.25–2.49	66
2.50–2.74	23
2.75–2.99	1
3.00–3.24	28
3.25–3.49	1
3.50+	3
	5,111

15.   Frequencies of errors in Minnesota preliminary farm price indexes (from Walter B. Garver, "The Reliability of Preliminary Price Indexes," *Journal of the American Statistical Association*, June, 1938, p. 383):

Per Cent Error of Index	Total for 16 Commodities
0.0–0.4................	108
0.5–0.9................	87
1.0–1.4................	36
1.5–1.9................	26
2.0–2.4................	22
2.5–2.9................	9
3.0–3.4................	4
3.5–3.9................	3
4.0–4.9................	10
5.0–5.9................	4
6.00 and over..........	3
	312

16.   Average weekly earnings during 1936 of urban Negro workers in the Mountain Region (*The Urban Negro Worker in the United States*, 1925–1936, Vol. 1, U. S. Department of Interior, p. 116):

Average Weekly Earnings	Total
Less than $5............	38
$ 5– 9................	17
10–14................	32
15–19................	25
20–24................	24
25–29................	10
30–34................	8
35–39................	9
40–44................	6
45–49................	1
50–74................	1
75–99................	2
	173

* * *

17.   Construct frequency polygons, as in Figure IV–9, for the distributions of weight per mille (*a*) at mobilization, 1917–1918, and (*b*) at demobilization, 1919, of United States Army Troops.   Compare the polygons and draw conclusions.   (From C. B. Davenport and A. G. Love, *The Medical Department of the United States Army in the World War*, Vol. 15, *Statistics*, Part I, "Army Anthropology," 1921, p. 121.)

Class Range	Weight per Mille	
	At Mob.	At Dem.
90– 99..............	0.21	.....
100–109..............	11.27	5.206
110–119..............	72.42	41.602
120–129..............	170.76	132.605
130–139..............	238.32	222.553
140–149..............	217.25	235.943
150–159..............	144.85	177.641
160–169..............	79.29	104.061
170–179..............	36.37	48.003
180–189..............	15.96	20.587
190–199..............	7.92	7.246
200 or over..........	5.40	4.561

18. The size of complete families (total progeny) of farmers (from Raymond Pearl, *The Biology of Population Growth*, Alfred A. Knopf, 1925, p. 206):

Total Progeny from Completed Marriages	Number
0..................	78
1..................	88
2..................	141
3..................	187
4..................	192
5..................	184
6..................	184
7..................	148
8..................	147
9..................	141
10..................	113
11..................	76
12..................	44
13..................	29
14..................	9
15..................	6
16..................	5
17..................	4
18..................	0
19..................	0
20..................	0
21..................	1
22..................	0
23..................	1
	1778

19. In what respects is Figure IV–12 below misleading or fallacious? The diagram is constructed from the following data:

Ages	Annual Death Rate per 1000
0– 4................	17.2
5– 9................	2.1
10–14................	1.6
15–19................	2.7
20–24................	2.8
25–29................	3.2
30–34................	4.0
35–44................	5.9
45–54................	10.9
55–64................	25.1
65–74................	55.3
75+................	135.9

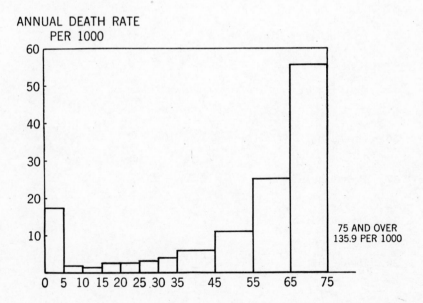

FIG. IV-12.   FREQUENCY POLYGON FOR DEATHS BY AGE GROUPS
(Fictitious Data).

Exercises on Summations

In Exercises 20–28, expand the term given.

20. $\sum_{i=1}^{n} F_i$ 23. $\sum_{i=1}^{7} x_i^2$ 26. $\sum_{i=1}^{n} (r_i + s_i)$

21. $\sum_{i=1}^{9} f_i$ 24. $\sum_{i=1}^{m} (x_i - x_0)$ 27. $\sum_{i=1}^{6} f_i(x_i + y_i)$

22. $\sum_{i=1}^{n} f_i y_i$ 25. $\sum_{i=1}^{n} f_i y_i^3$ 28. $\sum_{i=1}^{m} \dfrac{a}{x_i}$

*   *   *

In Exercises 29–35, write the terms as summations.

29. $X_1 + X_2 + X_3 + \cdots\cdots + X_{10}$

30. $f_1 x_1^2 + f_2 x_2^2 + \cdots + f_n x_n^2$

31. $\dfrac{f_1}{N} + \dfrac{f_2}{N} + \dfrac{f_3}{N} + \cdots + \dfrac{f_n}{N}$

32. $(x_1 - x_0) + (x_2 - x_0) + \cdots + (x_{15} - x_0)$

33. $f_1(y_1 + z_1) + f_2(y_2 + z_2) + \cdots + f_m(y_m + z_m)$

34. $f_1(x_1 - \bar{x})^2 + f_2(x_2 - \bar{x})^2 + \cdots\cdots + f_n(x_n - \bar{x})^2$

35. $x_1 y_1 + x_2 y_2 + \cdots\cdots + x_{50} y_{50}$

*   *   *

36. Prove that $\sum_{i=1}^{10} (x_i - k) = \sum_{i=1}^{10} x_i - 10k$

37. Prove that $\sum_{i=1}^{N} (X_i - Y_i) = \sum_{i=1}^{N} X_i - \sum_{i=1}^{N} Y_i$

38. Prove that $\sum_{i=1}^{n} \dfrac{f_i}{N} = 1$

39. Prove that $\sum_{i=1}^{N} \dfrac{(x_i - x_m)^2}{k} = \dfrac{1}{k}\left[\sum_{i=1}^{N} x_i^2 - 2x_m \sum_{i=1}^{N} x_i + Nx_m^2 \right]$

40. Prove that $\left(\sum_{i=1}^{N} x_i\right)^2 \neq \sum_{i=1}^{N} x_i^2$

41.   Prove that $\sum\limits_{i=1}^{N} x_i \sum\limits_{i=1}^{N} y_i \neq \sum\limits_{i=1}^{N} x_i y_i$

Exercises on Probability

42.   A bag contains 7 black balls and 3 white balls all of the same size, weight, and material.   If a ball is drawn at random, what is the probability that it is black?

43.   A president is to be chosen by lot from a club composed of 12 men and 8 women.   What is the probability that a man is selected?

44.   If 600,000 ordinary automobile registration numbers are issued in a given state, what is the probability that the next license number seen (*a*) is under 200,000?   (*b*) begins with 4?   Assume no out-of-state cars present.

45.   In cutting a pack of cards, what is the probability of cutting (*a*) an ace?   (*b*) a heart?   (*c*) a face card or ace?

46.   What is the probability that the throw of a pair of dice is (*a*) 5?   (*b*) 10?

47.   What is the probability that the throw of 2 dice is under 7?

48.   From Table IV–2 ,find the probability that a bill for electricity is (*a*) between \$5.00 and \$5.50; (*b*) \$7.00 or over; (*c*) under \$6.00.

49.   From Exercise 13, find the probability that a college girl wore (*a*) a size 6 shoe; (*b*) a shoe of any size from 4 to 7 inclusive; (*c*) a shoe of size larger than 7.

50.   From Figure III–4, find the probability that a freshman (*a*) is not absent during a semester; (*b*) is absent not more than twice; (*c*) is absent more than three times.

51.   From Exercise 17, find the relative frequency of weights at mobilization (*a*) between 150 and 160 pounds; (*b*) between 120 and 170 pounds; (*c*) under 120 pounds; (*d*) 180 pounds or over.

52.   From the Mortality Table, Table K of the Supplementary Tables, compute the probability (*a*) that a person ten years of age will live to be twenty; (*b*) that a person thirty years old will live to be fifty; (*c*) that a person eighty years old will live to be ninety.

THE ARITHMETIC, HARMONIC, AND GEOMETRIC MEANS

❖❖⫶||||||||||⫶||||||||||⫶||||||||||⫶||||||||||⫶||||||||||⫶||||||||||⫶||||||||||⫶||||||||||⫶||||||||||⫶||||||||||⫶||||||||||❖❖

"If the average man could be exactly determined, . . . he could be considered as a type of the beautiful; and all major deviations from his proportions and from his attitudes are to be classed as deformities and disease; whatever feature is not only dissimilar with respect to the proportions and forms, but departs still more from the observed limits, is to be ranked as a monstrosity."

L. A. J. QUETELET, *The Physics of Society* (1835).

1. Introduction. An *average* is a typical or representative value. It is a familiar notion even to a nonmathematical person. In general, he understands the average bill for electric current to be the sum of the amounts of the bills divided by the number of the bills. He is likely, also, to understand the average size of men's shoes sold in a given store to be the size for which there is the greatest sale. However, these two interpretations of the meaning of "average" are quite different. They illustrate a frequent mistake made by the "average" nonmathematical person. The sum of the sizes of all shoes sold in the given store divided by the number of shoes sold usually yields a fraction, say 8.2, and this does not correspond, as a rule, to any standard size sold. The "most popular" size and the "mean" size (the latter) are different concepts. Each has an important place in statistics; they must not be confused. There are many kinds of averages in statistics.   Chapters V, VI, and VIII will be devoted to the most important ones.

Yule (Ref. 7) has described admirably six conditions which a statistical average should satisfy.   They are as follows:

1.   The average should be rigidly defined and not left to the mere estimation of the observer.

2.   It should be based on all the observations made.

3.   It should possess some simple and obvious properties and not be mathematically too abstract.

4.   It should be calculated with reasonable ease and rapidity.

5.   It should be as stable as possible.

6.   It should lend itself readily to algebraic treatment.

(A)   THE ARITHMETIC MEAN

2.   Definitions.   *The arithmetic mean, $\bar{x}$ (read "x-bar"), of a set of variates x_1, x_2, x_3, . . . x_N is defined as their sum, $\sum\limits_{i=1}^{N} x_i$, divided by their number, N.   Thus,*

$$\bar{x} = \frac{1}{N} \sum_{i=1}^{N} x_i. \tag{1}$$

This average is not only the most familiar one in use today, but it is also the most basic in theory and the most useful in practice.   As an illustration, consider the following data:

The age at inauguration of the presidents of the United States from George Washington to Franklin Roosevelt:

57, 61, 57, 57, 58, 57, 61, 54, 68, 51, 49, 64, 50, 48, 65, 52, 56, 46, 54, 49, 50, 47, 55, 55, 54, 42, 51, 56 , 55, 51, 54, 51.

To find the arithmetic mean, we merely add the ages and divide by the number of presidents, 32.

$$\bar{x} = \frac{1735}{32} = 54.2.$$

The mean age of the presidents is therefore about 54 years. If an adding machine is not available, the simple operation of straightforward addition may often be made simpler by employing a *provisional mean*.   A glance at the data above shows that the mean is somewhere between 50 and 60 years. We choose 55 as a provisional mean, and add the positive and negative deviations from it. These deviations will be, in order:

2, 6, 2, 2, 3, 2, 6, −1, 13, −4, −6, 9, −5, −7, 10, −3
1, −9, −1, −6, −5, −8, 0, 0, −1, −13, −4, 1, 0, −4, −1, −4

Their sum, −25, divided by 32 yields −0.8 approximately. Hence, the mean age deviates from 55 by −0.8 and is 54.2 years. Formula (1) is used in practice when N is small, say under 50, and when it is not advisable to group the values into a frequency table.

In most statistical problems, the frequency distribution is employed, and in this case the definition of the arithmetic mean may be formulated as follows:

$$\bar{x} = \frac{1}{N} \sum_{i=1}^{n} f_i x_i, \tag{1a}$$

where f_i is the frequency of the class whose mid-value is x_i, n is the number of classes, and $N = \sum_{i=1}^{n} f_i$. Formulas (1) and (1a) represent essentially the same thing, for (1a) merely takes into account the fact that certain variates occur repeatedly, the number of repetitions being designated as the frequency f.

Formula (1a) gives precisely the same value for $\bar{x}$ as formula (1), provided that the arithmetic mean for each class interval is exactly the mid-value of the interval. This, however, is rarely the case, save possibly in a discrete set. Nevertheless, most frequency distributions in practice are of the roughly symmetrical type where the larger frequencies build up toward a maximum somewhere near the middle of the range of values. Thus, the mean value of each class interval in the lower half of the range is likely to be above the mid-value of the interval, and the mean value of each class interval in the upper half of the range is likely to be below the mid-value of the interval. As a consequence of these two compensating effects, formula (1a) will, in general, be accurate enough for most purposes, especially when N is large and the class interval reasonably small. In the case of the J-type of distribution there will be a distinct bias given to the mean in the direction of the largest class frequencies; and unless the class intervals are quite small, the error committed may be serious. For other more or less irregular distributions, no

TABLE V–1

COMPUTATION OF THE ARITHMETIC MEAN OF THE HEAD LENGTHS OF
462 ENGLISH CRIMINALS

(1)	(2)	(3)	(4)	(5)	(6)
				Check	
Mid-Value x_i	Frequency f_i	u_i	$f_i u_i$	$u_i + 1$	$f_i(u_i + 1)$
173.5	3	−5	−15	−4	−12
177.5	9	−4	−36	−3	−27
181.5	29	−3	−87	−2	−58
185.5	76	−2	−152	−1	−76
189.5	104	−1	−104	0	0
193.5 = x_0	110	0	0	1	110
197.5	88	1	88	2	176
201.5	30	2	60	3	90
205.5	6	3	18	4	24
209.5	4	4	16	5	20
213.5	2	5	10	6	12
217.5	1	6	6	7	7
			−394		−173
			198		439
Totals	462		−196		266

general rule can be stated save that small class intervals will increase the accuracy of formula (1a).

3. Computation of the mean. *The unit deviation, u_i, of a value, x_i, from a given value, x_0, is defined by the formula:*

$$u_i = \frac{x_i - x_0}{k}, \qquad (2)$$

where k is the width of the class interval. In Table IV–2, $k = 0.50$ (dollars); in Table IV–3, $k = 4$ (millimeters). By considering the class intervals to be of unit width and by finding the mean of the deviations of the mid-values from an arbitrary but convenient mid-value, x_0 (a provisional mean), the computation of $\bar{x}$ from a frequency table can be greatly simplified. We take as an example the data of Table IV–3, of which we use only columns 4 and 5. These appear as the first two columns in Table V–1. We select the somewhat central mid-value 193.5 as the provisional mean, x_0, from which the unit deviations, u_i, are recorded in column 3. These deviations are always integers, positive or negative (or zero), since the class intervals are reduced to unit width. For example,

$$u_1 = \frac{x_1 - x_0}{k} = \frac{173.5 - 193.5}{4} = -5$$

and

$$u_9 = \frac{x_9 - x_0}{k} = \frac{205.5 - 193.5}{4} = 3.$$

Instead of computing $\sum_{i=1}^{n} f_i x_i$, as required by formula (1a), we compute $\sum_{i=1}^{n} f_i u_i$, as shown in column 4, by multiplying the corresponding values of f and u in columns 2 and 3 and then dividing by the total frequency, 462. The result is the arithmetic mean of the u's, so that

$$\bar{u} = \frac{1}{N} \sum_{i=1}^{n} f_i u_i = \frac{-196}{462} = -0.424.$$

The number -0.424 represents the mean value of the unit deviations from 193.5. For a class width of 4, we get $4(-0.424) = -1.70$ as the mean of the deviations from 193.5; hence, if the head lengths deviate "on an average" by -1.70 from 193.5, their arithmetic mean must be 193.5 $-$ 1.70, or 191.8 (millimeters).

The preceding discussion leads us, therefore, to the formula

$$\bar{x} = k\bar{u} + x_0, \tag{1b}$$

which can be written in the more easily remembered form:

$$\bar{u} = \frac{\bar{x} - x_0}{k}. \tag{1c}$$

To obtain $\bar{x}$, we substitute the known values $\bar{u}$, x_0, and k in this formula, and solve for $\bar{x}$.

Thus,

$$- 0.424 = \frac{\bar{x} - 193.5}{4},$$

whence

$$\bar{x} = 191.8.$$

Equation (1c) may be formally established as follows:

$$u_i = \frac{x_i - x_0}{k};$$

hence, $\qquad \dfrac{1}{N}\Sigma f_i u_i = \dfrac{1}{N}\Sigma f_i\left(\dfrac{x_i - x_0}{k}\right);$

$$\bar{u} = \frac{1}{kN}\Sigma(f_i x_i - f_i x_0), \qquad \text{(Theorem 1, §IV-8)}$$

$$= \frac{1}{k}\left[\frac{1}{N}\Sigma f_i x_i - \frac{x_0}{N}\Sigma f_i\right], \qquad \text{(Theorems 1, 2, §IV-8)}$$

$$= \frac{1}{k}(\bar{x} - x_0). \qquad \text{(Formula (1a) and}$$
$$\text{Theorem 4, §IV-8).}$$

4. Change of scale. Reference was made in Section IV–5 to the effect on a graph of a change of scale. Let us discuss briefly the transformation which a frequency polygon or curve undergoes when the variate x_i is changed to u_i by means of equation (2):

$$u_i = \frac{x_i - x_0}{k}. \qquad (2)$$

In elementary algebra, we plot the graphs of simple functions. The position of a point in a plane is described by means of two numbers and a scale of measurement. A horizontal line, called the x-axis, is cut by a vertical line, called the y-axis, at a point O, called the *origin*. Distances measured horizontally to the right and vertically upward are considered to be positive; those measured in the opposite directions are negative, and thus the axes are said to be *directed*. The coordinates (x, y) of a point P consist of an *abscissa, x,* and an *ordinate*, y, which represent, respectively, the horizontal and vertical directed distances of P from the axes. (See Figure V–1.)   It is customary to designate a point as P: (x, y), which means, simply, that P has the coordinates (x, y).   For example, P_i: (x_i, y_i) designates the point P_i, whose abscissa is x_i and whose ordinate is y_i; P: $(-2, 3)$, the point P, whose abscissa is -2 and ordinate 3; and so on.   In

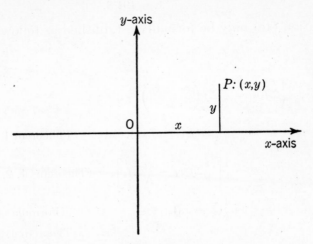

FIG. V-1.

constructing a frequency polygon, the frequency, f, is used as the ordinate, y.

It is often desirable to change a coordinate system by moving the origin horizontally.   Such a transformation is called a *translation*, and is illustrated in Figure V–2, where the new origin O' has been obtained by moving the old origin, O, a distance x_0 to the right.   The coordinates (x_i, y_i) of the point P_i referred to the original axes have become the coordinates $(x_i - x_0, y_i)$ referred to the translated axes.

If, now, we divide the new abscissa, $x_i - x_0$, by a factor k, where $k > 1$, as is illustrated in Figure V–3, the horizontal unit is reduced by this factor.   Such a transformation is called a *compression*.   If $k < 1$ (but > 0), the axes undergo a *stretching* or *elongation*.   The term *compression* may also be used in a generic sense to cover stretching as well.   Thus, we see that the transformation defined by equation (2) consists of both a translation and a compression.[1] The intrinsic character of a given frequency distribution is not changed by such transformations, although the shape and size of the corresponding frequency polygon or curve may change. We shall find it convenient later (Section IX–3) to speak of two curves as being of the same *type* if one can be made to coincide

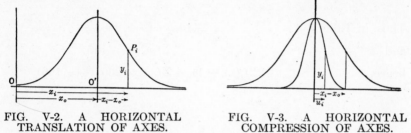

FIG. V-2. A HORIZONTAL
TRANSLATION OF AXES.

FIG. V-3. A HORIZONTAL
COMPRESSION OF AXES.

with the other by means of translations or compressions.

The preceding discussion has been concerned with changes in the horizontal scale only, but it applies to changes in the vertical scale also. For example, if, in a frequency polygon, we employ relative frequencies, $\dfrac{f_i}{N}$, instead of actual frequencies, f_i, we produce a vertical compression, since $N > 1$, always, and thus flatten the corresponding frequency polygon.

5. Remarks concerning the computation. (i) *Checking.*
The computation of the arithmetic mean may be verified by selecting a different provisional mean, x_0, and then applying the method of the preceding section. Referring to columns 5 and 6 of Table V–1, we have:

$$\bar{u} = \frac{266}{462} = 0.576 \text{ and } x_0 = 189.5,$$

so that
$$\bar{u} = \frac{\bar{x} - x_0}{k}$$

becomes
$$0.576 = \frac{\bar{x} - 189.5}{4},$$

whence
$$\bar{x} = 191.8.$$

This agrees with the result previously obtained.

---

[1] Stretchings and compressions may easily be made physical realities by means of coordinate rulings marked on a sheet of rubber. The rubber is attached to two vertical rods whose horizontal distance is made to vary.

If the new provisional mean selected is one adjacent to the old, the two summations should differ by exactly the total frequency, N. This is easily established as follows:

$$\Sigma f_i(u_i + 1) - \Sigma f_i u_i = \Sigma f_i u_i + \Sigma f_i - \Sigma f_i u_i$$
$$= \Sigma f_i$$
$$= N.$$

Thus, in Table V-1, $\qquad \Sigma f_i(u_i + 1) = 266$

and $\qquad\qquad\qquad\qquad \Sigma f_i u_i = -196;$

hence, $\qquad \Sigma f_i(u_i + 1) - \Sigma f_i u_i = 266 - (-196)$
$$= 462$$
$$= N.$$

(ii) *Significant digits.* The head lengths of the 462 English criminals were measured to the nearest millimeter, and hence with an accuracy of three significant digits. Their mean value has been computed to the nearest tenth of a millimeter and found to be 191.8. According to the remark in the last paragraph of Section II–7, we have good justification for saving four digits rather than three, since the total frequency, 462, is fairly large. However, the question of the precision of the arithmetic mean is not one which can be answered satisfactorily at this point. (See Sections XIV–4 and 5.) A good working rule for the present is to save one more digit than occurs in most of the individual items from which the frequency table is constructed.

(iii) *Unequal class intervals.* In some frequency distributions, the class intervals are not all of the same width, so that the method of Section 3 must be either modified or abandoned. If there is much irregularity among the widths, it is better not to attempt to make use of *unit* deviations, but to use *non-unit* deviations from a convenient provisional mean, as in Section 2. This means, merely, that k is omitted in formula (1c).

If there are but two different class widths, a desirable method is to select as the provisional mean, x_0, a suitable number lying between the two mid-values at which the change in width occurs. The method is illustrated in Table

V–2, where the last column and the computation at the right are to be omitted at present. The change in width from 5 units to 10 takes place from the mid-value 17.5 to the mid-value 25. If we choose $x_0 = 20$, the deviations, d_i, will have

TABLE V–2

COMPUTATION OF THE ARITHMETIC MEAN WHEN TWO DIFFERENT CLASS WIDTHS EXIST (*Fictitious Data*)

Class Boundaries	f_i	x_i	$d_i = x_i - 20$	$d_i' = \dfrac{d_i}{2.5}$	$f_i d_i'$	$f_i d_i'^2$
0 –5	4	2.5	−17.5	−7	−28	196
5–10	6	7.5	−12.5	−5	−30	150
10–15	10	12.5	− 7.5	−3	−30	90
15–20	20	17.5	− 2.5	−1	−20	20
20–30	45	25	5	2	90	180
30–40	30	35	15	6	180	1080
40–50	12	45	25	10	120	1200
50–60	6	55	35	14	84	1176
60–70	2	65	45	18	36	648
70–80	1	75	55	22	22	484
					−108	
					532	
Totals	136				424	5224

$$\bar{d}' = \frac{1}{N}\Sigma f_i d_i' = \frac{424}{136} = 3.12.$$

$$\bar{d} = 2.5 \times \bar{d}' = 2.5 \times 3.12 = 7.80.$$

$$\bar{x} = \bar{d} + x_0 = 7.80 + 20 = 27.8.$$

$$\sigma_{d'}^2 = \nu_{2d'} - \bar{d}'^2$$

$$= \frac{5224}{136} - (3.12)^2 = 28.7;$$

$$\sigma_x = k\sigma_{d'} = 2.5(28.7)^{1/2} = 13.4.$$

a common factor 2.5, so that we may employ reduced deviations, $d_i' = \dfrac{d_i}{2.5}$, to simplify the arithmetical work. The method may often be applied when there are more than two different class widths.

Sometimes the frequency distribution may be divided into several parts in each of which the class interval is uniform, the mean computed for each part, and then the *weighted arithmetic mean* of these means taken. The method is explained more fully in Section 8.

(iv)   *Non-symmetrical distributions.* In computing the arithmetic mean from a frequency distribution, we assumed that all the values lying within a given class interval could be replaced by the mid-value. This is a valid assumption provided that the distribution is a fairly symmetric one; but if the distribution exhibits considerable skewness, or if the data follow a highly irregular pattern, the methods of computation just outlined may be no longer valid. It may be necessary to employ very small class intervals or to dispense with the distribution and to revert to the raw data from which it was constructed. Occasionally more advanced techniques may be employed. Frequently the arithmetic mean must be abandoned in favor of a different, more representative average. (See Sections VI–11, 13, 15, and 16.)

6. Properties of the arithmetic mean. It is important to recall at this point the two formulas (1) and (1a):

$$\bar{x} = \frac{1}{N} \sum_{i=1}^{N} x_i; \tag{1}$$

$$\bar{x} = \frac{1}{N} \sum_{i=1}^{n} f_i x_i. \tag{1a}$$

These are equivalent under the assumption that each value x_i in (1a) occurs f_i times among the values x_i of (1) and that $\sum_{i=1}^{n} f_i = N$. In the future when algebraic relationships are studied, we shall use the simpler formula (1). For computational purposes we shall use (1a).

There are two important properties of the mean which can be easily established. They are stated in Theorems 1 and 2 below.

THEOREM 1. *The sum of the deviations of a set of variates from its arithmetic mean is zero.*

Proof: The sum of the deviations is represented by $\Sigma(x_i - \bar{x})$. Then,

$$\Sigma(x_i - \bar{x}) = \Sigma x_i - \Sigma \bar{x} \qquad \text{Theorem 2. §IV-8}$$
$$= \Sigma x_i - N\bar{x} \qquad \text{Theorem 3. §IV-8}$$

$$= \Sigma x_i - N\left(\frac{1}{N}\Sigma x_i\right) \qquad \text{by (1)}$$
$$= \Sigma x_i - \Sigma x_i$$
$$= 0.$$

THEOREM 2. *The sum of the squares of the deviations from the arithmetic mean is less than the sum of the squares of the deviations from any other value.*

Proof: The sum of the squares of the deviations from $\bar{x}$ and from any other value, x_0, are represented by $\Sigma(x_i - \bar{x})^2$ and $\Sigma(x_i - x_0)^2$, respectively. If the former is to be less then the latter, then,

$$\Sigma(x_i - \bar{x})^2 < \Sigma(x_i - x_0)^2.$$

Expanding,

$$\Sigma(x_i^2 - 2x_i\bar{x} + \bar{x}^2) < \Sigma(x_i^2 - 2x_ix_0 + x_0^2);$$

whence $\qquad \Sigma x_i^2 - \Sigma 2x_i\bar{x} + \Sigma\bar{x}^2 < \Sigma x_i^2 - \Sigma 2x_ix_0 + \Sigma x_0^2.$

Subtracting from each member of the inequality the first term, and noting that $\bar{x}$ and x_0 are constants, we have:

$$- 2\bar{x}\Sigma x_i + N\bar{x}^2 < - 2x_0\Sigma x_i + Nx_0^2.$$

If we divide by N, we get:

$$-2\bar{x}\cdot\frac{1}{N}\Sigma x_i + \bar{x}^2 < -2x_0\cdot\frac{1}{N}\Sigma x_i + x_0^2;$$

and if we use (1), we obtain:

$$-2\bar{x}^2 + \bar{x}^2 < - 2x_0\bar{x} + x_0^2;$$

whence, $\qquad\qquad 0 < \bar{x}^2 - 2\bar{x}x_0 + x_0^2,$

or $\qquad\qquad\qquad 0 < (\bar{x} - x_0)^2.$

Since $\bar{x} \neq x_0$, the right member is positive and the last inequality is therefore true. If we begin with the last inequality, known to be true, and reverse the order of our algebraic steps, we arrive at the first inequality written and thus prove the theorem.

Students of physics will be interested to note that the arithmetic mean in statistics is analogous to the center of mass or gravity in mechanics. If the histogram of a frequency distribution is conceived to be a uniform plane lamina, the abscissa of its center of mass will be $\bar{x}$. In statistics, the frequency, f_i, corresponds, in mechanics, to the mass, m_i, of the appropriate rectangle. For this reason, $\Sigma f_i x_i$ is called the *first moment* of the frequency distribution.

7. Uses of the arithmetic mean. In general, the arithmetic mean is a fairly stable average. It is not unduly affected by a few moderately small or moderately large values, and this stability increases with the total frequency, N. However, one or more extreme values may, at times, profoundly affect its value and render it useless. The general stability of the mean makes it a highly desirable statistical measure. It has a multitude of uses such as the following: in meteorology, for obtaining the average temperature or rainfall; in medicine, for discovering the average duration of a disease; in anthropology, for estimating certain average characteristics of a group of human beings; in economics, for computing average wages, prices, index numbers, and so on.

The arithmetic mean is dependent upon the *total* of the variates involved; hence, it is particularly useful in business statistics, as, for example, in averaging sales, production, prices, and so forth, over a specified period. In time series, totals are usually given for the week, month, or year, and from these we may find the average daily, weekly, or monthly figures. This use of the mean is additional to the one already mentioned in connection with moving averages. (Section III–8.)

Another use of the arithmetic mean is not so generally known. It occurs in connection with the study of curves, particularly the frequency curve. The ordinate, y, of a point, P, on a given curve varies as P moves along the curve. The average value of this ordinate, between two values, a and b, of the abscissa is always taken as the arithmetic mean, $\bar{y}$, of all possible values. In Figure V–4, the average ordinate between a and b is easily seen to be somewhere between the smallest value at a and the largest value at c. The method of obtaining the mean of an infinite set of values, the ordinates, requires a knowledge of calculus.

8. **The weighted arithmetic mean.** The *weight* of a variate is a number assigned to it in order to indicate its relative
importance.

Suppose that a student receives grades of 88, 81, 78, 74,
and 73 per cent in courses carrying credit hours of 2, 3, 4, 3,
and 3 hours, respectively. His average grade may be found
by multiplying each grade by the number of hours of credit
assigned to it. The sum of the weighted values thus obtained

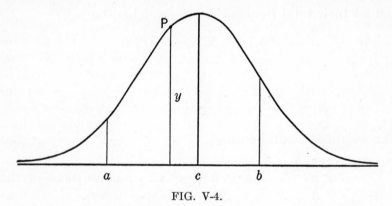

FIG. V-4.

is divided by the sum of the weights (the hours of credit), to
obtain the weighted mean. Thus,

$$\bar{x} = \frac{(2 \times 88) + (3 \times 81) + (4 \times 78) + (3 \times 74) + (3 \times 73)}{2 + 3 + 4 + 3 + 3}$$
$$= 78.1 \text{ (per cent)}.$$

The *weighted arithmetic mean* may therefore be defined by
the formula:

$$\bar{x} = \frac{\sum_{i=1}^{n} w_i x_i}{\sum_{i=1}^{n} w_i}, \tag{3}$$

where w_i is the weight assigned to x_i. A frequency table is a
table of weighted values, the frequencies being the weights.

THEOREM 3. *The arithmetic mean of a group of variates
divided into subgroups is equal to the weighted arithmetic mean
of the means of the subgroups, where the weights are equal to the
corresponding total frequencies of the subgroups.*

Proof: Assume that there are m subgroups, and let the variates in them be designated by:

$$x_i', x_i'', x_i''', \quad \cdots \quad x_i^{(m)},$$

where the superscript refers to the subgroup. Let the means of the subgroups be:

$$\bar{x}', \bar{x}'', \bar{x}''', \cdots \bar{x}^{(m)},$$

and let their total frequencies (the weights) be:

$$N', N'', N''', \cdots N^{(m)}.$$

Then, by (1),

$$\bar{x}' = \frac{1}{N'} \sum_{i=1}^{N'} x_i', \quad \bar{x}'' = \frac{1}{N''} \sum_{i=1}^{N''} x_i'', \quad \cdots \bar{x}^{(m)} = \frac{1}{N^{(m)}} \sum_{i=1}^{N^{(m)}} x_i^{(m)}.$$

The weighted mean becomes:

$$\frac{\sum_{i=1}^{m} N^{(i)} \bar{x}^{(i)}}{\sum_{i=1}^{m} N^{(i)}} = \frac{N' \bar{x}' + N'' \bar{x}'' + \cdots + N^{(m)} \bar{x}^{(m)}}{N' + N'' + \cdots + N^{(m)}}.$$

Replacing each mean by its value, and the denominator by its equal, N, we have:

$$\frac{\sum_{i=1}^{N'} x_i' + \sum_{i=1}^{N''} x_i'' + \cdots + \sum_{i=1}^{N^{(m)}} x_i^{(m)}}{N} = \frac{\sum_{i=1}^{N} x_i}{N} = \bar{x};$$

hence,

$$\bar{x} = \frac{1}{N} \sum_{i=1}^{m} N^{(i)} \bar{x}^{(i)}. \tag{4}$$

The preceding theorem may be applied advantageously to the computation of the arithmetic mean from a frequency distribution when there are several different class widths. The class intervals are divided into several groups in each of which the class interval is uniform, the mean is computed for each group, and then Theorem 3 is applied. Table V–3 illustrates the method.

TABLE V-3

COMPUTATION OF THE ARITHMETIC MEAN BY THE USE OF THE WEIGHTED MEAN OF MEANS (*Fictitious Data*)

Class Boundaries	f_i	x_i	u_i	$f_i u_i$	
0– 5	1	2.5	−3	−3	$\bar{u}' = \dfrac{\bar{x}'_i - x'_0}{k'}$
5– 10	3	7.5	−2	−6	
10– 15	2	12.5	−1	−2	$\dfrac{17}{30} = \dfrac{\bar{x}' - 17.5}{5}$
15– 20	6	17.5	0	0	
20– 25	8	22.5	1	8	$\therefore \ \bar{x}' = 20.3.$
25– 30	10	27.5	2	20	
Totals	30			17	
30– 40	25	35	−3	−75	$\bar{u}'' = \dfrac{\bar{x}'' - x''_0}{k''}$
40– 50	36	45	−2	−72	
50– 60	41	55	−1	−41	$\dfrac{-79}{205} = \dfrac{\bar{x}'' - 65}{10}$
60– 70	40	65	0	0	
70– 80	30	75	1	30	$\therefore \ \bar{x}'' = 61.1.$
80– 90	20	85	2	40	
90–100	13	95	3	39	
Totals	205			−79	
100–120	23	110	−1	−23	$\bar{u}''' = \dfrac{\bar{x}''' - x'''_0}{k'''}$
120–140	7	130	0	0	
140–160	2	150	1	2	$-\dfrac{21}{32} = \dfrac{\bar{x}''' - 130}{20}$
Totals	32			−21	$\therefore \ \bar{x}''' = 116.9.$

$$\bar{x} = \frac{N'\bar{x}' + N''\bar{x}'' + N'''\bar{x}'''}{N' + N'' + N'''} = \frac{(30 \times 20.3) + (205 \times 61.1) + (32 \times 116.9)}{30 + 205 + 32}$$

$$= \frac{16880}{267} = 63.2.$$

(B) THE HARMONIC MEAN

9. Definition and use. The program of a moving picture theater contained the following announcement:

"Patrons who consider the ushers uncivil should see the manager."

The effect of this statement on the reader is due to its two-fold meaning, one obvious, the other somewhat latent. A similar remark may be made concerning the average we are

to study next, for it is used as a measure of values the significance of which is often hidden. Let us first define this average and then illustrate its distinctive property.

The harmonic mean of a set of positive variates, $x_1, x_2, x_3 \cdots$
x_N, *is defined to be the number,* x_h, *whose reciprocal,* $\dfrac{1}{x_h}$, *is the*

arithmetic mean of $\dfrac{1}{x_1}, \dfrac{1}{x_2}, \dfrac{1}{x_3}, \cdots \dfrac{1}{x_N}$, *the reciprocals of the vari-*

ates.

$$\frac{1}{x_h} = \frac{1}{N} \sum_{i=1}^{N} \frac{1}{x_i}. \tag{5}$$

Suppose that the prices of a certain commodity for three
years are 10 cents, 20 cents, and 25 cents. If one purchases
the same quantity of this commodity each year, the average
price for the three years is quite properly given by the arithmetic mean:

$$\bar{x} = \frac{1}{3}(10 + 20 + 25) = 18\tfrac{1}{3}.$$

The average price is about 18.3 cents.

However, suppose that the quantity purchased depends
upon the price, so that one may buy twice as much at 10 cents
as at 20 cents. Then the average price paid over the three
years would be quite properly given by the weighted arithmetic mean where the weights are proportional to the quantities purchasable for a fixed sum, say one dollar. In this case,
the weights for the three years are 10, 5, and 4. Hence,

$$\bar{x} = \frac{(10 \times 10) + (5 \times 20) + (4 \times 25)}{10 + 5 + 4} = \frac{300}{19} = 15.8.$$

The weighted mean is about 15.8 cents. This may also be
found as a harmonic mean:

$$\frac{1}{x_h} = \frac{1}{3}\left(\frac{1}{10} + \frac{1}{20} + \frac{1}{25}\right) = \frac{19}{300};$$

$$x_h = \frac{300}{19} = 15.8.$$

Clearly, the lower the price, the greater the purchasing power of the dollar; and the latter is measured by the reciprocals of the prices measured in dollars.

The harmonic mean is thus used when the reciprocals of the variates have special significance. If x_i represents the price in dollars of a pound of flour, $\dfrac{1}{x_i}$ represents the number of pounds purchasable for a dollar, $\dfrac{1}{x_h}$, the (arithmetic) mean number of pounds purchasable for a dollar, and x_h the (harmonic) mean price in dollars per pound. Note that $x_h \neq \bar{x}$. (See Ex. V–28.) The harmonic mean is particularly useful in measuring purchasing power when prices are given. When the arithmetic mean and the harmonic mean are computed from a given set of data, different units of measurement are implied. The harmonic mean is not used widely, but it is of considerable importance in connection with index numbers. (See Chapter VII.)

(C) THE GEOMETRIC MEAN

10. Definition. *The geometric mean, x_g, of a set of N positive variates, x_1, x_2, x_3, $\cdots x_N$, is defined as the positive Nth root of their product.*

$$x_g = (x_1x_2x_3 \cdots x_N)^{1/N}. \tag{6}$$

For example, the geometric mean of the five numbers 2, 4, 8, 16, and 32 equals $(2 \times 4 \times 8 \times 16 \times 32)^{1/5} = 8$.

11. Properties. If we take the logarithms of both members of equation (6), we have:

$$\log x_g = \log (x_1x_2x_3 \cdots x_N)^{1/N}$$

$$= \frac{1}{N} \log (x_1x_2x_3 \cdots x_N) \qquad \text{Theorem 4, §II-12}$$

$$= \frac{1}{N} (\log x_1 + \log x_2 + \cdots + \log x_N). \quad \text{Theorem 1, §II-12}$$

Therefore,

$$\log x_g = \frac{1}{N} \sum_{i=1}^{N} \log x_i, \tag{7}$$

and we may state the following theorem.

THEOREM 4.   *The logarithm of the geometric mean of a set of positive variates is the arithmetic mean of their logarithms.*

This property is useful in computation (Section V–12).

THEOREM 5.   *The geometric mean of a set of positive variates, not all equal, is always less than their arithmetic mean.*

Proofs of this theorem may be found in Reference 21, page 195, or in Chrystal, *Algebra*, Black, Edinburgh, 1889, Chapter XXIV.

A useful illustration of this theorem occurs in the theory of index numbers.   (See Section VII–9.)   Relative changes in price are usually more significant than absolute changes. For example, if the price of an article changes from \$1.00 to \$2.00 while the price of a second article changes from \$1.00 to \$.50, the first article has been doubled in price while the second has had its price halved.   The arithmetic mean of these relative changes is $\frac{1}{2}(2 + \frac{1}{2}) = 1.25$.   On the other hand, the geometric mean of these relative changes is $\sqrt{2 \times \frac{1}{2}} = 1.00$. There has really been no net change in the ratios of the new prices to the old, as is indicated by the geometric mean.   The arithmetic mean, on the other hand, being larger, gives an "upward bias" to the average change in price, and for this reason is not considered to be as satisfactory an average when ratios are involved.

THEOREM 6.   *The **k**th power of the geometric mean of a set of positive variates equals the geometric mean of the **k**th powers of the variates.*

The proof is almost trivial:

$$x_g = (x_1 x_2 x_3 \cdots x_N)^{1/N}$$
$$x_g^k = [(x_1 x_2 x_3 \cdots x_N)^{1/N}]^k$$
$$= (x_1 x_2 x_3 \cdots x_N)^{k/N}$$
$$= (x_1^k x_2^k x_3^k \cdots x_N^k)^{1/N}.$$

This simple property of the geometric mean makes it a singularly appropriate average to use in comparing similar figures.   Area and volume vary with the second and third powers, respectively, of the linear dimension; hence, if we know the geometric mean of a set of linear dimensions, the geometric mean of the corresponding set of areas or of volumes is found by the simple operation of squaring or cubing the known mean.   Interesting applications of this property might be made, by way of illustration, in the field of insect physiology.   Some insects, like the ant, can lift weights of greater mass than their own bodies, and leaping insects, like the grasshopper, can project themselves great distances through the air.   Muscular power varies with cross-sectional area, that is, with the square of a linear dimension.   Thus, as the body of the insect decreases in size, the muscles become relatively more powerful.   A similar situation exists in the case of insects capable of locomotion by water.   The volume or mass of a body varies as the cube of its radius, whereas surface area varies as the square.   Thus, as the size of the insect body becomes smaller, its superficial area becomes relatively greater and thus the supporting forces of surface tension become relatively stronger.   Measurements connected with dimensional aspects of bodies of essentially the same density and shape but of different size may, at times, be advantageously averaged by means of the geometric mean and Theorem 6 above.

Attention should be called to the definition which introduces the geometric mean, x_g, at the beginning of this section. The variates involved are always positive quantities, so that x_g is intrinsically a positive number.   The same is true of the harmonic mean but not of the arithmetic.

12. Uses of the geometric mean. One of the most important applications of the geometric mean is made in estimating the average rate of change in a set of variates.   These variates usually constitute a time series.

EXAMPLE 1.   Suppose that a man invests $10,000 in various ways (bonds, stocks, savings bank accounts, and so forth) for five years, and that the amounts standing to his credit at the end of each year are as indicated in the second column of Table V–4.

The ratio of the amount at the end of a year to that of the beginning of the same year (the end of the preceding year) is given in Column 3, from which the average interest rate for that year (Column 4) is immediately obtained. For the first year, the interest rate is 3.98 per cent, since $\dfrac{10{,}398}{10{,}000} = 1.0398$;

TABLE V–4

Year i	Amount at End of Year A_i	Ratio $1 + r_i$	Interest Rate $100r_i\%$
	$10,000		
1	10,398	1.0398	3.98
2	10,713	1.0303	3.03
3	11,201	1.0456	4.56
4	11,576	1.0335	3.35
5	12,294	1.0620	6.20

for the third year, the rate is 4.56 per cent, since $\dfrac{11{,}201}{10{,}713} = 1.0456$. Thus,

$$A_1 = 10{,}000\ (1 + r_1)$$
$$= 10{,}000\ (1.0398)$$
$$= 10{,}398;$$
$$A_2 = 10{,}000\ (1 + r_1)(1 + r_2)$$
$$= 10{,}398\ (1 + r_2)$$
$$= 10{,}713;$$
$$A_3 = 10{,}000\ (1 + r_1)(1 + r_2)(1 + r_3)$$
$$= 10{,}713\ (1 + r_3)$$
$$= 11{,}201;$$

and so on.

We propose to find the average rate of interest for the entire five-year period. In other words, we seek the average ratio, $1 + r$, such that

$$10{,}000\ (1 + r)^5 = 10{,}000(1 + r_1)(1 + r_2)(1 + r_3)(1 + r_4)(1 + r_5)$$
$$= 10{,}000(1.0398)(1.0303)(1.0456)(1.0335)(1.0620);$$

whence,

$$(1 + r)^5 = (1.0398)(1.0303)(1.0456)(1.0335)(1.0620).$$

Clearly, the finding of the unknown, r, requires the extraction of a fifth root; that is, it requires the computing of the geometric mean of the five factors on the right of the last equation. Hence,

$$1 + r = [(1.0398)(1.0303)(1.0456)(1.0335)(1.0620)]^{1/5}.$$

By Theorem 4,

$$\log (1 + r) = \tfrac{1}{5}(\log 1.0398 + \log 1.0303 + \log 1.0456$$
$$+ \log 1.0335 + \log 1.0620)$$
$$= 0.01794;$$

whence,

$$1 + r = 1.0422.$$

Therefore,

$$r = 0.0422,$$

or

$$100r = 4.22 \text{ (per cent)}.$$

This means that the man would have received exactly the same return on his money at the end of five years if he could have replaced the five different interest rates by a single rate of interest equal to 4.22 per cent. Although this number may appear to equal the arithmetic mean of the interest rates, it is really less (Theorem 5), as computation to a greater number of decimal places will readily show. It should be noted that $1 + r_i$ of Table V–4 equals x_i of formula (6).

The preceding computation has been exhibited in detail in order to make clear the meaning of the geometric mean. The method is unnecessarily long and can be shortened considerably. The ratio of the amount at the end of the fifth year to that held initially is $\dfrac{12,294}{10,000}$, or 1.2294. In other words, the interest rate for the complete five-year period was 22.94 per cent. Assuming a uniform interest rate, r, throughout the five years,

$$10,000 (1 + r)^5 = 10,000 (1.2294)$$
$$(1 + r)^5 = 1.2294$$
$$1 + r = (1.2294)^{1/5}$$
$$= 1.0422;$$

whence, $\qquad\qquad\qquad r = 0.0422$, as before.

It is clearly unnecessary to multiply together the series of numbers, $1 + r_i$.

EXAMPLE 2. Table V-5 gives the number of claims paid for automobile accidents by a large accident insurance association. It is seen that there has always been an increase in

TABLE V-5

Year	No. of Claims	Ratio
1924	3612	
1925	4350	1.204
1926	4903	1.127
1927	5296	1.080
1928	5775	1.090
1929	5979	1.035
1930	6536	1.093

the number of claims paid. To find the average yearly rate of increase, we merely set, as in the work immediately preceding,

$$1 + r = \left(\frac{6536}{3612}\right)^{1/6}.$$

Note that the data for *seven* years yield *six* ratios.

Then, $\log (1 + r) = \frac{1}{6} \log \dfrac{6536}{3612}$

$= \frac{1}{6} (\log 6536 - \log 3612)$

$= 0.0429;$

whence, $1 + r = 1.104,$

and $r = .104.$

There has been, therefore, an average yearly increase of 10.4 per cent.

The geometric mean is often employed to interpolate values within an interval whose end-values are given. Suppose that we wish to estimate the number of automobile claims paid up to the end of the month of August, 1928. The rate of increase for the entire year 1928 was 9.0 per cent. If we assume a constant monthly rate of increase for the given year,

$$(1 + r)^{12} = 1.090$$
$$1 + r = (1.090)^{1/12}$$
$$= 1.0072,$$

and the average monthly increase is 0.72 per cent. Therefore, the number of claims paid at the end of August, the eighth month, equals $5296(1.0072)^8$, or 5609. If there had been considerable seasonal fluctuation in the number of claims paid, so that the increase from month to month varied considerably, this method would be unsatisfactory.

Under proper conditions, the geometric mean may be employed in *extrapolation*, that is, in estimating values *outside* of the range of those given. For example, suppose that we compute the probable number of claims to be paid in 1931 on the assumption that the rate of increase is that obtained from the geometric mean for the given series of years, namely, 10.4 per cent. Then,

$$6536 \ (1.104) = 7216,$$

and the estimated number for 1931 is 7216. The validity of this estimate, or of any estimate similarly made, depends upon the variability among the individual ratios or rates of change. The ratios in Table V–5 (Column 3) vary considerably from year to year, and we should not place too much confidence in the estimate just made for the year 1931. Nevertheless, this estimate has the advantage of being based on *all* the data available and, hence, on the general trend. When the successive ratios are fairly constant, the extrapolated value may be used with considerably more confidence.

At this point, the method discussed in Section III–9 becomes valuable. We may test a given set of values for a constant ratio by means of semi-logarithmic paper. If the graph exhibits a fair degree of linearity, the rate of change is approximately constant, and we may use the constant rate obtained from the geometric mean or the graph itself to extrapolate additional near-by values.

One of the most important uses of the geometric mean is in the computation of *index numbers* (Chapter VII), for then the averages of *relative numbers* or ratios are involved.   The value of the geometric mean in this connection is indicated under Theorem 5 and in the following theorem, whose proof is almost self-evident.

THEOREM 7.   *The geometric mean of the ratios of the corresponding values in two sets of variates,* x_1, x_2, x_3, $\cdots$ x_N *and* x'_1, x'_2, x'_3, $\cdots$ x'_N, *equals the ratio of the geometric means of the two sets.*

$$\left[\left(\frac{x_1}{x'_1}\right)\left(\frac{x_2}{x'_2}\right)\left(\frac{x_3}{x'_3}\right)\cdots\left(\frac{x_N}{x'_N}\right)\right]^{1/N} = \frac{(x_1 x_2 x_3 \cdots x_N)^{1/N}}{(x'_1 x'_2 x'_3 \cdots x'_N)^{1/N}}. \qquad (8)$$

It has been observed that the arithmetic mean computed from a frequency distribution exhibiting a fairly high degree of skewness may be inaccurate.   If the logarithms of the variates are computed, the resulting frequency distribution of the logarithms sometimes proves to be of the symmetric type. In such a case, the geometric mean might be a more appropriate average.   There are a number of questions involved in the computation associated with a logarithmic frequency distribution, and the student interested should consult a larger work on the subject.*

V—Exercises

Find the arithmetic mean for each set of ungrouped variates selected by your instructor from the data given in Exercises 1–5.

1.   Weights in pounds of the members of the Boston University football squad, 1936 (*Official Football Score Card*):

165, 140, 162, 155, 150, 158, 160, 166, 165, 180, 171, 192, 167, 176, 171, 163, 150, 179, 169, 162, 185, 196, 199, 201, 180, 205, 189, 180, 192, 179, 151, 173, 184, 140, 172, 183, 160, 160, 178, 153, 162, 164, 181, 194, 193, 184, 204, 190, 207, 155, 164, 190, 185, 186

2.   Average number of hours worked per day by males in 29 different industries, 1919 (*U. S. Bulletin of Labor Statistics*, No. 265, Table 5):

8.2, 8.3, 7.7, 7.8, 8.4, 7.8, 7.8, 8.1, 7.4, 5.5, 8.7, 7.9, 8.2, 8.5, 7.7, 7.7, 7.8, 8.1, 6.0, 7.2, 8.6, 8.2, 8.1, 7.1, 8.6, 7.1, 8.2, 8.0, 8.6

---

* See, for example, Ref. 2., Chap. XI.

3. Average July temperatures in New York City, 1915–1934 (*World Almanac*, 1936, p. 138):

72.5, 73.8, 74.1, 72.7, 74.0, 72.5, 76.2, 72.7, 72.3, 72.6, 72.5, 73.2, 73.0, 75.0, 74.1, 75.0, 76.5, 73.9, 73.7, 76.2

4. Amount of life insurance, in millions of dollars, in fraternal orders in the United States, 1920–1932 (*Statistical Abstract of the U. S.*, 1934, p. 274):

8,879.5, 9,159.0, 8,687.9, 8,758.6, 9,805.6, 9,769.6, 9,834.7, 9,726.7, 9,324.1, 9,155.4, 8,946.2, 7,301.0, 7,122.7

5. Average price, in cents per bushel, for sweet potatoes in 22 states, 1934 (*Yearbook of Agriculture*, 1935, p. 512):

89, 95, 80, 131, 96, 122, 70, 79, 76, 77, 71, 93, 96, 70, 66, 87, 79, 86, 73, 89, 90, 90

* * *

6. Could any of the preceding sets of data be grouped advantageously into a frequency distribution? What class intervals would you select?

* * *

Find the arithmetic mean for each frequency distribution selected from Exercises 7–13.

7. Precipitation in New York City.   (Ex. IV–7.)

8. Maximum temperatures in New York City.   (Ex. IV–8.)

9. Call discount rates.   (Ex. IV–9.)

10. Taxation for school support.   (Ex. IV–10.)

11. Brain-weight of Swedish males.   (Ex. IV–11.)

12. Intelligence quotients of runaway boys.   (Ex. IV–12.)

13. Sizes of shoes worn by college girls.   (Ex. IV–13.)

* * *

14. What factors make the value of the arithmetic mean daily wage determined from the frequency distribution, Ex. IV–14, open to criticism?

15. Which of the values of the mean obtained in Exercises 7–13 represent impossible but useful values?

16. Prove that the arithmetic mean of the deviations of a set of variates, x_1, x_2, x_3, $\cdots x_N$, from an arbitrary value, x_0, equals $\bar{x} - x_0$; that is, prove:

$$\frac{1}{N} \Sigma (x_i - x_0) = \bar{x} - x_0.$$

17. Criticize the statement on "the average man" quoted from Quetelet at the beginning of this chapter.

18. The frequency distribution of Ex. IV–18 is very skew. Would the arithmetic mean computed from it be inaccurate because of this fact?

19. Prove (a) Theorem 1 (§ V–6) and (b) Theorem 2 (§ V–6) by using $\Sigma f_i(x_i - \bar{x})$ instead of $\Sigma (x_i - \bar{x})$.

20. Compute the arithmetic mean for the data of Ex. IV–16. What factors make the result unreliable?

21. If the weight given to quiz grades is proportional to the time allowed for each quiz, find the average quiz grade of a student if he received 83 per cent on a half-hour quiz, 73 per cent and 79 per cent on two one-hour quizzes, and 84 per cent on a two-hour quiz.

22. Certain physical measurements were weighted according to the skill of the students making them. A has a weight of 2, B has a weight of 3, C, a weight of 1, D, a weight of 4, and E, a weight of 1. The following measurements were reported by the students: A, 16.49″; B, 16.48″; C, 16.55″; D, 16.48″; E, 16.54″. Find the average measurement.

23. In computing the "grade quotient" of a student at a certain college, $A = 4, B = 3, C = 2, D = 1, F = 0$. A plus sign adds 0.3, and a minus sign subtracts 0.3. The numerical equivalents of the grades are weighted according to the number of hours' credit. Find the grade quotient of a student with the following record: $A-$, 2 hrs.; $B+$, 3 hrs.; B, 3 hrs.; $C+$, 3 hrs.; $D-$, 4 hrs.

24. Compared according to grade quotients (see the preceding problem), which of the following two records is the better one?

    (a) B, 3 hrs.; $B-$, 2 hrs.; $C+$, 3 hrs.; D, 3 hrs.; F, 4 hrs.
    (b) $B-$, 3 hrs.; $C+$, 3 hrs.; $C-$, 4 hrs.; $D+$, 4 hrs.; $D-$, 1 hr.

25. The following data were taken from the *Statistical Abstract of the United States* for 1934:

Grain	Average Price: Cents per Bushel	Production: 1000 Bushels
Wheat	73	527,413
Corn	41	2,330,237
Oats	32	722,485
Barley	42	156,104
Rye	59	21,184

Find the average price of grain per bushel according to the following method. Let the prices be weighted according to the production; assign a weight of 1 to rye, and compute the corresponding weights for the other grains to the nearest integer.

26. Find the harmonic mean of the numbers 1 and 2.

27. Find the harmonic mean of the integers from 1 to 10 inclusive.

28. Assume the average retail price of bread per pound in three successive years to be 5, 6, and 10 cents. Compute the average number of loaves which can be purchased for a dollar over these three years. Use both the arithmetic mean and the harmonic mean of the bread prices in obtaining your answer, and compare the results.

29. Find the geometric mean of each of the following sets of numbers:

(a) 3, 8, 9;   (b) 6, 10, 12, 17, 20.

30. A sum of money was invested for five years. The average rates of return on the investment for the five successive years were as follows: 5.50 per cent, 4.73 per cent, 4.20 per cent, 3.91 per cent, 4.64 per cent. What was the average rate of interest for the five years?

31. If the average yields in bushels per acre of wheat in a certain locality were 11.0, 12.6, 12.9, 13.7, and 14.1 for five successive years, find the per cent of increase year by year and the average annual per cent of increase.

32. In 1890 there were 62 divorces per 1,000 marriages, and in 1932 there were 163. The increase has been fairly steady. What was the average yearly rate of increase expressed to the nearest tenth of a per cent?

33. The relative prices of grain for the year 1934, month by month, are given below.

Jan.	76	May	78	Sept.	112
Feb.	79	June	89	Oct.	109
Mar.	79	July	91	Nov.	109
Apr.	77	Aug.	106	Dec.	116

Find the average monthly per cent of increase expressed to the nearest tenth of a per cent.

34. The average price of a certain article in 1910 was $1.57 and in 1924 it was $1.88. Assuming a fairly uniform rate of increase in price for this period, what was the average annual per cent of increase, computed to the nearest tenth of a per cent? If this average rate of increase had continued, what would the price have been in 1927?

35. According to President Lowell's report for 1928–1929, the average ages at entrance of Harvard freshmen taken by five-year periods were as follows:

1866–1870.............. 18 yrs. 4.67 mos.
1886–1890.............. 19 yrs. 3.63 mos.

Assuming the rate of increase to be fairly constant, estimate the average age of a freshman, expressed in years and months, for the period 1881–1885.

36. From the semi-logarithmic graph of the population of the United States (Fig. III–11), estimate the population for the following years: (a) 1834; (b) 1859; (c) 1893.

37. Compute the populations required in the preceding exercise by making use of the geometric mean.

38. By making use of the inequality $(\sqrt{x} - \sqrt{y})^2 > 0$, where x and y are assumed to be positive numbers, $x \neq y$, show that the arithmetic mean of x and y is greater than their geometric mean.

39. Prove that the geometric mean of two numbers is the geometric mean between their arithmetic and harmonic means.

40. The weighted geometric mean of a set of n positive variates, $x_1, x_2, x_3, \cdots x_n$, having weights $w_1, w_2, w_3, \cdots w_n$, respectively, is defined by the formula:

$$x_g = (x_1^{w_1} x_2^{w_2} x_3^{w_3} \cdots x_n^{w_n})^{1/N}, \text{ where } N = \Sigma w_i.$$

Prove that

$$\log x_g = \frac{\Sigma w_i \log x_i}{\Sigma w_i}.$$

41. Discuss the three means of this chapter in the light of the six conditions which a statistical average should satisfy, as stated in Section 1.

42. Prove that the reciprocal of the harmonic mean of two positive numbers is greater than the reciprocal of their arithmetic mean.

CHAPTER

VI

THE MEDIAN AND OTHER POSITIONAL AVERAGES

❖❘❘❘❖

"Such is the past career, present condition, and certain future of
the Middle American. There are as many above him as below him,
and especially as many below him as above him."

JOSEPH JACOBS, "The Middle American,"
American Magazine, March, 1907.

1. Introduction. The averages to be studied in this chapter, with one exception, are sometimes called *positional
means*. They imply an ordered series of variates. The latter may be arranged individually in order of magnitude, beginning with the smallest and ending with the largest; or they
may be arranged collectively, as in a frequency distribution.
Sometimes only a qualitative order is possible, as in the case
of a group of persons arranged according to the color of their
hair, from the lightest to the darkest. A *positional mean*
marks a point of division in the scale of ordered variates.

2. Cumulative frequency. It is common experience to
hear questions of the following sort: How many tons of ship-
ping did Great Britain lose during the first six months of the
war. How many students received grades lower than
seventy per cent? What per cent of American girls twenty
years of age weigh less than 110 pounds? Such questions are
designed to elicit information of a special and significant type

and usually require, for their answers, certain partial sums obtained from data classified according to some convenient scheme. In statistics, these modes of expressing important facts center about the concept of *cumulative frequency*, a concept which has many practical applications in diverse fields.

TABLE VI–1

CUMULATIVE FREQUENCY TABLE OF HEAD LENGTHS

Mid-Value x_i	Frequency f_i	Boundary	Cum f_i
		171.5	
173.5	3		
		175.5	3
177.5	9		
		179.5	12
181.5	29		
		183.5	41
185.5	76		
		187.5	117
189.5	104		
		191.5	221
193.5	110		
		195.5	331
197.5	88		
		199.5	419
201.5	30		
		203.5	449
205.5	6		
		207.5	455
209.5	4		
		211.5	459
213.5	2		
		215.5	461
217.5	1		
		219.5	462
Total	462		

*The cumulative frequency (abbreviated to **cum f**) of the **m**th class in a frequency distribution is the sum of the frequencies, beginning with the first, f_1, and ending with the **m**th, f_m. Briefly,*

$$cum\, f_m = \sum_{i=1}^{m} f_i.$$

From the familiar data of Table IV–3, we construct Table VI–1 above. The latter includes the boundary values of each class as well as the cumulative frequencies. For example, cum $f_1 = 3$, cum $f_2 = f_1 + f_2 = 3 + 9 = 12$; cum $f_3 = f_1 + f_2 + f_3 = 12 + 29 = 41$; and so on. Of course, cum $f_n = N$; so that in Table VI–1, cum $f_{12} = 462$. When, for example, we say that cum $f_5 = 221$, we mean that 221 head lengths were less than 191.5 millimeters.

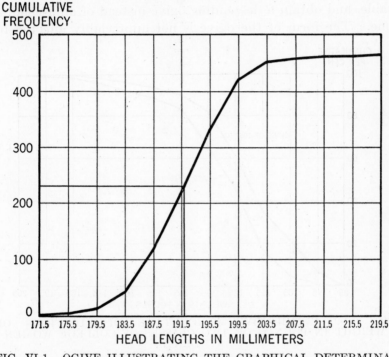

FIG. VI-1. OGIVE ILLUSTRATING THE GRAPHICAL DETERMINA-
TION OF THE MEDIAN HEAD LENGTH.

3. **The ogive.** The graph of the cumulative frequencies is called an *ogive,** and is obtained by plotting the cumulative frequencies against the boundary values or end-points of the class intervals. The plotted points are connected by line segments or by a smooth curve. The ogive has a number of

* The shape of this curve is not usually that suggested by the corresponding architectural term, which denotes a diagonal rib or pointed arch. The statistical word *ogive* is derived more directly from the word *ogee* (O. G.), which designates an S-shaped molding.

important uses.   From Figure VI–1, one can readily estimate
the number of head lengths below a given value.   If relative
frequencies or percentages are plotted instead of the frequencies themselves, we can estimate the proportion or percentage
of head lengths less than any assigned value.   By "accumu-
lating" the frequencies from the opposite end of the frequency
table, we derive a "more than" table instead of a "less than"
table, and obtain a descending ogive instead of an ascending
one.   The form of the ogive is not appreciably affected by

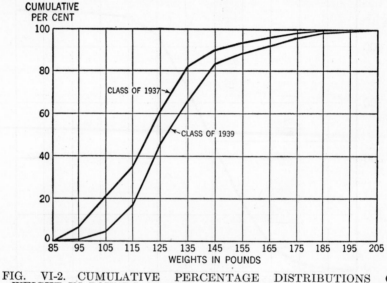

FIG.   VI-2. CUMULATIVE   PERCENTAGE   DISTRIBUTIONS   OF
WEIGHT IN POUNDS OF TWO CLASSES OF COLLEGE WOMEN
STUDENTS.

the presence of unequal class intervals, but, of course, care
must be exerted to take account of them in marking off the
horizontal scale.

   Two cumulative frequency distributions may often be compared advantageously by means of their ogives plotted to the
same scale or to comparable horizontal scales.   This is especially practical when the two sets of data have identical or
nearly identical classifications.   Unequal totals may be handled by the use of percentage frequencies.   Figure VI–2 illustrates these points.   It becomes clear from the two super-

imposed ogives that the Class of 1937 had more very light students (about 10 to 20 per cent) than the Class of 1939. There was a much smaller discrepancy among the students of heavier weight.

4. **The Lorenz curve.** A variation of the simple cumulative frequency graph or ogive is found in the curve bearing the name of its inventor, M. O. Lorenz. Cumulative percentages are plotted against each other on the horizontal and vertical axes. The information which such a curve imparts is best illustrated by an example. (See Table VI–2 and Figure VI–3.)

TABLE VI-2

NUMBER AND ACREAGE OF FARMS IN 1925 (*Statistical Abstract of the United States*, 1934, pp. 549–550)

Size of Farm in Acres	No. of Farms	No. of Acres in Thousands	% No. Farms	% No. Acres	Cum % No. Farms	Cum % No. Acres
Under 20	966,584	10,156	15.2	1.1	15.2	1.1
20– 49	1,450,643	46,405	22.8	5.0	38.0	6.1
50– 99	1,421,078	101,906	22.3	11.0	60.3	17.1
100–174	1,383,777	185,708	21.7	20.1	82.0	37.2
175–499	942,378	258,204	14.8	27.9	96.8	65.1
500–999	143,852	97,468	2.3	10.5	99.1	75.6
1,000 and over	63,328	224,472	0.9	24.3	100.0	99.9
Total	6,371,640	924,319	100.0	99.9		

From the data given in the first three columns of Table VI–2, the percentage numbers of farms and of acres are computed, and from these, the cumulative percentages. The paired values of cumulative per cents determine the points to be plotted on a square chart, through which a broken line or a smooth curve is drawn. Certain significant aspects of the data are clearly manifest. Figure VI–3 shows, for example, that (*a*) 50 per cent of the farms contain only about 12 per cent of the total acreage of farms in the United States; (*b*) 75 per cent of the farms contain only about 30 per cent of the acreage; (*c*) 50 per cent of the total acreage is contained in less than 12 per cent of the farms; and so on. The diagonal straight line from the lower left-hand corner to the upper right-hand corner is called a "line of equal distribution," for if 10 per cent of the farms had 10 per cent of the acreage, 20 per cent of the farms had 20 per cent of the acreage, and so on, the plotted points would lie on this diagonal.   The departure

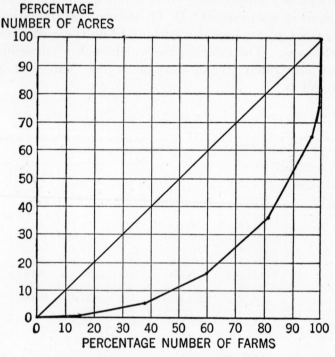

FIG. VI-3.   LORENZ CURVE FOR NUMBER AND ACREAGE OF FARMS
IN 1925 (Data of Table VI-2).

of the actual curve from the diagonal line gives a visual measure of the inequalities of distribution and in a form often strikingly effective for purposes of propaganda.   This departure may be measured algebraically as the horizontal or vertical deviation of the curve from the line for a given percentage.

Lorenz curves are admirably suited for comparing two or more distributions.   They have been used to advantage in investigations connected with distributions of wealth, incomes, expenses, and so forth.

5.   The Pareto curve.   This curve is related to the Lorenz curve in that logarithmic scales are employed.   It has distinct advantages in cases of data which have an extensive and detailed range, and which are considerably skewed.   (See Ref. 2, pp. 190–193.)

6.   The Z-chart.   Cumulative frequencies or totals are used in a form of chart which derives its name from the fact that the three broken line graphs composing it usually form the letter Z.   It is illustrated in Figure VI–4, constructed

TABLE VI–3

ANTHRACITE COAL-MINE FATALITIES IN THE UNITED STATES BY MONTHS, 1933 AND 1934. (*Coal-Mine Accidents in the U. S., 1935*, U. S. Bureau of Mines, Bull. 409, p. 88.)

Months	No. of Fatalities		Cumulative Total for 1934	Moving Annual Total for 1934
	1933	1934		
Jan.	26	27	27	232
Feb.	16	32	59	248
Mar.	23	28	87	253
Apr.	15	24	111	262
May	5	26	137	283
June	13	14	151	284
July	15	16	167	285
Aug.	20	16	183	281
Sept.	19	17	200	279
Oct.	29	28	228	278
Nov.	29	20	248	269
Dec.	21	20	268	268

from the data of Table VI–3.   The lowest graph represents anthracite coal-mine fatalities month by month for 1934. The middle or diagonal graph is an ogive; it represents the cumulative monthly total.   The uppermost graph represents the moving annual total, that is, the total number of fatalities for the twelve months ending with and including each month. The necessary computed values are shown in the last two columns of Table VI–3.   Notice, in the last column, that once the first moving annual total, 232, is obtained (by adding the numbers for February, 1933, to January, 1934, inclusive), each succeeding total may be easily obtained by adding

to the previous total the algebraic difference between the
corresponding figures for 1934 and 1933.   Thus,

$$248 = 232 + (32 - 16)$$
$$253 = 248 + (28 - 23)$$
$$\cdot \qquad \cdot \qquad \cdot$$
$$\cdot \qquad \cdot \qquad \cdot$$
$$\cdot \qquad \cdot \qquad \cdot$$
$$281 = 285 + (16 - 20)$$
$$\cdot \qquad \cdot \qquad \cdot$$
$$\cdot \qquad \cdot \qquad \cdot$$
$$\cdot \qquad \cdot \qquad \cdot$$
$$268 = 269 + (20 - 21)$$

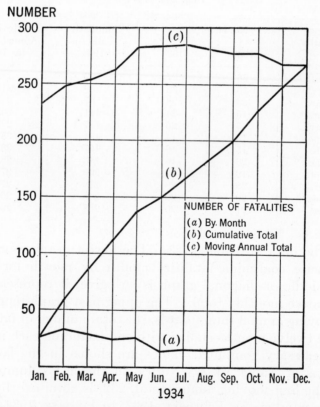

NUMBER OF FATALITIES
(*a*) By Month
(*b*) Cumulative Total
(*c*) Moving Annual Total

FIG. VI-4.   Z-CHART FOR ANTHRACITE COAL-MINE ACCIDENTS
IN THE UNITED STATES, 1934.

It is sometimes necessary to use two different vertical scales because of the disparity in the magnitudes of the monthly figures and of the totals. In such a case, the vertical scales at the left and right of the chart should be clearly marked and appropriately labeled.

7. The median for ungrouped data. Foremost in importance among the averages of this chapter is the median, the halfway or fifty per cent point in a scale of ordered variates. Let us assume that N variates have been arranged in the following order of magnitude,

$$x_1 \leqq x_2 \leqq x_3 \leqq \cdots \leqq x_N.$$

We then make the following definition:

The median of this ordered set of variates is the value $x_{\frac{N+1}{2}}$ *when* N *is odd, and the value* $\frac{1}{2}(x_{\frac{N}{2}} + x_{\frac{N+2}{2}})$ *when* N *is even.* *

In general, the median will have the desirable property that there will be as many variates greater as there are less.

When the total number of variates is odd, the median is merely the middle one in the ordered set. Thus, if we take the data for the average working day of males in 29 industries, Exercise V–2, and arrange the 29 numbers in order, we obtain:

5.5	6.0	7.1	7.1	7.2	7.4	7.7	7.7	7.7	7.8	7.8
7.8	7.8	7.9	8.0	8.1	8.1	8.1	8.2	8.2	8.2	8.2
8.3	8.4	8.5	8.6	8.6	8.6	8.7				

Here $x_1 = 5.5$, $x_2 = 6.0$, $x_3 = 7.1$, $\cdots x_{15} = 8.0$, $\cdots$ $x_{29} = 8.7$. The central number in order is the fifteenth, 8.0, hence the median number of hours worked per day was 8.0 hours. There were as many of the 29 industries with an average working day of more than 8.0 hours as there were industries with an average working day of less than 8.0 hours.

As defined, the median is always determinate, but it may not have statistical value. The median becomes useful when there are as many variates greater as there are less.

---

* For a purely mathematical discussion of definitions and properties of the median, see references (a) and (b) in Section 10 of this chapter.

When the number of variates is even, any number between the two middle ones of the ordered set usually possesses this property. Often two or more middle ones coincide in value. Whether or not they coincide, the value given by the definition (one-half the sum of the two middle variates) will have statistical significance. The median of the integers from 1 to 20 would be $\frac{1}{2}(10 + 11)$, or $10\frac{1}{2}$.

When some of the variates, other than the middle ones or a group of middle ones, are identical with the median, the median may be of doubtful value. Suppose that we arrange the ages at inauguration of the presidents of the United States in order (Section V–2):

42, 46, 47, 48, 49, 49, 50, 50, 51, 51, 51, 51,
52, 54, 54, 54, 54, 55, 55, 55, 56, 56, 57, 57,
57, 57, 58, 61, 61, 64, 65, 68.

The median of these 32 ages equals one-half the sum of the 16th and 17th ages, each of which is 54; and hence the median is 54 also. But the 14th and 15th ages are also 54, and 54 is not an age such that 16 presidents were older and 16 younger at the time of inauguration. For this reason the use of the median as a statistical measure of presidential ages is open to criticism. It would be better to say that 4 presidents were 54 years old, 13 presidents were younger, and 15 older. Difficulties of this type arise more often in the case of discrete variates.

8. The median for grouped data. When the number of variates is large enough to justify the use of a frequency table, the median may be readily computed from it with the aid of a column of cumulative frequencies. The definition which follows may be shown to be a natural extension of the definition in the preceding section. (See, for example, Ref. 21, Chap. IV.)

The median of a frequency distribution is the value of the variable, x, which corresponds to the cumulative frequency, $\frac{1}{2}N$.

This value may be estimated by the method of interpolation by proportional parts employed in finding logarithms.

In Table VI–1, $\frac{1}{2} N = 231$, cum $f_5 = 221$, and $231 - 221 = 10$; hence, the value of x corresponding to cum $f = 231$ is the tenth value among the 110 head lengths assumed to range in order from 191.5 to 195.5 millimeters. Hence, we take $\frac{10}{110}$ of the class interval, 4, and add the result to 191.5, the boundary corresponding to cum $f_5 = 221$. Thus, the median equals:

$$\left(\frac{10}{110} \times 4\right) + 191.5 = 191.9 \text{ (millimeters)}.$$

This means that there were as many head lengths greater than 191.9 millimeters as there were less.

9. Remarks concerning the computation. (i) *Significant Digits.* The statements concerning the precision of the mean [Section V–5(ii)] are, in general, applicable also to the median. For a relatively small number of items, say 40 or less, the number of digits to be used in writing the median value is usually equal to that occurring in most of the individual items. For a relatively large number, say between 40 and 400, an extra digit may be saved with some degree of justification.

(ii) *Distribution within an interval.* The method of interpolation just described assumes that the variates belonging to a class are uniformly spaced within the class interval. Such a distribution is, of course, not strictly in accord with experience. The assumption is open to criticism, particularly if the total frequency is fairly small, if the class interval is wide, or if the distribution is not reasonably symmetric. Nevertheless, for most frequency distributions arising in practice, the method outlined is considered satisfactory.

(iii) *Graphical computation.* The objections cited in the preceding paragraph may be partially eliminated by a graphical method of interpolation which many statisticians prefer. From the ogive or cumulative frequency polygon, the abscissa of the point corresponding to the ordinate, $\frac{1}{2} N$, is estimated. If more accurate results are desired, the broken line may be replaced by a smooth curve.   From Figure VI–1, the median head length is seen to be equal to about 191.9, in this case the same as the value obtained by arithmetic interpolation.

(iv)   *Unequal class intervals.*   The method of determination of the median of a frequency distribution by either arithmetic or graphic interpolation is still applicable when the class intervals are not uniform.

(v)   *Discrete distributions.*   In most frequency distributions of discrete variables, the method of interpolation is based upon the use of artificial class boundaries.   For this reason and for other reasons, the median is usually valueless in such distributions.   The data of Table VI–4 form an example of a discontinuous distribution for which the median value, 6, has practically no statistical value.

TABLE VI–4

NUMBER OF MICE DYING PER GROUP OF SIX UNDER
CERTAIN SERUM TESTS

No. of Mice Dying	f_i	Cum f_i
0	42	42
1	31	73
2	13	86
3	7	93
4	9	102
5	71	173
6	355	528
	528	

10.   Properties of the median.   The median of a frequency distribution varies somewhat with the method of grouping, that is, with the choice of class limits and widths of class intervals.   This is an undesirable characteristic, but it offers no serious difficulties in practice.

The median is not readily affected by a few abnormal values, extremely small or extremely large, and this stability makes it a useful average in many cases.   For example, in Table IV–2, the replacement of the last three electric current bills by three abnormally large ones, say each of $15.00, would in no wise affect the median, but would raise the arithmetic mean by an appreciable amount (about 29 cents).

A vertical line passing through the median value of a frequency distribution divides its histogram into two parts of equal area (See Figure VI–5). This follows from the definition of the median and from the fact that the areas of the constituent rectangles are proportional to the corresponding class frequencies.

If the histogram is replaced by the corresponding frequency curve, the area under the latter should be divided into two

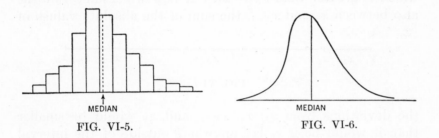

MEDIAN   MEDIAN

FIG. VI-5.   FIG. VI-6.

equal parts by the line erected perpendicular to the horizontal axis at the median value (See Figure VI–6). In fact, if the frequency curve is known, the corresponding median may be computed, if necessary, by more advanced methods. A good estimate of the median may sometimes be made with the aid of arithmetic probability paper (Section X–14).

The *absolute value* of a number, x, is its numerical value, that is, its value treated as a positive number, and is symbolized by $|x|$. Thus, $|-4| = 4$, $|6 - 13| = 7$, $|5| = 5$. The first of these equalities is read "the absolute value of -4 equals 4."

THEOREM. *The sum of the absolute deviations of a set of variates from a given value is a minimum when the given value is the median.*

Proof: Let the N variates, arranged in order of increasing magnitude, be $x_1, x_2, x_3, \cdots x_N$. Represent them as points on a straight line (Fig. VI–7), and let x_0 be any value of x lying between x_1 and x_N, so that $x_1 < x_0 < x_N$. The sum of the absolute deviations of x_1 and x_N from x_0 is:

$$| x_1 - x_0 | + | x_N - x_0 | = (x_0 - x_1) + (x_N - x_0)$$
$$= x_N - x_1.$$

Suppose that x_0 were not between x_1 and x_N. For example, suppose that $x_0 > x_N$. Then the sum of the absolute values of the deviations would be:

$$| x_1 - x_0 | + | x_N - x_0 | = (x_0 - x_1) + (x_0 - x_N)$$
$$= (x_N - x_1) + 2 (x_0 - x_N),$$

which is greater than $x_N - x_1$. If now we assume x_0 to lie also between x_2 and x_{N-1}, the sum of the absolute values of

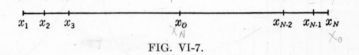

FIG. VI-7.

the deviations from x_1, x_2, x_{N-1}, and x_N would be smaller than it would be if x_0 lay anywhere outside of the interval from x_2 to x_{N-1}. Continuing this process, by assuming x_0 to lie between x_3 and x_{N-2}, then between x_4 and x_{N-3}, and so on, we see that the sum with respect to all the variates is a minimum when x_0 has exactly as many variates less as greater, that is, when x_0 is the median. If the number of variates is odd, the last choice of x_0 must be the middle variate.

Note that the sum of the absolute values of the deviations of x_0 from any two values between which it lies, say x_1 and x_N, is the same regardless of the position of x_0 *within* the interval.

The property of the median stated in the preceding theorem may be used as its definition. For a careful treatment of this subject and related topics, one should consult the following articles: (*a*) E. L. Dodd, "Definitions and Properties of the Median, Quartiles, and Other Positional Means," *American Mathematical Monthly*, May, 1938; (*b*) D. Jackson, "Note on the Median of a Set of Numbers," *Bulletin of the American Mathematical Society*, January, 1921.

11. Applications of the median. It has already been noted that the median is not very useful in dealing with discrete variables. It is also of doubtful value when the number of variates involved is relatively small, say below 20, and the spread throughout the range is very uneven.

When observations are made which contain some extremely high or low values, the median is generally a better average than the mean. Two groups of men might have practically the same median weights but somewhat different arithmetic means owing to the presence of a few abnormally heavy (or a few abnormally light) men in one of the groups. A higher median in one group would indicate generally heavier men throughout the set. (See Exercise VI–16.)

Certain distributions quite definitely tend to be skew because of some natural limit at one end of the range of variation. Thus, the hourly wages of a certain class of workers might exhibit skewness due to the fact that no worker receives less than zero cents per hour, while many workers (theoretically at least) can attain exceedingly high wages. In such cases, the median might well be more truly typical of the average wage than the arithmetic mean.

The median is often useful when an accurate determination of the arithmetic mean is impossible. This occurs when a frequency table is "open" at one end or both ends. (See, for example, Exercises IV–14 and 15.) Indefinite classes at the ends of a distribution will not affect the position of the median.

The median is employed as a useful average throughout a wide range of statistical investigations. Among them the following may be mentioned: in mortality studies for finding the average length of life (probable lifetime), in various kinds of price and wage statistics, in the theory of errors of physical measurements or of observations, and in problems dealing with data which are arranged according to some qualitative criterion.

12. The quartiles. *The first quartile, Q_1, of a frequency distribution is the value of the variable, x, which corresponds to the cumulative frequency $\frac{1}{4}N$. The third quartile, Q_3, corre-*

sponds to the cumulative frequency $\frac{3}{4}N$.   The second quartile is, of course, the median.

Thus, Q_1 is usually a value such that one-fourth of the variates are smaller and three-fourths of them larger. Q_3 is usually a value such that three-fourths of the variates are smaller and one-fourth larger.   The vertical lines through the quartiles divide the area of the histogram and the area under the frequency curve into four equal areas (Figure VI–8).   This means that the area under the curve to the left of

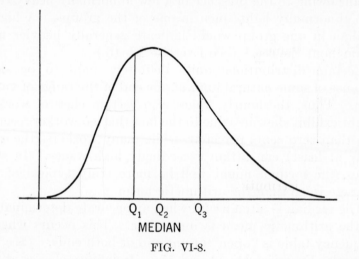

FIG. VI-8.

Q_2, the area under the curve to the right of Q_2, the area between Q_1 and Q_3, and the sum of the two areas "outside" of Q_1 and Q_3, are each equal to 50 per cent of the total area.

The quartiles have important uses in connection with the measurement of the degree of dispersion of the data about the center and with the measurement of the skewness of the distribution.   (See Sections VIII–2 and 3.)

As defined, a *quartile* is a point or a mark in an ordered set of values but it is often used also to designate an interval or a range of values.   We find it convenient to state, for example, that a value lies in the second quartile, that is, between the marks Q_1 and Q_2.

The method of computation is basically the same as that

used for the median. We illustrate with the data of Table VI–1:

$$\tfrac{1}{4}N = \tfrac{1}{4}\,(462) = 115.5$$

The value of x corresponding to cum $f = 115.5$ lies between the boundaries, 183.5 and 187.5, within which 76 variates are found.

$$115.5 - 41 = 74.5.$$

Hence, the value we seek,

$$Q_1 = \left(\frac{74.5}{76} \times 4\right) + 183.5 = 187.4.$$

One-fourth of all the 462 head lengths, then, were less than 187.4 millimeters. Similarly,

$$\tfrac{3}{4}N = \tfrac{3}{4}(462) = 346.5;$$
$$Q_3 = \left(\frac{346.5 - 331}{88} \times 4\right) + 195.5 = 196.2.$$

All the remarks of Section 9 concerning the median hold without exception for the other quartiles. In particular, attention should be called to the graphical methods of estimating the quartiles.

13. The mid-mean. *The mid-mean of a frequency distribution is the arithmetic mean of that portion of the distribution which lies between the first and third quartiles.* It has the advantage of being an average of the more typical half of the distribution and thus avoiding the inclusion of abnormally large and relatively small items. The mid-mean has, therefore, a stability which, at times, is highly desirable. We should find it useful when we wish to discard the influences of non-typical values.

We illustrate one method of computing it from the data of Table VI–1, without attempting to make use of unit deviations. From the work of the preceding section,

$$\tfrac{1}{4}N = 115.5, \qquad Q_1 = 187.4,$$
$$\tfrac{3}{4}N = 346.5, \qquad Q_3 = 196.2,$$

from which we find that $117 - 115.5$, or 1.5 variates had values between 187.4 and 187.5, and that $346.5 - 331$, or

15.5 variates had values between 195.5 and 196.2. Multiplying frequencies by appropriate mid-values, we have:

$$1.5 \times \tfrac{1}{2}(187.4 + 187.5) = \quad 281$$
$$104 \times \quad 189.5 \quad\quad\quad = 19{,}708$$
$$110 \times \quad 193.5 \quad\quad\quad = 21{,}285$$
$$15.5 \times \tfrac{1}{2}(195.5 + 196.2) = \quad 3{,}036$$
$$\text{Total} \quad\quad\quad\quad\quad \overline{44{,}310}$$

$$\text{Mid-mean} = \frac{44{,}310}{231} = 191.8.$$

We note the following facts: (1) some of the frequencies are fractional; (2) the sum of the frequencies employed equals $\tfrac{1}{2}N$; (3) the value of the mid-mean lies close to the arithmetic mean in fairly symmetric distributions. In the example, the agreement is unusually close, 191.8 for both the mid-mean and the mean.

14. The percentiles. *The mth percentile, P_m, of a frequency distribution is the value of the variable, x, which corresponds to m per cent of N.* It is conceived as the value for which m per cent of the variates are smaller and $(100 - m)$ per cent are larger. A percentile is computed by the familiar method of interpolation. Referring again to Table VI–1, we compute the 30 percentile, P_{30}.

$$0.30N = 0.30 \times 462 = 138.6$$
$$P_{30} = \left(\frac{138.6 - 117}{104} \times 4 \right) + 187.5 = 188.3.$$

Thus, 30 per cent of the head lengths were less than 188.3 millimeters and 70 per cent were greater.

Of major importance among the percentiles are the *deciles*. The rth decile, D_r, corresponds to the $10r$ percentile, where $r = 1, 2, 3, \cdots 9$. Thus, the third decile, D_3, is the 30 percentile. The deciles divide the ordered set of variates into ten portions of equal frequency. They are employed occasionally to give in greater detail the range of distribution of the variates and to characterize the nature of a set of qualitatively ordered variates. An example of the latter might be a group of students arranged according to native ability.

15. The mode. Although the mode might be questioned as being a positional mean in the same sense that the median, quartiles, and percentiles mark points of division in a scale, it does mark a point of highest frequency and for that reason is included among the averages of this chapter.

The modal class of a frequency distribution is the class corresponding to the maximum frequency. More generally, we may define the modal class as that class of greater frequency than any near-by class, in order to cover the possibility of *multimodal* data, that is, of frequency distributions whose polygons or curves have more than one distinct "peak." In the data of Table VI–1, the modal class is the class whose mid-value is 193.5 mm. This fact is clearly shown graphically in Figure IV–1, where the tallest rectangle corresponds to the class interval 191.5 − 195.5.

The preceding definitions are usually useful, however, only in the case of discrete data. For example, if a certain shoe store sold more men's shoes of size 8 than any other size, 8 would be the modal size. It is obvious in Table IV–4 or in Figure IV–2 that three heads appeared most often; hence, the modal value is 3.

These definitions, save in cases of the type just cited, are open to serious criticism. In the first place, data may be assembled into class intervals in various ways, and the modal value will vary with the choice of the class intervals. In the second place, the above definitions concern a *modal class*, an interval, and not a *mode*, a single value. Since we conceive of a frequency distribution as determining a frequency curve, the value of the variable, x, corresponding to the maximum point of this curve is precisely the mode of the distribution, and the maximum point on the curve rarely coincides exactly with the peak of the polygon. The accurate determination of the mode belongs to a more advanced chapter in statistics.

Statistically, the mode represents the most typical, the most frequent, value. It is often confused popularly with the arithmetic mean.

16. The appropriateness of an average. The desirable properties of a statistical average have been summarized in

Section V–1, and the peculiar advantages of each have already been discussed. Nevertheless, it is not always easy to decide which statistical average is most suitable in a given case. The nature of the data and the use to which the average is to be put may influence its selection. Let us illustrate with a few examples.

A certain college is raising endowment funds from its graduates. It is announced that 100 members of the class of 1930 have subscribed a total of $21,400, or an average of $214 per graduate. Suppose that two of these subscriptions were for $5,000 and that the remaining 98 ranged from $10 to $250, with most of them in the neighborhood of $100. Obviously, $214 is not typical of the class as a whole. In this case, the median would have been more truly representative, for its value would have been negligibly affected by the two unusually generous subscriptions. The employment of the arithmetic mean has succeeded in doubling approximately the "average" subscription as measured by the median. Some might argue that the worthy end justifies the mean! At any rate, it is clear that an unrepresentative average may be highly deceptive. We should recall at this point also the fact that solicitors of funds are often faced with the question, "What is the usual subscription?" In such cases, the mode is often a truly typical average.

The health department of a certain town reports annually the median bacteria counts of the milk from dairies selling milk in the town. There are usually twelve counts per year for each dairy. The median is employed as an average in order to minimize the effect of extreme items, for a single, unusually high count might so affect an arithmetic mean count as to create a misleading impression concerning the purity of the milk. An occasional high bacteria count ordinarily is not serious, for the bacteria in the milk of most United States cities are relatively harmless. However, frequent high counts would indicate dirty milk and would be reflected in the median. It is possible to argue that in the case of virulent bacteria, a single high count might lead to fatal results, and—after all, death is permanent. Nevertheless, particularly virulent bacteria are dangerous even in normal counts. It would seem that the median count, on the whole, is as good an average as any, although it does conceal interesting aspects of the data. The range of bacteria counts would supply a valuable additional item of information.

A manufacturer of articles of clothing is not generally interested in mean or median sizes, but in those most frequently demanded. For him, the most typical size is the one most frequently used, and this average we designate as the *mode*. In like manner, a social worker might be interested in the customary wage of men employed in a certain factory, not the mean or the median wage. The commonest wage might convey certain desired implications. For other purposes, the mean or median wage is usually more suitable.

Let us summarize briefly the uses of the three most common measures of central tendency, the mean, median, and mode. For fairly symmetric distributions, the three averages are very nearly equal and may be considered to be equally valid. The selection, then, might be made solely on the basis of ease of computation or the degree of familiarity on the part of those for whom the average is intended. The arithmetic mean is easily understood and computed without difficulty, as a rule. Skew distributions of the type illustrated in Figure VIII–2 do not always permit the mean to be as truly representative as it ordinarily is. If a fairly high degree of skewness is present, the mode or the median may be a better average. Thus, when the median differs markedly from the mean, the former is more likely to be a better average. The median, as has been pointed out, is useful when the frequency table is incomplete at an end, when a few extremely large or small variates are present, or when the classification is according to a qualitative order. In educational statistics, the desirability of dividing a class of pupils according to ability into two or more parts makes the median particularly useful at times. We may wish to know if Susie Smith stands in the upper half of the class or the lower. The median marks this division.

The mode is likely to have genuine practical value for discrete data.   It is also singularly appropriate when one value or class interval is predominant.

VI—Exercises

Find the median for each of the sets of ungrouped data indicated in Exercises 1–4.

1. Weights of members of the B. U. football squad. (Ex. V–1.)

2. Average July temperatures in New York City.   (Ex. V–3.)

3. Average price of sweet potatoes.   (Ex. V–5.)

4. Marks in Higher Mathematics.   (Ex. IV–3.)

* * *

5. The College Entrance Examination Board stated in 1935 that the median age of the readers of examination papers should be in the vicinity of 40 years.   What does this mean?

6. (a)   In which of Exercises IV–7 to 18, inclusive, is the median of doubtful statistical value?   (b)   In which would non-graphical interpolation be inaccurate?

* * *

Construct a cumulative frequency table and compute the median for each of the frequency distributions indicated in Exercises 7–14. Use the method of interpolation with an ogive when directed to do so by your instructor.

7. Precipitation in New York.   (Ex. IV–7.)

8. Maximum temperatures in New York.   (Ex. IV–8.)

9. Call discount rates.   (Ex. IV–9.)

10. Rate of taxation for school support.   (Ex. IV–10.)

11. Brain-weight of Swedish males.   (Ex. IV–11.)

12. Intelligence quotients of runaway boys.   (Ex. IV–12.)

13. Weekly earnings of Negro workers.   (Ex. IV–16.)   Note (a) the change in class interval, and (b) the unsymmetrical character of the distribution.   Do these affect the computation of the median?

14. Weight per mille of United States Army Troops.   (Ex. IV–17.)   Compare the median weights at mobilization and at demobilization.

* * *

15. The appearance of a group of salesmen is given in the follow-

ing table. How would you characterize the "median appearance" of salesmen of this group? (From Donald R. G. Cowan, *Sales Analysis from the Management Standpoint*, University of Chicago, 1938, p. 2.)

Appearance	Number
Excellent.............	297
Good.................	1231
Fair.................	393
Bad.................	18

16. The arithmetic means of the weights of two football squads were 170 lbs. for Squad *A* and 175 lbs. for Squad *B*. The median weights were 171 lbs. and 172 lbs., respectively. What can you conclude about the relative weights of the two squads?

17. The arithmetic means of the grades of two small classes in mathematics were 76 per cent and 74 per cent. The median grades were 75 per cent and 77 per cent, respectively. What conclusion do you draw concerning the classes?

18. The social classes of the parents of 760 English convicts are given in the table below. How would you characterize the median social class? (From Charles Goring, *The English Convict*, His Majesty's Stationery Office, London, 1913, page 176. By permission of The Controller of His Britannic Majesty's Stationery Office.)

Social Class	Number
Well-to-do or upper middle........	105
Prosperous poor or lower middle....	391
Poor or lower...................	243
Very poor or destitute...........	21

19. Construct on the same scale the two ogives for the data of Exercise IV–17. Compare them and draw conclusions.

20. Suppose that the ogive for a given frequency distribution were a straight line. What would this indicate?

* * *

Construct Lorenz curves for the data of Exercises 21 and 22 below. Draw conclusions from them.

21. Income tax returns for 1934, showing number of returns and net incomes. (Adapted from *Statistics of Income for 1934*, Part I, United States Treasury Department, Bureau of Internal Revenue, Washington, D. C., page 6.)

Net Incomes in $1000	Total No. of Returns	Amount in $1000
Under 1............	320,460	211,113
1– 2.........	1,608,095	2,277,726
2– 3.........	980,682	2,467,851
3– 5.........	762,536	2,839,348
5–10.........	290,824	1,952,891
10–25.........	102,892	1,513,592
25–50.........	20,931	708,530
50 and over....	8,000	825,751

22. Number and tonnage of vessels sailing from a certain port during a given year:

Tonnage	No. Vessels	Total Tonnage
Under 1,000........	57	31,900
1,000– 2,000........	85	113,800
2,000– 4,000........	42	121,800
4,000– 6,000........	26	129,100
6,000– 8,000........	10	73,400
8,000–10,000........	5	44,300
10,000–15,000........	3	41,800
Over 15,000........	1	18,700

*   *   *

Compute the quartiles Q_1 and Q_3 for the data indicated in Exercises 23–29.   Compute also such deciles or percentiles as your instructor requires.

23. Marks in Higher Mathematics.   (Ex. IV–3.)

24. Call discount rates.   (Ex. IV–9.)

25. Maximum New York temperatures (Ex. IV–8.)

26. Taxation for school support.   (Ex. IV–10.)

27. Brain-weight of Swedish males.   (Ex. IV–11.)

28. Intelligence quotients of runaway boys.   (Ex. IV–12.)

29. Weekly earnings of Negroes.   (Ex. IV–16.)

*   *   *

30. Find the modal class of each of the frequency distributions of Exercises IV: 7–12, 14–16.

⌐31.   Find the mode of the distribution of Exercise IV–13.

32.   Do the quartile values as computed by interpolation from a frequency distribution give the precise points at which the histogram is divided into four equal areas?   Why?

*   *   *

Construct Z-charts for the data of Exercises 33 (year 1930) and 34 (year 1932).

33.   Volume of Trading in Corn Futures, 1929 and 1930.   (*Year-book of Agriculture*, 1935, page 388.)

Month	Millions of Bushels	
	1929	1930
Jan.	690	196
Feb.	373	252
Mar.	416	328
April	466	283
May	526	290
June	475	322
July	520	498
Aug.	453	611
Sept.	296	433
Oct.	269	461
Nov.	261	418
Dec.	199	649

34.   Precipitation at New York City, 1931 and 1932.   (*World Almanac*, 1936, page 139.)

Month	Inches	
	1931	1932
Jan.	2.43	4.23
Feb.	2.44	2.38
Mar.	4.74	5.52
Apr.	3.30	2.69
May	3.93	1.81
June	4.00	3.57
July	4.55	0.85
Aug.	3.26	2.72
Sept.	1.15	1.56
Oct.	2.87	5.03
Nov.	0.61	5.87
Dec.	2.22	2.62

*   *   *

35. Why would Z-charts be inappropriate for the data of Exercises III: 24–26?

36. Why would a Lorenz curve be unsatisfactory for the following data on income tax returns?

Net Incomes in $1000	Total No. of Returns	Amount in $1000
Under 5...........	3,671,773	6,300,199
5– 10...........	290,824	1,199,393
10– 25...........	102,892	701,215
25– 50...........	20,931	236,287
50– 100...........	6,093	107,874
100– 150...........	982	26,439
150– 300...........	690	21,860
300– 500...........	116	3,583
500–1000...........	86	2,341
1000 and over........	33	1,265

37. In Europe the term *probable lifetime* means the age at which just half of the persons born contemporaneously will be estimated to be living. How would this average be found?

In some districts, the mortality of children in the first year is fifty per cent. According to the preceding definition, what would be the probable lifetime of a newborn child in such districts? How would the *expectation of life*, the mean number of years that persons of a given age will probably survive, compare with the probable lifetime in such cases?

38. In the United States, the probable lifetime, or better, *the most probable afterlifetime*, of a person of a given age is "the number of years that persons of a given age will most probably survive, obtained by finding the mode of the remaining lengths of life of all persons who attain that age." From the Mortality Table (Table K), find the most probable afterlifetime of persons of age 25. Of age 40. Of age 60.

39. In a certain town, 500 people reported their incomes. All of these ranged from $1,000 to $5,000, with $1500 as the usual income. The single exception was that of the town's richest man, who reports an income of about $90,000. How would you report the average income of the town?

40. The fees charged by a specialist often vary with the capacity of the patient to pay. The charges per one initial examination of a certain doctor are as follows: nothing for very poor patients, $5 for persons of limited means, $10 for persons in comfortable circumstances, $15 for persons of substantial means, and $25 for those of great wealth. Discuss the average fee (mean, median, or mode) from the point of view of (a) the physician, (b) the patient.

CHAPTER

VII

INDEX NUMBERS

❖❖⊐||||||||||||⊏⊐||||||||||||⊏⊐||||||||||||⊏⊐||||||||||||⊏⊐||||||||||||⊏⊐||||||||||||⊏⊐||||||||||||⊏⊐|||||||||||⊏⊐||||||||||||⊏⊐||||||||||||⊏⊐||||||||||||⊏❖❖

"Men learnt in the nineteenth century that the subject of economics, at all events, was suitable in parts for mathematical treatment, and that it would be the better throughout for dispassionate and expert study."

WILLIAM C. D. DAMPIER-WHETHAM, *A History of Science.**

1. Introduction. There is hardly any subject in statistics which requires a more accurate knowledge of the differing characteristics of the statistical averages than the subject of index numbers, a subject of particular importance to the economist and sociologist. · Index numbers are the results of attempts to measure changes in a variable which is itself a complex of interdependent variables. For example, "the cost of food" is a variable depending upon many other variables such as the prices of flour, beef, pork, potatoes, milk, eggs, and so forth. These simpler variables are, in general, interrelated. A rise in the price of beef may bring about a greater demand for pork, thus raising the price of pork also. Prices of dairy products may affect one another. Clearly, "the cost of food" cannot be uniquely defined; it must be estimated from a group of many properly chosen items.

In subsequent sections we shall consider mainly index numbers of commodity prices. There are, of course, index numbers of wages, of volume of trade, of employment, of stock

---

* New York, Macmillan, 1930.

quotations, and so on. There are also index numbers used to measure variables not associated with the economic world. Index numbers for school efficiency, physical fitness, intelligence, and other concepts are not unknown. Index numbers usually measure changes from *time to time*, say year to year, or month to month; but they may also indicate changes from *place to place*, as in the cost of living in New York, Chicago, and San Francisco.

The subject of this chapter is extensive, and, at times, intricate. Moreover, it includes much of a controversial char-

TABLE VII–1

FARM PRICE OF BUTTER

Year	Price in Cents per Pound p_i	Relative $100 \dfrac{p_i}{p_1}$
1923......	$40.4 = p_1$	100
1924......	39.4	98
1925......	40.7	101
1926......	41.1	102
1927......	42.3	105
1928......	43.7	108
1929......	43.8	108
1930......	36.8	91
1931......	27.4	68
1932......	$20.7 = p_{10}$	51

acter. We shall merely indicate some of the main features of the subject and a few of the principal conclusions.

2. Relatives. *A relative of a variable is the ratio, multiplied by 100, of its value at one time (or place) to its value at another time (or place).*

Consider the average farm price of butter for the years 1923 to 1932 inclusive, shown in Table VII–1. Denote the successive prices for the ten given years by p_1, p_2, p_3, $\cdots$ p_{10}. Let us compare prices with the price for 1923 as a base. The ratio, multiplied by 100, of each price to the base price, 40.4, is given in the third column and forms a series of *price relatives* for butter. Clearly, relatives above 100 indicate increased prices and relatives below 100 indicate decreased prices.

Some writers call these relatives index numbers. In a sense, they are index numbers of the simplest possible type, but we shall refer to them as relatives.

The study of relatives embraces two aspects, both of which are familiar and which are inseparably joined—the aspect of the frequency distribution and that of temporal variation. In Table VII–1, the variation of a single variable, the farm price of butter, is clearly shown from year to year. This set of relatives forms a time series, and could therefore be studied by the graphical methods of Sections III–8 and XI–10. It is important to note that the variable concerns always the same commodity, but that the time is changing.

On the other hand, we might keep the time fixed and study the relatives for a great many different variables, such as the prices of butter, milk, eggs, flour, bacon, potatoes, and so forth. A large number of relatives are often employed in forming an index number, and the form of their distribution has not only direct economic significance, but also a bearing on the choice of a representative average. A sample frequency distribution of relatives is exhibited in Table VII–2. Note that the time is constant (July, 1927). Many distributions of relatives have been found to be skew, but there seems to be no completely acceptable evidence that this is generally true. A set of relatives may be studied in the same manner as any frequency distribution—for central tendency by evaluating various means, for dispersion, for skewness, and for other characteristics.

The prices of various commodities for different years are symbolized by the letter p with appropriate subscripts and superscripts. Thus, we have:

$p_1', p_1'', p_1''', \cdots p_1^{(N)}$ for the prices of N commodities in the first year,

$p_2', p_2'', p_2''', \cdots p_2^{(N)}$ for the prices of N commodities in the second year,

.   .   . . . .

.   .   . . . .

.   .   . . . .

$p_i', p_i'', p_i''', \cdots p_i^{(N)}$ for the prices of N commodities in the ith year.

Briefly, then, $p_i^{(j)}$ represents the price of the jth commodity in the ith year. It is customary, provided no ambiguity results, to omit the superscript when writing summations. It follows that Σp_i denotes the sum of the prices of N commodities in the ith year, that is,

$$\Sigma p_i = p_i' + p_i'' + p_i''' + \cdots + p_i^{(N)}.$$

Corresponding to a price, p_i, is a quantity, q_i, to be discussed later. Thus, $\Sigma p_i q_i$ denotes the sum of the products of

TABLE VII–2

FREQUENCY DISTRIBUTION OF RELATIVE WHOLESALE PRICES FOR JULY, 1927 (Leonard Ascher, "Variations in Price Relative Distribution, January 1927 to December 1936," *Journal of the American Statistical Association*, Vol. 32, No. 198, p. 275.)

Relative	Frequency
40.0– 49.9	2
50.0– 59.9	2
60.0– 69.9	17
70.0– 79.9	30
80.0– 89.9	82
90.0– 99.9	192
100.0–109.9	146
110.0–119.9	25
120.0–129.9	15
130.0–139.9	9
140.0–149.9	3
150.0–159.9	3
160.0–169.9	1
170.0–179.9	1
180.0–189.9	1

N prices in the ith year by their respective quantities or weights for the ith year. $\Sigma p_i q_1$ represents the sum of the products of N prices in the ith year by their respective quantities for the first year.

3. Unweighted averages of relatives. The choice of a proper average to be employed for a group of price relatives is guided, as usual, by the desire to find a simple, understandable measure which lends itself readily to mathematical treatment and is sufficiently responsive to price movements. We shall discuss briefly each average.

(a) *The arithmetic mean.* For N commodities in the ith year, the arithmetic mean is defined by the formula:

$$\frac{1}{N} \Sigma \left(\frac{p_i}{p_1}\right).\qquad(1)$$

The arithmetic mean is always sensitive to extreme values and may be unduly affected by the more widely fluctuating prices. A more serious criticism arises, however, from the *bias* which is imparted to the mean by rising prices.

TABLE VII–3

ILLUSTRATION OF BIAS

Commodity	Price in 1st year p_1	Price in 2nd year p_2	Relative $\dfrac{p_2}{p_1}$	Relative $\dfrac{p_1}{p_2}$
No. 1	$1.00	$2.00	200	50
No. 2	$2.00	$1.00	50	200
Arithmetic Mean ·			125	125

Consider the prices shown in Table VII–3. In the first place, we agree that, regardless of the choice of year as a base, there has been no net movement in prices for this simple group of two commodities, yet the arithmetic mean of the relatives, for either base, shows an advance of 25 per cent in price. The undue emphasis placed on the advancing price results from the fact that although the absolute (not relative) increase is the same as the absolute (not relative) decrease, namely, $1.00, the divisor used to obtain the relative is relatively smaller when prices increase than when they decrease. This fact may be demonstrated more formally as follows:

Let $p_i = p_1 + \Delta p_i$, where Δp_i (read "delta-p-sub-i") represents the change in price (positive or negative) from the price in the base year, p_1. Hence, formula (1) may be written as:

$$\frac{1}{N} \Sigma \left(\frac{p_1 + \Delta p_i}{p_1}\right) = 1 + \frac{1}{N} \Sigma \left(\frac{\Delta p_i}{p_1}\right).$$

From the expression on the right, it becomes clear that the smaller a given denominator, that is, the smaller the basic price of a given commodity, the greater the weight given to the change in price of that commodity. When prices are generally rising above a basic price p_1, the latter price is relatively small. Hence, rising prices receive more emphasis than falling prices. When prices are generally falling below a basic price p_1, the latter price is relatively large. Thus, underemphasis is given to a general fall in prices. For example, if a price rises from \$0.80 to \$1.00, the increase is 25 per cent; when it falls from \$1.00 to \$0.80, it decreases by 20 per cent.

(b)   *The harmonic mean.* For N commodities in the ith year, we define this average (Section V–9) by means of the formula:

$$\frac{N}{\Sigma\left(\dfrac{p_1}{p_i}\right)}. \tag{2}$$

The harmonic mean has been recommended as an appropriate average measure of change in purchasing power (See Section V–9), since this varies inversely with prices. It is the reciprocal of the arithmetic mean with reversed base. Hence, the direction of bias in the arithmetic mean is reversed in the harmonic mean.

(c)   *The geometric mean.* For N commodities in the ith year, this average is defined as:

$$\sqrt[N]{\left(\frac{p_i'}{p_1'}\right)\left(\frac{p_i''}{p_1''}\right)\cdots\left(\frac{p_i^{(N)}}{p_1^{(N)}}\right)}, \tag{3}$$

and may be written in the form:

$$\frac{1}{\sqrt[N]{\left(\dfrac{p_1'}{p_i'}\right)\left(\dfrac{p_1''}{p_i''}\right)\cdots\left(\dfrac{p_1^{(N)}}{p_i^{(N)}}\right)}}. \tag{3a}$$

Thus, the geometric mean is the reciprocal of the geometric mean with reversed base. A further form,

$$\frac{\sqrt[N]{p_i'p_i''\cdots p_i^{(N)}}}{\sqrt[N]{p_1'p_1''\cdots p_1^{(N)}}}, \tag{3b}$$

shows that the geometric mean of relatives is the same as the relative of the geometric means of prices. (Sections V: 10–12.)

The geometric mean is free of many of the faults which characterize the preceding means.   It is free of bias, and this is what we should expect, since it averages *rates* of change. In Table VII–3, the geometric mean of the two relatives equals

$$\sqrt{200 \times 50} = 100,$$

regardless of which year is chosen as the base.   Since there has been no net movement in prices for the pair of commodities, the geometric mean of the relatives remains at 100 despite the reversal of base.

Some statisticians maintain that frequency distributions of relatives are nearly always skew because, theoretically, prices can rise to any level but cannot fall below the zero level. Hence they argue, for reasons stated at the end of Section V–12, that the geometric mean is a natural average for data possessing such skewness.   There is much disagreement on this point, however.

There is no question that the geometric mean is an average peculiarly appropriate to rates of change, and that these are highly significant in any study of price movements.   However, the labor of calculating a geometric mean operates against its more frequent use.

(*d*)   *The median.*   For a small number of relatives, the median is apt to be erratic.   It is generally very stable in a large group, and this property is sometimes an asset and sometimes a liability.   It is an asset when we wish to discount the effect of a few abnormal values; it is a liability when price changes are confined principally to one side of the median. Despite the simplicity and general reliability of the median, it has not come into frequent use.

(*e*)   *The mode.*   For a small group of relatives, the mode has no practical meaning; for a large group, the mode is essentially an approximation.   For these and other reasons, the mode is usually avoided in the theory of index numbers.

4.   Index numbers.   *"Index numbers" are numbers which measure the relative changes in the magnitude of a group of related variables.*   Suppose that we have the prices of wheat, corn, and oats for two years, say 1926 and 1936, and let us choose 1926 as the base year.   If we compute two appropriate numbers which enable us to make a direct comparison of the price of *grain* in 1936 with that for 1926, we call them *index numbers of the price of grain.*   Whereas a relative number involves but one commodity or item, an index number involves a group of them.   It is a sort of composite average, an average based on individual prices.

Index numbers may be *aggregative* or *relative*.   In the former type, the prices, for each year, of a group of commodities may be appropriately averaged, or combined into an aggregate, and a series of relatives, index numbers, formed from the series of averages or aggregates of prices for the years.   In the latter type, the relatives for each commodity are computed and then a proper average of these relatives is computed for each year.   This distinction will be illustrated presently with the aid of Tables VII–4 and 5.

5.   Aggregative index numbers.   *An "aggregative index number" is the ratio, multiplied by* 100, *of a weighted aggregate of values associated with a time* (*or place*) *to a corresponding weighted aggregate of values associated with another time* (*or place*), *usually fixed.*   One such index number may be expressed as:

$$\frac{\Sigma p_i q_1}{\Sigma p_1 q_1}, \tag{4}$$

where q_1 is the weight associated with both p_i and p_1, and where the basic time (usually a year or month) is denoted by the subscript 1.

Table VII–4 will furnish an illustration.   Assume the weights to be proportional to the quantities sold in the base year, 1930.   The column of weighted means of prices is found by the method described in Section V–8.   For example, the weighted average price for the base year, 1930, is found thus:

$$\frac{\Sigma p_1 q_1}{\Sigma q_1} = \frac{(3 \times 67) + (8 \times 59) + (4 \times 32)}{3 + 8 + 4} = 53.4.$$

The average price of a bushel of grain was 53.4 cents in 1930.

The index numbers in the last column are merely relatives formed from the weighted averages in the preceding column where 1930 is used as the base year. These index numbers give a simple direct picture of the variations in the price of grain over the years 1930 to 1934 inclusive.

Since Σq_1 is fixed for all weighted averages, it is really unnecessary to compute it in obtaining the aggregative index numbers, for it merely cancels out each time. Thus,

$$\frac{\Sigma p_i q_1}{\Sigma q_1} \div \frac{\Sigma p_1 q_1}{\Sigma q_1} = \frac{\Sigma p_i q_1}{\Sigma p_1 q_1}.$$

$$\frac{\Sigma w_i x_i}{\Sigma w_i}$$

However, the values in the next-to-the-last column seem to have more practical meaning in their present form. Pres-

TABLE VII–4 _Weighted arithmetic mean_

Weights, q_1		Wheat	Corn	Oats	Weighted Mean of Prices in Cents per Bushel $\dfrac{\Sigma p_i q_1}{\Sigma q_1}$	Aggregative Index Number $\dfrac{\Sigma p_i q_1}{\Sigma p_1 q_1}$
		3	8	4		
Year	i	Cents per Bushel p_i				
1930	1	67 p_1	59 p_1	32 p_1	53.4	100
1931	2	39 p_2	32 p_2	21 p_2	30.5	57
1932	3	38 p_3	32 p_3	16 p_3	28.9	54
1933	4	74 p_4	52 p_4	33 p_4	51.3	96
1934	5	88 p_5	85 p_5	49 p_5	76.0	142

ently we shall merely use the weighted aggregates or totals instead of the weighted averages.

6. Relative index numbers. _A relative index number is the average of a group of relatives associated with a given time (or place)._ Whereas, in finding an aggregative index number we first average the prices and then calculate their relatives, here we first find the relatives, and then average them. One such index number may be defined by the formula:

$$\frac{\Sigma \left(\dfrac{p_i}{p_1}\right) p_1 q_1}{\Sigma p_1 q_1}, \tag{5}$$

where p_1q_1 is the weight associated with the relative, $\dfrac{p_i}{p_1}$. The weight, p_1q_1, represents *money value* in the base year, obtained as the product of the price, p_1, by the quantity, q_1.

Since the numerator of (5) reduces to Σp_iq_1, it is obvious that this formula is merely a disguised form of (4). The reason for this apparent repetition of calculations will become evident later.

Let us compute a set of relative index numbers for the data of Table VII–4. These data, with the necessary calculations,

TABLE VII–5

Weights		Wheat		Corn		Oats		Weighted Mean of Relatives
		3×67		8×59		4×32		
Year	i	Cents per Bushel	Rel-ative	Cents per Bushel	Rel-ative	Cents per Bushel	Rel-ative	$\dfrac{\Sigma\left(\dfrac{p_i}{p_1}\right)p_1q_1}{\Sigma p_1q_1}$
1930	1	67	100	59	100	32	100	100
1931	2	39	58	32	54	21	66	57
1932	3	38	57	32	54	16	50	54
1933	4	74	110	52	88	33	103	96
1934	5	88	131	85	144	49	153	142

appear in Table VII–5. The relatives of each grain are computed, and then the weighted mean of the three relatives for each year. Note that the weights are the products of the numbers, q_1 (assumed to be proportional to the quantities sold in the base year), by the prices, p_1, in the base year, 1930. For example, the relative index number, 57, for the year 1931, found in the last column, is calculated as follows:

$$\frac{(58 \times 3 \times 67) + (54 \times 8 \times 59) + (66 \times 4 \times 32)}{(3 \times 67) + (8 \times 59) + (4 \times 32)} = 57.$$

Again we note that since $58 = \dfrac{39}{67} \times 100$, $54 = \dfrac{32}{59} \times 100$, and $66 = \dfrac{21}{32} \times 100$, the result is identical with that obtained in the preceding section.

Since the set of relative index numbers just found is identical with the set of aggregative index numbers previously found, the reader might well request the reason for such duplication of effort. There is, briefly, a twofold justification for this. In the first place, data often come to us in the form of relatives already calculated and published. These relatives are frequently combined to construct other indexes. For example, a set of index numbers on manufacturing production has been computed from thirteen other index numbers, such as those for foods, textiles, iron and steel, lumber, and so forth (see Ex. VII–12), and each of these, in turn, was composed of varying numbers of constituents. (See Ex. VII–13.) In the second place, individual price relatives as well as groups of them are often subjected to separate or composite analysis.

Another question which arises is that of weighting. Why should we weight the relatives of Table VII–5 according to value? In answering this question, we must bear in mind that a relative taken by itself reveals nothing concerning either the magnitude of the prices involved or the associated quantities. The importance of a relative is not bound up solely with the quantity involved, for even a very small quantity of a very expensive commodity may constitute an important item in a group. Neither is the importance of a relative bound up solely with the price involved, for a low price may be offset by the large quantity produced or consumed. A properly weighted relative takes account of both price and quantity, and for this reason is usually weighted by money value, pq.

7. Weighting. We have characterized an index number as a composite average of different items. These items are consumed, produced, or sold in varying amounts; furthermore, they are measured or priced in diverse ways. Eggs are measured and priced by the dozen, wheat by the bushel, coal by the ton, and so on. Obviously, the most accurate index number takes account of these factors.

Averages of relatives can sometimes be computed with sufficient accuracy without the use of weights, particularly when the number of items is large and when prices do not fluctuate abnormally. The possibility of correlation between the importance of a commodity and its variational tendencies in price as well as violent fluctuations in price contributes toward lack of faith in some unweighted averages of relatives.

In the case of aggregative index numbers, weighting becomes a necessity, and the weights, in general, are the quantities involved. The weight for a given year is often the quantity consumed, produced, sold, and so forth, during the base year. It may be the average amount for a period of years; or, for more precise work, the weight for each year may be the amount involved that year. Weights of the last-named type necessitate much more labor in computing.

The method of weighting depends, first of all, upon the particular index number desired. Where living costs are involved, the price of a commodity is usually weighted according to the amount consumed. Where volume of trade or production is concerned, the amount produced or exchanged is employed. The question as to whether the amounts to be used as weights should be those of the base year, those of the year compared, or some other combination of amounts depends largely upon the purpose of the index number. If one is comparing food costs with a fixed food budget in mind, then the amounts consumed will be fixed for all years. If one, however, is interested in actual amounts expended for food, the weights will vary from year to year with the amounts consumed. Sometimes the mean proportional, $\sqrt{q_1 q_i}$, of the amounts involved for the base year and the year compared is used. The method of weighting also varies with the mathematical type of formula used. In choosing weights, round numbers have been found to be sufficiently accurate, and varying degrees of approximation are used. Surprisingly good results are obtained with exceedingly rough weighting.

8. The base. In choosing a year as base, one should avoid years in which price conditions are abnormal. Sometimes a more representative base may be obtained by using the mean of a number of years, perhaps of all of the years

involved.   A moving base in which the base for a given year
is the preceding year is sometimes employed.   Instead of the
set of relatives:

$$\frac{p_2}{p_1}, \frac{p_3}{p_1}, \frac{p_4}{p_1}, \ldots$$

for a given commodity, we obtain the set:

$$\frac{p_2}{p_1}, \frac{p_3}{p_2}, \frac{p_4}{p_3}, \ldots,$$

called *chain* or *link relatives*.   These are frequently used in
the study of seasonal variations.

The mean proportional between two prices for two years
may be advantageously utilized as a base when the prices for
these two years are being compared.   A relative for the *i*th
year becomes then, $\dfrac{p_i}{\sqrt{p_i p_1}}$.

9. Bias.   In Section VII–3(*a*) it was observed that the
arithmetic mean of relatives, among other things, gives undue
emphasis to rapidly rising prices.   Such undue emphasis is
called *bias*.   A choice of index number is largely guided by an
endeavor to reduce bias to a minimum.   For a given type of
index number, bias may be of several kinds.   First, the bias
may be *fixed*, that is, it may exist independently of the numerical values of the items involved.   This is sometimes called
type bias.   Second, the bias may be *variable*, that is, its direction and magnitude may be dependent upon the numerical
values.

The existence of bias is detected by the *time-reversal test*.
Let the average of the relatives (divided by 100) computed
with reference to one year as a base be multiplied by the
average (divided by 100) computed with reference to the
other year as a base.   The product of the two averages with
reversed bases should be unity.   If the product is greater
than one, there is said to be an upward bias.   If the product
is less than one, there is a downward bias.

Let us refer back to Table VII–3 for an example.   The
arithmetic means of the relatives (divided by 100) with re-

versed bases are both 125 divided by 100 or 1.25. The product

$$1.25 \times 1.25 \doteq 1.56;$$

hence, there is a marked upward bias. This is a characteristic fault of the arithmetic mean.

It is possible to give formal proofs of the existence of type bias or lack of it in the common averages.* The facts may be summarized as follows:

Arithmetic Mean. . .	Upward bias
Harmonic Mean . . .	Downward bias
Geometric Mean . . .	No bias
Median	No bias
Mode	No bias

Not only may the form of average yield a certain kind of bias, but also the method of weighting. Space does not permit us to dwell upon the effects of different systems of weighting upon the various averages.

10. The selection of an index number. The choice of an index number will be influenced by availability of data, ease of computation, mathematical properties, and the purpose for which it is intended.

If weights are not to be used, the selection is likely to be made from either the median or geometric mean of relatives, for each is free of bias. Many prefer the latter. Since the arithmetic mean has an upward bias and the harmonic a downward bias, a blend of the two is sometimes recommended. This may be obtained through the arithmetic mean:

$$\frac{1}{2}\left[\frac{1}{N}\Sigma\left(\frac{p_i}{p_1}\right) + \frac{N}{\Sigma\left(\frac{p_1}{p_i}\right)}\right] \tag{6}$$

or the geometric mean:

$$\sqrt{\Sigma\left(\frac{p_i}{p_1}\right) \div \Sigma\left(\frac{p_1}{p_i}\right)}. \tag{7}$$

---

* See, for example, W. V. Lovitt and H. F. Holtzclaw, *Statistics*, Prentice-Hall, Inc., New York, 1929, Chap. X.

Formula (6) will be found to eliminate much of the bias and formula (7) all of it.

When weights are to be used, one of the most practical index numbers is that found from the weighted aggregate of prices (Section 5). This index number is in common use in the United States, particularly in the study of wholesale and retail prices.

The sum, $\Sigma p_i q_i$, is a weighted aggregate of prices of N commodities for the ith year. Here the weight q_i represents the quantity involved in the ith year. If the weight chosen is the quantity consumed or produced in the base year, then the above aggregate becomes $\Sigma p_i q_1$. A relative obtained by finding the ratio of weighted aggregates to a basic aggregate is a most practical index number. Such an index number for the ith year is defined either as:

$$\frac{\Sigma p_i q_i}{\Sigma p_1 q_i}, \tag{8}$$

or as:

$$\frac{\Sigma p_i q_1}{\Sigma p_1 q_1} \tag{9}$$

according as the weight chosen is based on quantities, q, for the ith year or the base year.

Fisher's *ideal index number* is obtained by taking the geometric mean of the two formulas (8) and (9), and is, therefore:

$$\sqrt{\frac{\Sigma p_i q_i}{\Sigma p_1 q_i} \times \frac{\Sigma p_i q_1}{\Sigma p_1 q_1}}. \tag{10}$$

As (10) is difficult to compute, a close approximation to it is obtained by using the arithmetic mean of the weights, q_i and q_1. This leads to:

$$\frac{\Sigma p_i (q_1 + q_i)}{\Sigma p_1 (q_1 + q_i)}. \tag{11}$$

This formula is practically as accurate as (10) and is relatively easy to compute. Its field of application is limited, as a rule, to prices, for the necessary weights for other data are often difficult to obtain.

Many statisticians hold that a good index number should meet, as far as is possible, two mathematical tests, the time-reversal test and the factor-reversal test. The former has been described.

In most of the index numbers, prices and quantities are involved. The product of a price by its corresponding quantity yields a *total expenditure* or a *money value*. It is considered desirable to employ a formula such that if it is used to compute an index number of prices, the corresponding index number of quantities can be obtained by interchanging the p's and the q's in the formulas. In the factor-reversal test, the product of the two indexes thus obtained should be consistent with the index number for total expenditure. Fisher's Ideal Formula meets this test admirably.

11. An important aspect. The most basic problem in computing an index number is the selection of a representative series of items. The most careful mathematical analysis may be vitiated when the index number is constructed from component parts poorly chosen. In general, the larger the number of appropriate items, the greater the accuracy of the result. Fisher has concluded that the lower limit for the number of items should run from 20 to 50, with preference for the larger figure, and that an upper limit of 200 is quite sufficient.

It is probably safe to say that index numbers which are expected to have wide use because of national importance, such as those connected with wholesale prices, cost of living, general production, and so on, will probably be constructed from a large series of items. Nevertheless, an expert selection of ten or a dozen "barometric" prices has frequently been found to be remarkably serviceable. The nature and number of the items to be employed are determined largely by the distinctive purpose of the index.

VII—Exercises

Compute relatives for the series of items in Exercises 1–4.

1. Average price of eggs (Ex. III–16). Use January as a base.

2. Average freight rates on wheat (Ex. III–17). Use 1916 as a base.

3.   Average weekly car loadings (Ex. III–26).   Use the data for 1929 only, with January as a base.

4.   Average prices of 25 industrial stocks (Ex. XI–6).   (a)   Use 1913 as a base.   (b)   Use the mean of the prices for the years 1913–1915 inclusive as a base.

*   *   *

5.   Construct on the same chart, for the purposes of comparison, three graphs of relatives covering the years 1913–1920 inclusive for the following data.   Use 1913 as a base.   (i)   Average freight rates on wheat (Ex. III–17).   (ii)   Average prices of 25 industrial stocks (Ex. XI–6).   (iii)   Revised indexes of physical production (Ex. XI–8).

6.   Using the arithmetic mean of the yearly earnings from 1929 to 1936 as a base, compute the relative earnings of member banks of the Federal Reserve System for the eight years given in each of the following categories: (a)   Total earnings.   (b)   Earnings on loans. (c)   Earnings on investments.   (d)   All other earnings.   Construct on the same chart the graphs of these four sets of relatives.

Earnings, in Millions of Dollars, of Member Banks of the Federal Reserve System.   (Carson, William J., "Trends of Principal Earning Assets and Their Significance," *Journal of the American Statistical Association*, Vol. 33, No. 202, p. 316.)

Year	Total	Loans	Investments	Others
1929	2399	1563	473	363
1930	2158	1349	472	337
1931	1841	1073	480	288
1932	1554	851	458	245
1933	1237	604	426	207
1934	1244	540	474	230
1935	1207	498	467	242
1936	1271	513	487	271

7.   Compute the relatives for yearly sales of confectionery and competitive chocolate products by 277 manufacturers for the years 1928–1936.   (a)   Use 1928 as a base.   (b)   Use 1935 as a base. (From *Confectionery Production and Distribution*, 1936, United States Department of Commerce Bulletin No. 97, p. 14.)

Year	1928	1929	1930	1931	1932
Thousands of Dollars........	242,106	258,293	236,248	200,961	156,498

(Table continued on page 166.)

Year	1933	1934	1935	1936
Thousands of Dollars........	157,649	181,528	199,558	218,117

8. The approximate production in millions of bushels in 1933, and the corresponding average price per bushel on December first of that year, are given for each of five grains. What is the average price of a bushel of grain weighted according to production?

Grain	Wheat	Rye	Corn	Oats	Barley
Production........	500	20	2300	730	160
Price.............	74¢	62¢	52¢	33¢	43¢

9. Given the following prices, with appropriate weights, of three dairy products. Using the weighted arithmetic means of the prices, find aggregate index numbers for the prices of these dairy products for the three years given, with 1926 as the base year.

	Milk (Cents per Quart)	Butter (Cents per Lb.)	Cheese (Cents per Lb.)
1926	14.5	44.4	23.1
1927	14.7	47.1	26.3
1928	15.2	47.5	25.0
Weights	30	6	3

10. A candy manufacturer used certain quantities of ingredients in making a standard amount of a given product in 1937. In 1938 he changed the relative amounts. The corresponding quantities and prices for the two years are given below. Find a simple index number, for 1938, of the cost of a standard amount, with 1937 as the base year.

	Amounts in Lbs.		Price in Cents per Lb.	
	1937	1938	1937	1938
Sugar.......	100	90	4.5	4
Cocoa.......	20	25	7	8
Peanuts.....	10	12	4	6.5
Milk........	10	13	10	12

11.　The prices of five basic commodities are given for the years 1926–1931 with appropriate weights.　Compute the index numbers for this group, with the year 1926 as a base, by either or both of the following methods and for such years as directed by your instructor. (a)　Use the relatives of the weighted aggregates of prices.　(b) Use the relatives of the prices weighted according to money value.

	Potatoes (per lb.)	Bread (per lb.)	Milk (per qt.)	Flour (per lb.)	Sugar (per lb.)
Weights	709	435	324	260	148
1926	.049	.094	.140	.060	.069
1927	.038	.093	.141	.055	.073
1928	.027	.091	.142	.054	.071
1929	.032	.090	.143	.051	.066
1930	.036	.087	.140	.048	.062
1931	.023	.076	.123	.035	.057

12.　The following data were used to compute an index number of *Manufacturing Production* for the year 1935 on the year 1919 as a base.　Verify that this number equals 106.1.　Use the weighted geometric mean.　(From V. S. Kolesnikoff, "Index of Manufacturing Production Derived from Census Data, 1935," *Journal of the American Statistical Association*, Vol. 32, No. 200.)

Industry	Index No.	Weight
Food and Kindred Products..................	118.3	125
Textiles and Their Products..................	114.4	167
Iron, Steel, and Their Products..............	92.1	233
Lumber and Its Remanufactures..............	57.2	66
Leather and Its Finished Products............	106.0	37
Paper and Printing..........................	159.5	106
Chemicals and Allied Products...............	149.4	107
Stone, Clay, and Glass Products..............	117.3	33
Nonferrous Metals	95.8	40
Tobacco Manufactures.......................	137.2	16
Vehicles for Land Transportation.............	130.1	36
Ship and Boat Building	2.0	12
Rubber Products............................	134.4	22

13.　The following data were used to compute the index number of manufacturing production for *Chemicals and Allied Products* found in the table of the preceding exercise.　Show how this index number was computed and verify it.　Use the weighted geometric mean.

Industry	Index No.	Weight
Chemicals and Acids.........................	169.8	24
Coke...	78.9	5
Gas...	97.5	16
Fertilizers..................................	77.0	5
Explosives...................................	66.8	3
Paint and Varnish	143.3	12
Petroleum Refining..........................	295.1	27
Oil and Cake, Cottonseed....................	82.0	4
Turpentine and Rosin	159.3	2
Salt...	115.2	2
Soap..	106.0	7

14. Compare the unweighted arithmetic, harmonic, and geometric means of the index numbers listed in the preceding table.

15. Given the prices of two items in two different years shown below. Determine the bias in the arithmetic mean of the relatives.

Item	p_1	p_2
No. 1.......	1.00	1.30
No. 2.......	1.80	0.90

16. Given the prices of three commodities in two different years as shown below. Apply the time-reversal test to (a) the arithmetic mean of their relatives; (b) the geometric mean of their relatives.

Commodity	p_1	p_2
No. 1.......	1.00	0.80
No. 2.......	0.90	1.20
No. 3.......	2.00	1.50

17. Given the prices of four items in two different years as shown below. Is there a net change in the prices from the first year to the second? Apply the time-reversal test to (a) the arithmetic mean of the relatives; (b) the geometric mean of the relatives.

Item	p_1	p_2
No. 1.......	1.00	1.20
No. 2.......	1.00	0.70
No. 3.......	0.80	1.10
No. 4.......	1.00	0.80

18. Show that the index numbers of formulas (7), (10), and (11) satisfy the time-reversal test.

19. Prove that the median of a set of relatives meets the time-reversal test. Note that the relatives for one base are always the reciprocals of those with the reversed base.

20. Prove that the mode in a frequency distribution of relatives meets the time-reversal test. Observe the hint in the preceding exercise.

21. Prove that the geometric mean of a set of relatives has no bias.

22. Which of formulas (8), (9), (10), and (11) satisfy the factor-reversal test?

23. Suppose you were asked to compute index numbers for the average yearly cost of a college education in the United States. List the items you would include in the order of importance. Discuss difficulties arising.

CHAPTER

VIII

MEASURES OF DISPERSION

>:||||||||||||[:]||||||||||[:]||||||||||[:]||||||||||[:]||||||||||[:]||||||||||[:]||||||||||[:]||||||||||[:]||||||||||[:]||||||||||[:]||||||||||[:]||||||||||[:]||||||||||[:]:<

"Every scheme for the analysis of nature has to face these two facts, change and endurance."

ALFRED N. WHITEHEAD, *Science and the Modern World.**

1. Introduction. Statistical data in the form of frequency distributions often exhibit certain general characteristics already noted, namely, a building-up of relatively large frequencies about the center and a steady falling-off of frequencies toward the ends. Frequency curves corresponding to such distributions may be symmetric or asymmetric. In the case of a frequency curve corresponding to a distribution of the symmetric, bell-shaped type, the mean, median, and mode coincide (Figure VIII–1). In the case of a skew frequency curve, these three averages will ordinarily be distinct, as in Figure VIII–2. (See also Section IX–12.)

One of the objects of a statistical investigation is to describe, as effectively as possible, significant characteristics of data. In the case of a frequency distribution, we may exhibit the frequency table, the histogram, and the frequency curve; we may compute the average best typifying the data; and we may describe the apportionment of the data by means of positional averages. Yet all these devices may fail to char-

---

* New York, Macmillan, 1925.

170

acterize properly the nature of the distribution at hand. The way in which variates are dispersed about the mean may be suggested by the devices just mentioned, but we desire more than a suggestion; we need a numerical measure of such dispersion. One of the aims of this chapter will be to devise and compare various measures of dispersion.

2. **The quartile deviation.** It has been pointed out (Section VI–12) that 50 per cent of the total distribution is com-

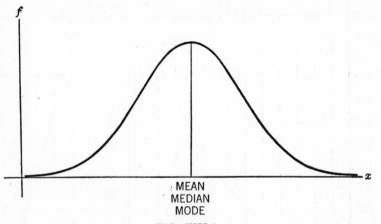

FIG. VIII-1.

prised of variates lying between the first and third quartiles. This suggests that one-half the interval $Q_3 - Q_1$ would measure the "average" deviation of the variates from the median or other intermediate value. We therefore define the *quartile deviation* or *semi-interquartile range*, Q, as:

$$Q = \tfrac{1}{2}(Q_3 - Q_1). \tag{1}$$

It is an appropriate measure of dispersion to accompany the median. Referring to Section VI–12, the quartile deviation for the head lengths of 462 criminals is:

$$\tfrac{1}{2}(196.2 - 187.4) = 4.4.$$

This means, roughly, that 50 per cent of the head lengths deviated from the median (or other intermediate value) by less than 4.4 millimeters. The other 50 per cent deviated by more than 4.4 millimeters.

3. The quartile coefficient of skewness. In a symmetric distribution, the intervals between the median, Q_2, and the first and third quartiles are always equal, that is, $Q_3 - Q_2 = Q_2 - Q_1$, but in an asymmetric distribution they rarely are. In other words, there is greater dispersion on one side of the

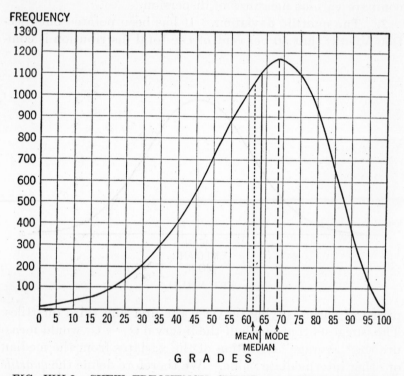

FIG. VIII-2. SKEW FREQUENCY CURVE OF THE RATINGS OF APPROXIMATELY TEN THOUSAND CANDIDATES. (*Thirty-First Annual Report of the Secretary of the College Entrance Examination Board*, 1930, page 17. Published by the Board, New York, 1931. The curve shown in this report has been slightly modified by the addition of the median line.)

median than on the other. This suggests, as a measure of the asymmetry or skewness, the difference between these two intervals. Of course, the magnitude of this difference will also depend upon the units in which the variates are expressed. In order to make the measure of skewness independent of the units used, it may be divided by twice the quartile deviation, $2Q$. Hence, we define:

$$\text{Skewness} = \frac{(Q_3 - Q_2) - (Q_2 - Q_1)}{2\left(\frac{Q_3 - Q_1}{2}\right)} = \frac{Q_1 + Q_3 - 2Q_2}{Q_3 - Q_1}. \quad (2)$$

If $Q_3 - Q_2$ is greater than $Q_2 - Q_1$, the skewness is positive and the longer range of values extends to the right, as in Figure VIII–3. In other words, there is greater dispersion to the right. The value of the coefficient of skewness, as defined in (2), ranges between -1 and $+1$. This can be shown informally as follows. Take, for example, an exaggerated case of

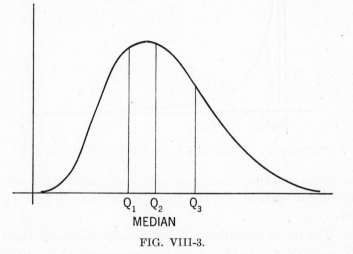

FIG. VIII-3.

positive skewness such as is illustrated in the J-curve of Figure VIII–4. Q_1 and Q_2 are fairly close together, but Q_3 is far to the right. Hence, $Q_3 - Q_2$ is very nearly equal to $Q_3 - Q_1$, and $Q_2 - Q_1$ is very small. Hence, according to the first form of (2), the skewness will be somewhat under $+1$. The steeper the descent of the curve and the larger the range of values to the right, the nearer, relatively, do Q_1 and Q_2 become. For negative skewness, the situation is similar.

Using again the values of Q_1, Q_2, and Q_3 for the head lengths of English criminals, we obtain (see Section VI–8):

$$\text{Skewness} = \frac{Q_1 + Q_3 - 2Q_2}{Q_3 - Q_1} = \frac{187.4 + 196.2 - 2(191.9)}{196.2 - 187.4} = -0.023.$$

The value here is quite near zero, since the distribution is fairly symmetric.

The quartile measure of skewness is not one which is used extensively. It is best suited to data for which other meas-

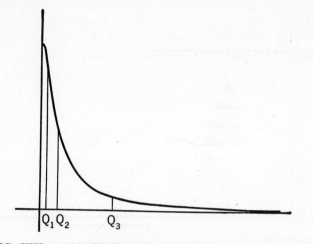

FIG. VIII-4. AN EXAMPLE OF EXTREME SKEWNESS.

ures, to be described later, are not applicable. A frequency distribution open at one end or both ends would be a case in point.

4.   The mean deviation. *The mean deviation, M.D., of a set of N variates, x_1, x_2, x_3, $\cdot$ $\cdot$ $\cdot$ x_N, is defined as the arithmetic mean of their absolute deviations from their arithmetic mean.*

$$\textbf{M.D.} = \frac{1}{N} \sum_{i=1}^{N} | x_i - \bar{x} | . \tag{3}$$

For example, suppose that the maximum temperatures at 20 selected towns of a certain region at a given date were as follows:

47,   38,   32,   35,   41,   46,   45,   46,   42,   43,
43,   38,   40,   39,   36,   44,   33,   29,   42,   41.

The mean temperature is readily found to be 40°. The absolute deviations are:

$$7, \quad 2, \quad 8, \quad 5, \quad 1, \quad 6, \quad 5, \quad 6, \quad 2, \quad 3,$$
$$3, \quad 2, \quad 0, \quad 1, \quad 4, \quad 4, \quad 7, \quad 11, \quad 2, \quad 1,$$

with a sum equal to 80.

Hence, $\qquad\qquad\qquad$ M. D. $= \dfrac{1}{20}(80) = 4.$

This means that the temperatures deviated, on an average, 4° from the mean temperature.

In the case of a frequency distribution, we have:

$$\mathbf{M.D.} = \frac{1}{N} \sum_{i=1}^{n} f_i \,|\, x_i - \bar{x} \,| \,. \tag{3a}$$

The mean deviation is not an important measure, although it is occasionally used in connection with laboratory measurements. The theorem of Section VI–10 suggests that the absolute deviations from the median might be more appropriate than those measured from the mean, but the indeterminateness of the median is a disadvantage, and so the mean is commonly used as the reference value. Moreover, the median and the mean are nearly equal in many common distributions. The mean deviation, although a good measure of the dispersion of the data, is not readily susceptible to algebraic treatment.

5. The standard deviation. Next to the arithmetic mean in fundamental importance in statistical analysis comes the measure of dispersion known as the *standard deviation* (or, sometimes, as the *root-mean-square deviation*). It has practically all the advantages of the mean deviation with the added property of being manipulated readily in algebraic expressions. In order to keep all deviations positive, we square them, instead of taking their absolute deviations. The square root of the mean of these squared deviations becomes, then, the measure of the deviations. More formally:

The standard deviation, σ (read "sigma"), of a set of $\mathbf{N}$ *variates,* $x_1, x_2, x_3, \cdots x_N$*, with arithmetic mean* $\bar{x}$*, is the positive square root of the arithmetic mean of the squares of the deviations from the arithmetic mean.*

Thus, $$\sigma = \left[\frac{1}{N} \sum_{i=1}^{N} (x_i - \bar{x})^2 \right]^{\frac{1}{2}}.\tag{4}$$

In the case of a frequency distribution,

$$\sigma = \left[\frac{1}{N} \sum_{i=1}^{n} f_i (x_i - \bar{x})^2 \right]^{\frac{1}{2}}.\tag{4a}$$

The square of the standard deviation, σ^2, is called the *variance*. Other names for this measure are the *second moment* and the *mean-square deviation*.

As a simple example of the use of formula (4), let us refer to the 20 maximum temperatures of the preceding section. From the deviations already computed, we obtain their squares:

$$49, \quad 4, \quad 64, \quad 25, \quad 1, \quad 36, \quad 25, \quad 36, \quad 4, \quad 9,$$
$$9, \quad 4, \quad 0, \quad 1, \quad 16, \quad 16, \quad 49, \quad 121, \quad 4, \quad 1,$$

with a sum equal to 474.   Then,

$$\sigma = \left[\frac{1}{20} \times 474 \right]^{\frac{1}{2}} = (23.7)^{\frac{1}{2}} = 4.87.$$

The standard deviation is, therefore, about $4.9°$.

It might be noted, at this point, that for distributions which are fairly symmetric, the mean deviation can be shown to be about four-fifths of the standard deviation.   Thus, for the ungrouped data on maximum temperatures, M.D. = 4, $\sigma = 4.9$, and M.D. = $\frac{4}{5}\sigma$, approximately.

6. Properties of the standard deviation. Theorem 1.
The mean of the squares of the deviations of a set of variates from an arbitrary value, x_0, equals the mean of the squares of the deviations from the mean, $\bar{x}$, plus the square of the deviation of x_0 from $\bar{x}$. That is,

$$\frac{1}{N} \Sigma (x_i - x_0)^2 = \frac{1}{N} \Sigma (x_i - \bar{x})^2 + (x_0 - \bar{x})^2.\tag{5}$$

Proof: If we square the binomial terms on the right, as indicated, we get:

$$\frac{1}{N}\Sigma(x_i - \bar{x})^2 + (x_0 - \bar{x})^2$$

$$= \frac{1}{N}\Sigma(x_i^2 - 2x_i\bar{x} + \bar{x}^2) + x_0^2 - 2x_0\bar{x} + \bar{x}^2$$

$$= \frac{1}{N}\Sigma x_i^2 - 2\bar{x}\left(\frac{1}{N}\Sigma x_i\right) + \bar{x}^2 + x_0^2 - 2x_0\left(\frac{1}{N}\Sigma x_i\right) + \bar{x}^2$$

$$= \frac{1}{N}\Sigma x_i^2 - 2\bar{x}^2 + \bar{x}^2 + \frac{Nx_0^2}{N} - \frac{2x_0}{N}\Sigma x_i + \bar{x}^2$$

$$= \frac{1}{N}\Sigma x_i^2 - \frac{2x_0}{N}\Sigma x_i + \frac{Nx_0^2}{N}$$

$$= \frac{1}{N}\Sigma(x_i^2 - 2x_0x_i + x_0^2)$$

$$= \frac{1}{N}\Sigma(x_i - x_0)^2.$$

Thus, the right member of (5) is shown to be equivalent to the left member.

Formula (5) may be written in the more compact form:

$$\nu_{2x} = \mu_{2x} + (x_0 - \bar{x})^2, \tag{5a}$$

where the Greek letter ν (read nu) denotes deviations with respect to an arbitrary value, the Greek letter μ (read mu) denotes deviations with respect to the mean, the first subscript, 2, denotes the second power of the deviation (or the second moment), and the second subscript, x, denotes the variable involved. Note that $\mu_{2x} = \sigma_x^2$.

Students of physics will be interested in the fact that the standard deviation is analogous to the radius of gyration with respect to the center of gravity of a system of particles. In fact, formula (5) or (5a) is similar to the theorem of mechanics which states that the moment of inertia of a system of particles about any axis equals its moment of inertia about a parallel axis through its center of gravity, plus the moment of inertia about the arbitrary axis of the mass of the system considered concentrated on the axis through the center of gravity.

THEOREM 2. *The sum of the squares of the deviations is a minimum when taken with respect to the arithmetic mean.*

This theorem is exactly the same as Theorem 2 of Section V–6. A second, simpler proof follows directly from formula

(5). The last term $(x_0 - \bar{x})^2$ in its right member becomes a minimum, zero, when $x_0 = \bar{x}$; hence, $\dfrac{1}{N} \Sigma (x_i - x_0)^2$ is a minimum when $x_0 = \bar{x}$.

7. Computation of the standard deviation. The computation of σ from a frequency distribution follows the same general pattern as that for $\bar{x}$ and may be regarded as a logical extension of it. We employ again unit deviations, u_i, where $u_i = \dfrac{x_i - x_0}{k}$, k being the class interval. It will be shown in Section IX–8 that when u_i replaces x_i, formula (5a) becomes the following:

$$\nu_{2u} = \mu_{2u} + \bar{u}^2, \tag{6}$$

where

$$\nu_{2u} = \frac{1}{N}\Sigma f_i (u_i - u_0)^2 = \frac{1}{N}\Sigma f_i u_i^2, \text{ since } u_0 = 0;$$

$$\mu_{2u} = \frac{1}{N}\Sigma f_i (u_i - \bar{u})^2 = \sigma_u^2;$$

and

$$\bar{u} = \frac{1}{N}\Sigma f_i u_i.$$

Hence, from (6) we obtain the formula useful in practice,

$$\sigma_u^2 = \nu_{2u} - \bar{u}^2. \tag{7}$$

It is then easy to show that:

$$\sigma_x = k\sigma_u. \tag{8}$$

The proofs of these statements will be given in Section IX–8.

Let us apply formulas (7) and (8) to the data of Table V–1. All the work included there is transferred to Table VIII–1, which follows. Column 5, headed $f_i u_i^2$, is obtained by multiplying the corresponding pairs of values in columns 3 and 4; $u_i(f_i u_i) = f_i u_i^2$. The last three columns are for checking purposes. The successive steps in the computation are exhibited below the table, where the standard deviation is found to be 6.48, or about 6.5, millimeters. The variance equals $(6.48)^2$, or about 42.0.

8. Remarks concerning the computation of σ. (i) *Checking.* As in the case of the arithmetic mean, the value

TABLE VIII–1

COMPUTATION OF THE STANDARD DEVIATION OF HEAD LENGTHS

(1)	(2)	(3)	(4)	(5)	(6)	(7)	(8)
Mid-Value						Check	
x_i	f_i	u_i	$f_i\,u_i$	$f_i\,u_i^2$	u_i+1	$f_i(u_i+1)$	$f_i(u_i+1)^2$
173.5	3	−5	−15	75	−4	−12	48
177.5	9	−4	−36	144	−3	−27	81
181.5	29	−3	−87	261	−2	−58	116
185.5	76	−2	−152	304	−1	−76	76
189.5	104	−1	−104	104	0	0	0
193.5	110	0	0	0	1	110	110
197.5	88	1	88	88	2	176	352
201.5	30	2	60	120	3	90	270
205.5	6	3	18	54	4	24	96
209.5	4	4	16	64	5	20	100
213.5	2	5	10	50	6	12	72
217.5	1	6	6	36	7	7	49
			−394			−173	
			198			439	
Totals	462		−196	1300		266	1370

$$\bar{u} = \frac{1}{N}\Sigma f_i u_i = \frac{-196}{462} = -0.424$$

$$\nu_{2u} = \frac{1}{N}\Sigma f_i u_i^2 = \frac{1300}{462} = 2.81$$

$$\sigma_u^2 = \nu_{2u} - \bar{u}^2 = 2.81 - (-0.424)^2 = 2.63$$

$$\sigma_x = k\sigma_u = 4\,(2.63)^{1/2} = 6.48$$

$\Sigma f_i(u_i+1) - \Sigma f_i u_i = 266 - (-196) = 462$ √

$(4)\,f_i(u_i+1)^2 - (4)\,f_i u_i^2 = 2\,\Sigma f_i u_i + N$

$1370 - 1300 = 2\,(-196) + 462$

$70 = 70$ √

of the standard deviation as found from a frequency distribution may be verified by selecting a new provisional mean adjacent to the original one chosen. Since

$$\Sigma f_i(u_i + 1)^2 - \Sigma f_i u_i^2 = \Sigma f_i u_i^2 + 2\Sigma f_i u_i + \Sigma f_i - \Sigma f_i u_i^2$$
$$= 2\Sigma f_i u_i + N,$$

we may compare, in Table VIII–1, the difference of the totals in columns 8 and 5 with twice the total of column 4 added to the total frequency, N. Thus, as shown in the lower right-hand portion of this table,

$$1370 - 1300 = 2(-196) + 462,$$

or $$70 = 70,$$

which verifies the answer.

(ii) *Significant digits.* The discussion of Section V–5 (ii) can be shown to be generally valid for the standard deviation, whose value, taken from Table VIII–1, we shall express finally as 6.5 millimeters. This implies a precision of one more decimal place than occurs in the individual head lengths, since these were measured to the nearest millimeter. Moreover, Sheppard's corrections discussed in paragraph (v) below do not enhance the precision of this value of σ. Perhaps even more important than any of these considerations is the fact that the second decimal place would have little if any statistical significance in any practical problem connected with the standard deviation of head lengths. A good working rule is to save, at most, one more decimal place than occurs in most of the individual items, the variates. In practice, this often means that two significant digits are sufficient, and therefore the slide rule can often be employed to advantage in the computation of the square roots connected with σ.

(iii) *Ungrouped data.* In Section 5 the direct computation of the standard deviation was illustrated for the simple set of maximum temperatures. For more extensive sets, not amenable to grouping, the use of a provisional mean will often simplify the arithmetical labor. The formula to be used when the unit of measurement of x remains unchanged is:

$$\sigma_x^2 = \nu_{2x} - (x_0 - \bar{x})^2. \tag{9}$$

(See Exercise VIII–31.)

(iv) *Unequal class intervals.* If a frequency distribution contains groups of unequal class intervals, the standard deviation may often be calculated advantageously by making a wise choice of x_0 and by taking proper account of the inequalities in the intervals. This method works well when only two differing groups exist, and is illustrated in Table V–2.

In other cases, particularly when there are more than two groups with unequal class intervals, it may be wiser to compute the mean and variance of each group separately and then to apply the following formula:

$$N\sigma_x^2 = \sum_{i=1}^{m} N^{(i)}\sigma_x^{(i)2} + \sum_{i=1}^{m} N^{(i)}(\bar{x}^{(i)} - \bar{x})^2, \tag{10}$$

where the notation is the same as that described under Theorem 3, Section V–8, with the addition of the symbol $\sigma^{(i)}$ to designate the standard deviation of the ith group.

TABLE VIII–2

COMPUTATION OF THE STANDARD DEVIATION WHEN THE CLASS INTERVALS ARE UNEQUAL

u_i	$f_i\, u_i$	$f_i\, u_i^2$	
			$\bar{x} = 63.2$
-3	-3	9	$N' = 30 \qquad k' = 5 \qquad \bar{x}' = 20.3$
-2	-6	12	
-1	-2	2	$\nu'_{2u} = \dfrac{71}{30} = 2.37;$
0	0	0	
1	8	8	$\sigma_u'^2 = 2.37 - \left(\dfrac{17}{30}\right)^2 = 2.05;$
2	20	40	
Totals	17	71	$\sigma_x'^2 = 5^2\,(2.05) = 51.2.$
-3	-75	225	
-2	-72	144	$N'' = 205 \qquad k'' = 10 \qquad \bar{x}'' = 61.1$
-1	-41	41	
0	0	0	$\nu''_{2u} = \dfrac{637}{205} = 3.11;$
1	30	30	
2	40	80	$\sigma_u'' = 3.11 - \left(\dfrac{-79}{205}\right)^2 = 2.96;$
3	39	117	
Totals	-79	637	$\sigma_x''^2 = 10^2\,(2.96) = 296.$
-1	-23	23	$N''' = 32 \qquad k''' = 20 \qquad \bar{x}''' = 116.9$
0	0	0	
1	2	2	$\nu'''_{2u} = \dfrac{25}{32} = 0.781;$
Totals	-21	25	$\sigma_u'''^2 = 0.781 - \left(-\dfrac{21}{32}\right)^2 = 0.351;$
			$\sigma_x'''^2 = 20^2\,(0.351) = 140.$

$$N\sigma_x^2 = \sum_{i=1}^{3} N^{(i)}\,\sigma_x^{(i)2} + \sum_{i=1}^{3} N^{(i)}\,(\bar{x}^{(i)} - \bar{x})^2;$$

$267\,\sigma_x^2 = [(30 \times 51.2) + (205 \times 296) + (32 \times 140)] + [30\,(203 - 63.2)^2 + 205\,(61.1 - 63.2)^2 + 32\,(116.9 - 63.2)^2] = 215{,}000;$

$\sigma_x = 28.4.$

To illustrate the use of formula (10), we reproduce in Table VIII–2 a portion of Table V–3, and make use of the values $\bar{x}'$, $\bar{x}''$, $\bar{x}'''$, and $\bar{x}$ already found.

(v) *Sheppard's correction.* As stated in Section V–2, the assumption that the variates are so distributed within a class interval that each may be replaced by the mid-value of the interval is not a valid one. In computing the arithmetic mean, no harm is done when such an assumption is applied to moderately symmetric distributions; but in the case of the standard deviation, objectionable errors might arise. W. F. Sheppard has developed correction formulas to apply to the standard deviation and to other moments computed from frequency distributions which are of the continuous, approximately normal type. Owing to the question of significant digits, the application of Sheppard's correction is hardly worth while unless the total frequency, N, is very large, say at least 1,000, and unless the number of class intervals is at least 20.

The corrected value of the variance, σ^2, is found, according to Sheppard, by subtracting $\dfrac{k^2}{12}$ from the computed variance, k, as usual, being the class interval. Thus,

$$\sigma_x^2 \text{ (corrected)} = \sigma_x^2 - \frac{k^2}{12}. \tag{11}$$

If we apply this formula to the data of Table VIII–1, we obtain:

$$\sigma_x^2 \text{ (corrected)} = 42.0 - \frac{16}{12}$$

$$= 40.7,$$

whence, σ_x (corrected) = 6.38.

The net practical effect is to change the standard deviation of the head lengths from 6.5 to 6.4, not a serious matter.

9. Uses of the standard deviation. There is no question that σ is the most widely used measure of dispersion. A relatively small value of σ denotes close clustering about the mean; a relatively large value, wide scattering about the mean. Figures VIII–5 and 6 illustrate such a difference in spread of the data.

The standard deviation constitutes a convenient statistical unit used in the construction of other statistical constants and in the comparison of these with one another. In other words, many measures are expressed in terms of σ as a unit. (See Section IX–4.) For the present, it is worth while to note that a spread of 3σ on each side of the arithmetic mean of a moderately symmetric distribution of fairly large total frequency includes at least 99 per cent of all the variates, as a

FIG. VIII-5.   FIG. VIII-6.

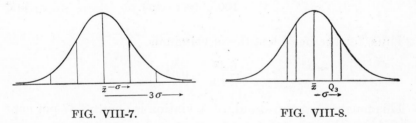

FIG. VIII-7.   FIG. VIII-8.

rule. A corresponding spread of σ includes about 68 per cent (Figures VIII–7 and VIII–8). The first fact may be used as a rough check on our calculation of σ. The second shows that σ is somewhat greater than the quartile deviation, Q; for the quartile range, $Q_3 - Q_1$, includes 50 per cent of the variates. For example, for the data of head lengths (Table VIII–1), $3\sigma = 3(6.48) = 19.4$; hence, the range from $\bar{x} - 3\sigma$ to $\bar{x} + 3\sigma$ is from 172.4 to 211.2 millimeters approximately, and this includes all but 5 or 6 of the 462 head lengths. Also, $Q = 4.4$, which is about two-thirds of σ, where $\sigma = 6.5$.

10. The coefficient of variation. The value of the standard deviation of a set of positive variates, grouped or ungrouped, depends, among other things, upon the units in which the variates are expressed. It is often desirable to compare the dispersion of two sets of positive variates measured in the same or in different units. Examples of data subject to such comparison might be the hourly wages of coal miners and of steel workers or the lengths and weights of some living body. In order to reduce a statistical measure to a number which is independent of the unit of measurement used, this measure is divided by some other one expressed in the same unit. The result is a so-called *pure number* or *absolute measure*. Formula (2) for skewness (Section VIII–3) is an example.

A common absolute measure of dispersion is the *coefficient of variation, V*, defined as:

$$V = \frac{\sigma_x}{\bar{x}}, \tag{12}$$

or as:

$$V = 100 \frac{\sigma_x}{\bar{x}} \text{ (per cent).} \tag{13}$$

Thus, for the head lengths of criminals,

$$V = \frac{6.48}{191.8} = 0.0337.$$

This means that the standard deviation is about 3.37 per cent of the arithmetic mean.

The amount of dispersion of data seems to be connected, in a vague way, with the distance from the origin or zero point to the mean value; therefore, the coefficient of variation should be used only in cases where an origin is inherent in the data. Measurements of lengths, weights, hourly wages, prices of goods, school grades in per cent, and so forth, cannot be less than zero; hence, for such data, the quantity, V, has significance. On the other hand, temperature readings are entirely relative to the particular scale used. A reading of 0° Centigrade is equivalent to 32° Fahrenheit; there is no temperature intrinsically zero. The reason for the restriction of the use of V to positive variates should, by now, be apparent. Surely the presence of $\bar{x} = 0$ in formula (12) or (13) would be embarrassing to the would-be statistician.

VIII—Exercises

1. Given the numbers 2, 7, 2, 6, 8, 4, 6, 5. Find (*a*) the mean; (*b*) the mean deviation; (*c*) the standard deviation.

2. The temperature of a thermostat was read at two-minute intervals for a period of 20 minutes, with the following results:

Time	0	1	2	3	4	5
Temp.	3.161	3.158	3.159	3.160	3.152	3.162

Time	6	7	8	9	10
Temp.	3.152	3.158	3.162	3.162	3.155

Find the mean temperature and the mean deviation. (From *Journal of Chemical Education*, Feb. 1935.)

3. Find the standard deviation of the integers from 1 to 19 inclusive.

*   *   *

Find the standard deviation for each of the sets of ungrouped data indicated in Exercises 4–6.

4. Hours of work in 29 industries. (Ex. V–2.)

5. July temperatures in New York City. (Ex. V–3.)

6. Prices of sweet potatoes. (Ex. V–5.)

*   *   *

Find the standard deviations for the frequency distributions designated in Exercises 7–12. Check the computation as directed by your instructor. Give both the uncorrected and the corrected values (according to Sheppard) of σ. Find also the coefficient of variation when directed to do so by your instructor.

7. Precipitation in New York City. (Ex. IV–7.)

8. Daily temperatures in New York City. (Ex. IV–8.)

9. Call discount rates. (Ex. IV–9.)

10. Taxation for school support. (Ex. IV–10.)

11. Brain-weight of Swedish males. (Ex. IV–11.)

12. Intelligence quotients of boys. (Ex. IV–12.)

*   *   *

Find the mean deviation for each of the sets of ungrouped data indicated in Exercises 13–15.

13. Hours of work in 29 industries. (Ex. V–2.)

14. July temperatures in New York City. (Ex. V–3.)

15. Prices of sweet potatoes. (Ex. V–5.)

*   *   *

Find the mean deviation for each of the frequency distributions indicated in Exercises 16–18.

16. Call discount rates. (Ex. IV–9.)

17. New York City temperatures. (Ex. IV–8.)

18. Precipitation in New York City. (Ex. IV–7.)

*   *   *

Find (a) the quartile deviation, and (b) the quartile coefficient of skewness for the data indicated in Exercises 19–25.

19. Precipitation in New York City. (Ex. IV–7.)

20. Call discount rates. (Ex. IV–9.)

21. New York City temperatures. (Ex. IV–8.)

22. Taxation for school support. (Ex. IV–10.)

23. Wages of male employees. (Ex. IV–14.)

24. Intelligence quotients of boys. (Ex. IV–12.)

25. Brain-weight of Swedish males. (Ex. IV–11.)

*   *   *

26. Given the frequency distribution below, where the class intervals are not all equal. Compute the arithmetic mean and standard deviation by two methods, as follows:

Method 1. Let $u_i = \dfrac{x_i - x_0}{k}$, where $x_0 = 40$ and $k = 10$. See Table V–2.

Method 2. Use formula (10), Section VIII–8. See Table VIII–2.

Class Interval	Frequency
0 — 10	1
10 — 20	4
20 — 30	15
30 — 40	20
40 — 60	20
60 — 80	8
80 — 100	2
Total	70

27. What would you say about the usefulness of any measure of dispersion computed from a J-distribution? Assume that all grouping errors have been properly eliminated.

28. What is the value of the quartile coefficient of skewness when the distribution is perfectly symmetric? Prove your statement.

29. Prove formally that if $X_i = x_i - \bar{x}$, $\sigma_X = \sigma_x$.

$\times$ **30.** Prove that $\sigma_x^2 = k^2 \sigma_u^2$.

31. Show that formula (9), Section VIII–8 (iii), is true.

32. Prove Theorem 2, Section V–6, by using the value for σ^2 obtained from formula (4a), Section VIII–5.

$\times$ **33.** Prove formula (10), Section VIII–8.

CHAPTER

IX

UNIFORM SCALES: MOMENTS

❖❖❖⫘⫘⫘⫘⫘⫘⫘⫘⫘⫘⫘⫘⫘⫘⫘⫘⫘⫘⫘⫘⫘⫘⫘⫘⫘⫘⫘⫘⫘⫘⫘⫘⫘❖❖

"Though counting in the usual way,
Years twenty-one I've been alive,
Yet reckoning by my natal day,
I am a little boy of five!"

W. S. GILBERT, *The Pirates of Penzance.*

(A) UNIFORM SCALES

1. Introduction. The notion of a reference point is familiar to us all. The Christian uses "the year of our Lord" as a point of departure or origin for measuring time, but a Mohammedan employs the year of the Hegira (622 A. D.) for the beginning of his era. The lapse of time between two historical events is, however, the same for both Christian and Moslem. Longitude is reckoned from the Greenwich meridian, but it could be reckoned as well from the meridian passing through Baraboo. In either case, the difference in longitude between any two given points on the earth's surface would be the same. A change of origin does not change the scale of measurement, and this is a simple but important fact.

Another familiar notion is that of unit of measurement—the fact that we select from time to time such units as seem of appropriate size for the purpose in hand. A sprinter's time for a 100-yard dash is measured in seconds, the age of a person is given in years—unless he happens to be an infant, when it may be given in months. In *The Pirates of Penzance*, the hero Frederic suffers from the fact that he is only "a little boy of five" despite the fact that twenty-one years have elapsed since he was born—on February 29.

The comparison of two or more sets of data often becomes more vivid when they are measured with the same unit and placed in juxtaposition. A striking example of this occurs when one follows the suggestion made in H. G. Wells' *Outline of History*. The author points out that if the time diagrams showing the geological and the glacial ages of the earth were plotted to the same scale, the geological diagram would be from 41 to 410 feet long, as compared with the glacial diagram about four inches long. And the historical period of man appears then as an interval of about one-sixteenth of an inch!

A judicious choice of unit is necessary in many regions of statistical investigation. For example, it makes a great deal of difference in drawing certain conclusions whether we measure aviation transportation in terms of number of trips, number of passengers carried, number of passenger-miles flown, or number of passenger-flight-hours. Attention should also be called to the fact that a deliberate choice of a relatively small or a relatively large unit is sometimes made in order to produce a misleading impression. Figures of astronomical proportions may amaze or startle one; magnitudes expressed in figures of moderate size may soothe or deceive.

In some of the work of the preceding chapters, advantages were gained by a change of scale, either by a shifting of origin or a uniform reduction or magnification of scale, or by both. We called these transformations *translations* and *stretchings* or *compressions*. (Section V–4.) Let us review them briefly and characterize them more carefully.

2. The translation of coordinate axes. When axes are displaced so that their new positions remain parallel to the old, the axes are said to have undergone a *translation*. Suppose that a point, P, has coordinates (x, y) with reference to axes whose origin is O. Let the axes be translated horizontally a distance h and vertically a distance k, thus giving the new origin, O', the coordinates (h, k). (Figure IX–1.) If

(x', y') are the coordinates of P referred to the new axes, we see that

$$x = x' + h$$
$$y = y' + k \, ; \tag{1}$$

whence,

$$x' = x - h$$
$$y' = y - k \tag{1a}$$

The first pair of equations gives the original coordinates x and y in terms of the new, x' and y'; the second pair gives x' and

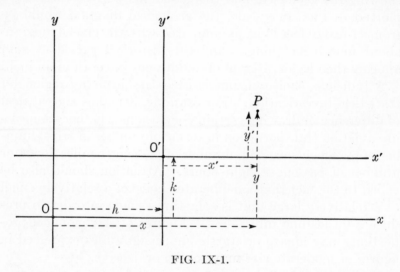

FIG. IX-1.

y' in terms of x and y. These equations can easily be shown to be valid for any position whatsoever of O' relative to O, provided the new axes remain respectively parallel to the old.

As a simple practical illustration of the use of translated axes, consider the positions of the frequency curves in Figures IX–2 and 3. In Figure IX–3, the y-axis of Figure IX–2 has been translated horizontally to the right a distance equal to the arithmetic mean, $\bar{x}$. The axes have not been translated vertically. In other words, the values of h and k in formulas (1) and (1a) are $\bar{x}$ and 0, respectively. Thus,

$$x' = x - \bar{x};$$
$$y' = y.$$

Obviously, x' represents the deviation from the mean. In the future, we shall find it more convenient to refer to frequency curves constructed with origins at their mean values.

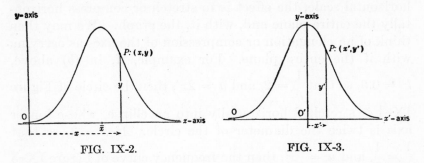

FIG. IX-2.   FIG. IX-3.

Up to the present we have used only horizontal shifts of origin, but in Chapters X and XI we shall have occasion to employ both horizontal and vertical displacements. Note that a translation of axes in no wise affects the size and shape of the curve involved.

3. Change of scale. It has already been found advantageous, on occasion, to vary the unit in which a set of variates is expressed. For purposes of computing the arithmetic mean and standard deviation of a frequency distribution of variates, we changed from their values, x_i, to their corresponding unit deviations, u_i, by setting:

$$u_i = \frac{x_i - x_0}{k}. \tag{2}$$

In Section V–4, we showed that this formula really represents two transformations of axes:

(a)   a translation, $x' = x - x_0$, and

(b)   a stretching or compression, $u = \frac{1}{k} x'$.

Type (a) has been discussed. The new origin has been moved horizontally (only) a distance equal to x_0, the provisional mean. The new abscissa, x', represents a deviation from this provisional mean. Type (b) represents a horizontal compression of the x-axis if k is greater than one, a stretching if k is less than one. When the x-axis is stretched or compressed by a factor, k, each horizontal unit is, of course, stretched or compressed by the same amount. If all points of the plane are then determined according to the modified horizontal scale, the effect is to stretch or compress horizontally the entire plane and, with it, the graph. We may then think of an elongation or compression of the axes as carrying with it the entire plane. For example, if, in (b) above, $k = 0.5$, so that $\dfrac{1}{k} = 2$, and $u = 2x'$, then the circle of Figure IX–4 is stretched horizontally into an ellipse, whose longer axis is twice the diameter of the circle. If $k = 3$, so that $\dfrac{1}{k} = \dfrac{1}{3}$, and $u = \dfrac{1}{3}x'$, then the frequency curve of Figure IX–5 is compressed horizontally to one-third its width. It is helpful to conceive of the coordinate plane as a flat sheet of rubber

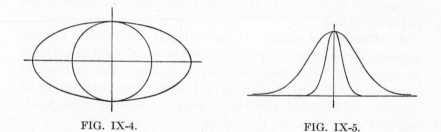

FIG. IX-4.   FIG. IX-5.

upon which the coordinate axes are drawn. If the rubber is attached to two vertical rods which are then pulled apart horizontally, the rubber will be stretched horizontally. Any scale of measurement laid off on the x-axis will be elongated, but the vertical scale will remain unchanged. Clearly, then, equation (2) defines both a shifting of the origin or zero-point of the x-scale and a modification of its unit of length.

A stretching or compression may alter both the size and shape of a given curve, but not the type. Curves may appear to be of different types when in reality they are not. Thus, the circle may be treated as a special case of a horizontal or vertical ellipse, that is, as an ellipse the major and minor axes of which happen to be of the same length. The two frequency curves of Figure IX–5 are really of the same type —symmetrical, bell-shaped, asymptotic to the x-axis. Thus, the change from the original unit, x, to the standard unit (see the next section) will not affect the type of the curve involved, but it may affect both its size and shape.

4. Standard units. Statistics involves, among other things, a comparative study of data, particularly of data in the form of frequency distributions. This study necessitates a reduction of different units of measurement to a common measure, or, better still, to pure numbers which are independent of the units used. For this and for other reasons, it has become universal practice to measure variates in terms of their standard deviation as a unit. We therefore employ the *standard variable*, σ_x, and introduce t, defined by the formula:

$$t = \frac{x - \bar{x}}{\sigma_x}. \tag{3}$$

Equation (3) defines a transformation of the variable x into the variable t. Geometrically, this means that the origin on the x-axis has been translated to the arithmetic mean, $\bar{x}$, and that the scale has been divided by the factor, σ_x. The old (x, y)-axes become the new (t, y)-axes. Since $x - \bar{x}$ and σ_x are directly proportional to the unit of measurement used, $\frac{x - \bar{x}}{\sigma_x}$ is a pure number, independent of the original unit.

5. Uniform and non-uniform scales. It has been tacitly assumed throughout the discussion of the preceding sections that the unit of measurement is constant throughout the length of a given axis; in other words, that the geometric distances from 0 to 1, 1 to 2, 2 to 3, −1 to −2, and so forth, are all the same. If equal numerical intervals determine equal geometric intervals on a straight line, the scale of measurement is said to be uniform.

Non-uniform scales have been used occasionally in this book. The scale of the slide rule (Figure II–2), the vertical scale of semi-logarithmic paper (Figure III–11), and the vertical scale of probability paper (Figure X–13) are examples. A change from a uniform to a non-uniform scale may change profoundly the type of curve. Thus, the graph of Figure III–10 changes practically to a straight line in Figure III–11.

(B) MOMENTS

6. Introduction. Frequency distributions have already been described in two different ways. *Geometrically*, the common bell-shaped type has been characterized by its symmetry or skewness, by the location of certain important points such as the mean, median, and mode, and by its degree of dispersion. Such a geometric description is readily comprehended but is essentially qualitative and often fails to reveal significant latent properties. *Algebraically*, the attributes of a frequency distribution have been precisely measured with the aid of certain functions of the variates, among which the mean, $\frac{1}{N}\Sigma f_i x_i$, and the variance, $\frac{1}{N}\Sigma f_i(x_i - \bar{x})^2$, are of chief importance. A value, such as $\bar{x}$ or σ_x, calculated from a given set of variates, is often called a *statistic*. There is one group of statistical constants or *statistics* which serves admirably to characterize frequency distributions. The important members of this group are calculated with relative ease. They serve, not merely to describe the chief features of the distribution, but also to fit the latter with an appropriate curve. The members of this group of statistical constants are called *moments*. They are not entirely unfamiliar to us, for the arithmetic mean is a first moment (Section V–6), and the variance, a second moment (Section VIII–5).

7. Definitions. *The rth moment, with reference to x_0, of a set of variates, x_1, x_2, x_3, $\cdots$ x_n, whose frequencies are f_1, f_2, f_3, $\cdots$ f_n, respectively, is defined by the formula:*

$$\frac{1}{N} \sum_{i=1}^{n} f_i(x_i - x_0)^r. \tag{4}$$

The reference value, x_0, is entirely arbitrary. The index, r, indicates the *order* of the moment. The *zero*th moment is unity, for:

$$\frac{1}{N}\Sigma f_i(x_i - x_0)^0 = \frac{1}{N}\Sigma f_i = 1.$$

If, for example, we choose $x_0 = 0$, the first moment becomes the arithmetic mean:

$$\frac{1}{N}\Sigma f_i x_i = \bar{x}.$$

If we choose $x_0 = \bar{x}$ and $r = 2$, we have the second moment with respect to the mean, which is the variance, for:

$$\frac{1}{N}\Sigma f_i(x_i - \bar{x})^2 = \sigma^2.$$

Two important reference values are in common use with moments, the value 0 and the value $\bar{x}$. When $x_0 = 0$, the moments are designated by ν_r; when $x_0 = \bar{x}$, they are designated by μ_r. These symbols, with $r = 2$ and with secondary subscripts to indicate the variate involved, were described in Section VIII–6.   Thus, $\frac{1}{N}\Sigma f_i(x_i - x_0)^r$ where the $x_0 = 0$

$$\nu_{rx} = \frac{1}{N}\Sigma f_i x_i^r, \tag{5}$$

and

$$\nu_{ru} = \frac{1}{N}\Sigma f_i u_i^r, \text{ where } u_i = \frac{x_i - x_0}{k}. \tag{6}$$

Also

$$\mu_{rx} = \frac{1}{N}\Sigma f_i(x_i - \bar{x})^r, \tag{7}$$

and

$$\mu_{ru} = \frac{1}{N}\Sigma f_i(u_i - \bar{u})^r. \tag{8}$$

8. **Properties of the moments.**   Let us examine the four moments obtained by setting $r = 1, 2, 3,$ and 4, in turn, in each of the four formulas above.   Obviously, the *zeroth* moment equals unity in all four cases.

$$\nu_{1x} = \frac{1}{N}\Sigma f_i x_i = \bar{x} \qquad\qquad \nu_{1u} = \frac{1}{N}\Sigma f_i u_i = \bar{u}$$

$$\nu_{2x} = \frac{1}{N}\Sigma f_i x_i^2 \qquad\qquad \nu_{2u} = \frac{1}{N}\Sigma f_i u_i^2$$

$$\text{(5a)} \qquad\qquad \text{(6a)}$$

$$\nu_{3x} = \frac{1}{N}\Sigma f_i x_i^3 \qquad\qquad \nu_{3u} = \frac{1}{N}\Sigma f_i u_i^3$$

$$\nu_{4x} = \frac{1}{N}\Sigma f_i x_i^4 \qquad\qquad \nu_{4u} = \frac{1}{N}\Sigma f_i u_i^4$$

An interesting case is that of the first moment, for it corresponds to the arithmetic mean. The four moments of (6a) will be useful in the practical problems of computation.

$$\mu_{1x} = \frac{1}{N}\Sigma f_i(x_i - \bar{x}) = 0.$$

$$\mu_{2x} = \frac{1}{N}\Sigma f_i(x_i - \bar{x})^2 = \sigma_x^2.$$

$$\mu_{3x} = \frac{1}{N}\Sigma f_i(x_i - \bar{x})^3.$$

$$\mu_{4x} = \frac{1}{N}\Sigma f_i(x_i - \bar{x})^4.$$

$$\left.\right\} \text{(7a)}$$

$$\mu_{1u} = \frac{1}{N}\Sigma f_i(u_i - \bar{u}) = 0.$$

$$\mu_{2u} = \frac{1}{N}\Sigma f_i(u_i - \bar{u})^2 = \sigma_u^2.$$

$$\mu_{3u} = \frac{1}{N}\Sigma f_i(u_i - \bar{u})^3.$$

$$\mu_{4u} = \frac{1}{N}\Sigma f_i(u_i - \bar{u})^4.$$

$$\left.\right\} \text{(8a)}$$

Note that the first moments of (7a) and (8a) reduce to zero by virtue of Theorem 1, Section V–6, and that the second moments correspond to the variances, σ_x^2 and σ_u^2.

In applying moments to frequency distributions for the purpose of interpreting their characteristics, we employ the μ-moments. These may be expressed in terms of the ν-moments, which are readily calculated. We proceed to develop important relationships between the μ's and ν's:

$$\mu_{2u} = \frac{1}{N}\Sigma f_i(u_i - \bar{u})^2$$

$$= \frac{1}{N}\Sigma f_i(u_i^2 - 2u_i\bar{u} + \bar{u}^2)$$

$$= \frac{1}{N}\Sigma f_i u_i^2 - 2\bar{u} \cdot \frac{1}{N}\Sigma f_i u_i + \bar{u}^2$$

$$= \nu_{2u} - 2\bar{u}^2 + \bar{u}^2.$$

Therefore,

$$\mu_{2u} = \nu_{2u} - \nu_{1u}^2, \text{ since } \nu_{1u} = \bar{u}. \tag{9}$$

$$\mu_{3u} = \frac{1}{N}\Sigma f_i(u_i - \bar{u})^3$$

$$= \frac{1}{N}\Sigma f_i(u_i^3 - 3u_i^2\bar{u} + 3u_i\bar{u}^2 - \bar{u}^3)$$

$$= \frac{1}{N}\Sigma f_i u_i^3 - 3\bar{u} \cdot \frac{1}{N}\Sigma f_i u_i^2 + 3\bar{u}^2 \cdot \frac{1}{N}\Sigma f_i u_i - \bar{u}^3$$

$$= \nu_{3u} - 3\bar{u}\nu_{2u} + 3\bar{u}^2\nu_{1u} - \bar{u}^3$$

$$= \nu_{3u} - 3\nu_{1u}\nu_{2u} + 3\nu_{1u}^2\nu_{1u} - \nu_{1u}^3.$$

Therefore,

$$\mu_{3u} = \nu_{3u} - 3\nu_{2u}\nu_{1u} + 2\nu_{1u}^3. \tag{10}$$

$$\mu_{4u} = \frac{1}{N}\Sigma f_i(u_i - \bar{u})^4$$

$$= \frac{1}{N}\Sigma f_i(u_i^4 - 4u_i^3\bar{u} + 6u_i^2\bar{u}^2 - 4u_i\bar{u}^3 + \bar{u}^4)$$

$$= \frac{1}{N}\Sigma f_i u_i^4 - 4\bar{u}\cdot\frac{1}{N}\Sigma f_i u_i^3 + 6\bar{u}^2\cdot\frac{1}{N}\Sigma f_i u_i^2 - 4\bar{u}^3\cdot\frac{1}{N}\Sigma f_i u_i + \bar{u}^4$$

$$= \nu_{4u} - 4\nu_{1u}\nu_{3u} + 6\nu_{1u}^2\nu_{2u} - 4\nu_{1u}^3\nu_{1u} + \nu_{1u}^4.$$

Therefore,

$$\mu_{4u} = \nu_{4u} - 4\nu_{3u}\nu_{1u} + 6\nu_{2u}\nu_{1u}^2 - 3\nu_{1u}^4. \tag{11}$$

Inasmuch as equations (9), (10), and (11) are still true if we replace the u's by x's, we now assemble these three important formulas for the μ-moments with the secondary subscript omitted:

$$\mu_2 = \nu_2 - \nu_1^2. \tag{9}$$

$$\mu_3 = \nu_3 - 3\nu_2\nu_1 + 2\nu_1^3. \tag{10}$$

$$\mu_4 = \nu_4 - 4\nu_3\nu_1 + 6\nu_2\nu_1^2 - 3\nu_1^4. \tag{11}$$

Note that the law of formation of the coefficients, of the subscripts of the moments higher than 1, and of the exponents attached to ν_1 is analogous to that for the terms of the binomial expansion, $(a - b)^n$. Thus, if $n = 4$,

$$(a - b)^4 = a^4 - 4a^3b + 6a^2b^2 - 4ab^3 + b^4,$$

which is similar in form to the next-to-the-last equation obtained in the derivation of (11). Instead of an exponent for a, we have a primary subscript for the first ν of each term.

A final, but important, relationship is that expressed by the following formula:

$$\mu_{rx} = k^r\mu_{ru}. \tag{12}$$

It is established as follows. Since:

$$u_i = \frac{x_i - x_0}{k},$$

$$ku_i = x_i - x_0. \tag{13}$$

TABLE IX-1
Computation of Moments of Head Lengths

x_i	f_i	u_i	f_iu_i	$f_iu_i^2$	$f_iu_i^3$	$f_iu_i^4$	Check				
							u_i+1	$f_i(u_i+1)$	$f_i(u_i+1)^2$	$f_i(u_i+1)^3$	$f_i(u_i+1)^4$
173.5	3	-5	-15	75	-375	1875	-4	-12	48	-192	768
177.5	9	-4	-36	144	-576	2304	-3	-27	81	-243	729
181.5	29	-3	-87	261	-783	2349	-2	-58	116	-232	464
185.5	76	-2	-152	304	-608	1216	-1	-76	76	-76	76
189.5	104	-1	-104	104	-104	104	0	0	0	0	0
193.5	110	0	0	0	0	0	1	110	110	110	110
197.5	88	1	88	88	88	88	2	176	352	704	1408
201.5	30	2	60	120	240	480	3	90	270	810	2430
205.5	6	3	18	54	162	486	4	24	96	384	1536
209.5	4	4	16	64	256	1024	5	20	100	500	2500
213.5	2	5	10	50	250	1250	6	12	72	432	2592
217.5	1	6	6	36	216	1296	7	7	49	343	2401
			-394		-2446			-173		-743	
			198		1212			439		3283	
Totals	462		-196	1300	-1234	12,472		266	1370	2540	15,014

$v_{1u} = \bar{u} = -\frac{196}{462} = -0.424$

$v_{2u} = \frac{1300}{462} = 2.81$

$v_{3u} = \frac{-1234}{462} = -2.67$

$v_{4u} = \frac{12,472}{462} = 27.0$

$\mu_{2u} = v_2 - v_1^2$
$= 2.81 - (-.424)^2 = 2.63$

$\mu_{3u} = v_3 - 3v_2v_1 + 2v_1^3$
$= -2.67 - 3(2.81)(-.424) + 2(-.424)^3 = 0.75$

$\mu_{4u} = v_4 - 4v_3v_1 + 6v_2v_1^2 - 3v_1^4$
$= 27.0 - 4(-2.67)(-.424) + 6(2.81)(-.424)^2 - 3(-.424)^4$
$= 25.4$

$\Sigma f_i(u_i+1) = \Sigma f_i u_i + \Sigma f_i$
$266 = -196 + 462$ ✓

$\Sigma f_i(u_i+1)^2 = \Sigma f_i u_i^2 + 2\Sigma f_i u_i + \Sigma f_i$
$1370 = 1300 - 2(196) + 462$ ✓

$\Sigma f_i(u_i+1)^3 = \Sigma f_i u_i^3 + 3\Sigma f_i u_i^2 + 3\Sigma f_i u_i + \Sigma f_i$
$2540 = -1234 + 3(1300) + 3(-196) + 462$ ✓

$\Sigma f_i(u_i+1)^4 = \Sigma f_i u_i^4 + 4\Sigma f_i u_i^3 + 6\Sigma f_i u_i^2 + 4\Sigma f_i u_i + \Sigma f_i$
$15,014 = 12,472 + 4(-1234) + 6(1300) + 4(-196)$
$+ 462$ ✓

From formula (1c), Section V–3,

$$k\bar{u} = \bar{x} - x_0. \tag{14}$$

Subtracting (14) from (13), we obtain:

$$k(u_i - \bar{u}) = x_i - \bar{x}. \tag{15}$$

By definition, $\qquad \mu_{rx} = \frac{1}{N}\Sigma f_i(x_i - \bar{x})^r.$

Substituting (15) in the right member of the last equation, we have:

$$\mu_{rx} = \frac{1}{N}\Sigma f_i[k(u_i - \bar{u})]^r$$

$$= k^r \cdot \frac{1}{N}\Sigma f_i(u_i - \bar{u})^r$$

$$= k^r \mu_{ru}, \quad \text{which is formula (12).}$$

9. Computation of the moments. The method of computing moments is an extension of that employed for the standard deviation. We illustrate with the data of Table VIII–1, which we repeat in Table IX–1. The column headed $f_i u_i^3$ is obtained by multiplying the numbers $f_i u_i^2$ in the preceding column by the numbers u_i. The column headed $f_i u_i^4$ is obtained in a similar manner. For checking purposes, we also compute $f_i(u_i + 1)^3$ and $f_i(u_i + 1)^4$. The moments ν_{ru} are computed from formulas (6a). The moments μ_{ru} are computed from the moments ν_{ru}, by means of formulas (9), (10), and (11). It is seen that $\mu_{3u} = 0.75$ and that $\mu_{4u} = 25.4$.

10. Remarks on the computation of the moments.

(i) *Arithmetical work.* The multiplication of $f_i u_i^2$ and $f_i u^3$ by u_i to obtain $f_i u_i^3$ and $f_i u_i^4$, respectively, may often be done mentally. For distributions of considerable size, the computing machine or Barlow's tables are helpful. The computation of the μ's from the ν's constitutes the most troublesome part, but much labor can be eliminated here by free use of the slide rule and of tables of powers of numbers.

(ii) *The Charlier check.* The formulas in the lower right-hand portion of Table IX–1 are derived from the work of a Swedish statistician, C. V. L. Charlier. They are easily derived and are left as exercises for the student. Each

ν-moment should be carefully checked before proceeding to the computation of the next ν-moment and the μ-moments. The detection of early errors will eliminate a great deal of unnecessary and tedious correction.

(iii) *Significant digits.* It is probably a safe rule to save one more significant digit in the final value of a moment than occurs in most of the variates. In any case, three significant digits should be ample.

(iv) *Sheppard's corrections.* Errors due to grouping may, in the case of many appropriate bell-shaped distributions, be partially corrected by means of other formulas of Sheppard similar to the one used for the standard deviation. It has been established that:

$$\mu_{3x} \text{ (corrected)} = \mu_{3x} \text{ (uncorrected)}.$$

This fact may be made plausible by recalling that a third moment involves the sum of the third powers of the deviations. Since deviations may be positive or negative (or zero), their third powers are also. For perfectly symmetric distributions, the odd powers of the positive and negative deviations balance each other; that is, they add to zero. For fairly symmetric distributions, the errors due to grouping on one side of the mean will generally be neutralized by the errors on the other side.

For the fourth moment, Sheppard's formula is:

$$\mu_{4x} \textbf{ (corrected)} = \mu_{4x} - \tfrac{1}{2}k^2\mu_{2x} + \frac{7}{240}\, k^4, \tag{16}$$

where k equals the class interval and where μ_{2x} is uncorrected. Thus, in the case of the 462 head lengths, we find with the aid of Table IX–1 and formula (12) that:

$$\mu_{2x} \text{ (uncorrected)} = k^2\mu_{2u}$$
$$= 4^2 \times 2.63$$
$$= 42.1,$$

and that

$$\mu_{4x} \text{ (uncorrected)} = k^4\mu_{4u}$$
$$= 4^4 \times 25.4$$
$$= 6500.$$

Hence,

$$\mu_{4x} \text{ (corrected)} = 6500 - (\tfrac{1}{2} \times 4^2 \times 42.1) + \left(\frac{7}{240} \times 4^4\right)$$
$$= 6170.$$

11. Moments and units. It is perhaps prudent at this time to emphasize the role which each type of moment plays in statistical work. In order to simplify the work of computation, we employ unit deviations, u_i, with respect to a provisional mean, x_0, and their corresponding moments ν_{ru}. By means of these moments and formulas (9), (10), and (11), we compute the moments μ_{ru}. The latter are expressed in terms of unit deviations, u_i, with respect to the mean, $\bar{u}$. By virtue of formula (12), we may change easily to moments in terms of the original variable, x, referred to the mean value, $\bar{x}$. In particular, we note that:

$$\sigma_x^2 = \mu_{2x} \tag{17}$$
$$= k^2 \mu_{2u}.$$

An interesting fact which can be quite easily overlooked here is that the value of μ_{ru}, and, hence, of μ_{rx} [See formula (12)], does not depend in any way upon the choice of the provisional mean, x_0, with respect to which u_i is measured. This may be stated differently as follows:

The moment μ_r remains unchanged for any horizontal translation of axes.

In addition to the ν- and μ-moments, we need a third type of moment, one which is of practical importance in comparing the shape of the distribution with that of a normal frequency curve. The α-moments are expressed in terms of the standard variable, t, discussed in Section 4 of this chapter. Recalling that

$$t = \frac{x - \bar{x}}{\sigma_x}, \tag{18}$$

we define α_r by the formula:

$$\alpha_r = \frac{1}{N} \Sigma f_i t_i^r, \tag{19}$$

where α_r is read "alpha sub-r."

Since t is a pure number, independent of the units in which the variates, x_i, are measured, α_r is a pure number also. This fact makes the α-moments useful for the purpose of comparing frequency distributions arising from different sources. Of particular significance are α_3 and α_4, to be discussed presently.

12. Skewness. Bell-shaped distributions which are moderately skew form perhaps the largest and most important type occurring in nature. The degree of skewness ranges from negligible asymmetry to asymmetry of the J-type. Where "near symmetry" ceases and "moderate asymmetry" begins is difficult to judge. The quartile coefficient of skewness is one measure which has already been discussed (Section VIII–3), but there are others.

A second measure of skewness is given by α_3, so that we may write:

$$\text{Skewness} = \alpha_3 \tag{20}$$

$$= \frac{1}{N}\Sigma f_i t_i^3$$

$$= \frac{1}{N}\Sigma f_i \left(\frac{x_i - \bar{x}}{\sigma_x}\right)^3.$$

Since σ_x is constant for a given distribution, we may place $\dfrac{1}{\sigma_x^3}$ in front of the summation sign and write:

$$\text{Skewness} = \frac{1}{\sigma_x^3} \cdot \frac{1}{N}\Sigma f_i(x_i - \bar{x})^3$$

$$= \frac{\mu_{3x}}{\sigma_x^3}$$

$$= \frac{k^3 \mu_{3u}}{k^3 \sigma_u^3}$$

$$= \frac{\mu_{3u}}{\sigma_u^3}. \tag{21}$$

From these last results one can easily prove the following:

THEOREM. *The moment α_r remains unchanged for any horizontal translation, stretching, or compression of axes.*

The choice of α_3 as a suitable measure of skewness depends upon the fact that the third moment, as already pointed out, vanishes; that is, equals zero in a perfectly symmetric distribution. Thus, any nonvanishing third moment indicates some degree of asymmetry. If α_3 is positive, there must be more dispersion above the mean than below; if α_3 is negative, the reverse must be the case. Similar remarks apply to all odd moments.

As an illustration, let us compute α_3 for the head lengths of English criminals. From Table IX–1, we find $\mu_{3u} = 0.75$, $\sigma_u^2 = \mu_{2u} = 2.63$; hence:

$$\alpha_3 = \frac{\mu_{3u}}{\sigma_u^3}$$

$$= \frac{0.75}{(2.63)^{3/2}}$$

$$= 0.176.$$

There is no limit to the value which the skewness, as defined by formula (20), may have; but, in practice, moderately asymmetric curves yield values ranging from -2 to $+2$.

The significance which a numerical value for the skewness has for the shape of a given frequency curve can only be appreciated after extensive experience with many curves. Reference to Figures IX: 6–9 may aid in establishing this appreciation.

A third measure of skewness occasionally used involves the mode. In a perfectly symmetric distribution, the mean, median, and mode all have the same value, $Q_2 - Q_1 = Q_3 - Q_2$, and the skewness is zero. The skewness is said to be positive when the longer range of values is to the right, that is, when the "hump" of the curve is to the left. In Figure VIII–2, the curve has negative skewness. The longer range of values pulls the mean to the left, the mode is to the right, and the median appears between the two. In fact, it may be shown that, for moderately asymmetric distributions of the type illustrated in Figure VIII–2, the distance from the mean to the median is approximately one-third the distance *from* the mean *to* the mode. The positions of the mode and the

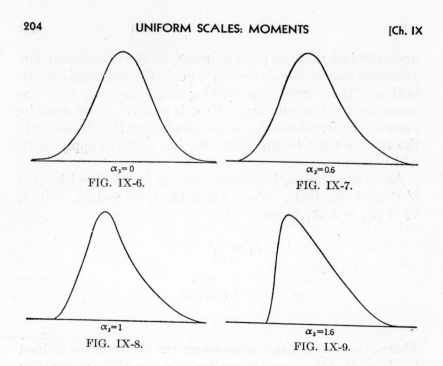

$\alpha_3 = 0$

FIG. IX-6.

$\alpha_3 = 0.6$

FIG. IX-7.

$\alpha_3 = 1$

FIG. IX-8.

$\alpha_3 = 1.6$

FIG. IX-9.

mean lead to an easily understandable measure of skewness defined as follows:

$$\text{Skewness} = \frac{\text{Mean} - \text{Mode}}{\text{Standard Deviation}}. \tag{22}$$

One objection to this measure is its dependence on the mode, which, for an asymmetric frequency curve, can be determined only after considerable preliminary computation. As stated in Section VI–15, the accurate determination of the mode (not the modal class) involves more advanced mathematics than is presupposed in this book. However, it is interesting to discover that for a certain type of asymmetric frequency curve* the last two measures of skewness are equivalent, for

$$\frac{\alpha_3}{2} = \frac{\text{Mean} - \text{Mode}}{\sigma}. \tag{23}$$

Because of this relationship, some statisticians prefer to use $\dfrac{\alpha_3}{2}$ instead of α_3 as a definition of skewness. Formula (23) is

---

* Pearson's Type III. (See Ref. 3, Part II, Chap. III, or Ref. 1, Part II, Chap. III.)

also useful in computing the mode when α_3 is known.　For example, for the distribution of head lengths, we obtain from (23):

$$\frac{0.176}{2} = \frac{191.8 - \text{Mode}}{6.48};$$

whence,　　　　　Mode $= 191.2$.

Thus, the mode would be six-tenths of a unit (one millimeter) to the left of the mean if a moderately skew frequency curve were fitted to the given data.

13. Kurtosis. Attention has previously been called to the important fact that the size and the shape of a given frequency polygon or frequency curve depend upon the units of measurement employed.　A given polygon or curve may be made to look flatter by increasing the horizontal unit of measurement; it may be made more peaked by decreasing the unit.　Two frequency polygons arising from widely different observations may be found, upon change to a common unit of measure, to be essentially the same in size and shape. In order to eliminate such deceptive influences, we place all frequency distributions upon the same basis by employing the standard unit.　Furthermore, we recall that fairly symmetric frequency distributions may be conceived to be samples selected from an ideal distribution whose graph is represented by a so-called normal frequency curve (Fig. IV–11). In other words, all bell-shaped frequency distributions which may be classified as essentially normal or symmetric are assumed to exhibit in their *ideal*, not their *actual*, form precisely the size and shape of the so-called normal frequency curve *when the same scales of measurement are employed.* Therefore, if all actual frequency distributions which are fairly symmetric are reduced to the same scale of measurement, the standard unit, their polygons may be compared with the ideal frequency curve.　In particular, their relative flatness or peakedness in the neighborhood of the mode may be observed and appropriately measured.　The word *kurtosis* is used to describe the "humpedness" of a curve.　When the polygon is relatively flatter than the normal curve, it is said to have kurtosis or to be *platykurtic*. When the polygon is relatively more peaked, it is said to lack kurtosis or to be *leptokurtic*. A normal curve is *mesokurtic*. An amusing mnemonic quoted by Yule (Ref. 7) is the following: "Platykurtic curves, like the platypus, are squat with short tails. Leptokurtic curves are high with long tails like the kangaroo —noted for 'lepping'!'"

It might appear that a sharply peaked curve implies a relatively small value for the standard deviation, while a flat curve implies a relatively large value; but these implications are by no means necessary. Two perfectly symmetric distributions with the same value for the standard deviation might differ noticeably in shape. This is illustrated by two hypothetical frequency distributions of heights shown in Table IX–2. They are perfectly symmetric distributions, and each has a mean of 67 inches and a standard deviation of 2.37 inches. Reference to their corresponding frequency polygons (Figure IX–10) shows a marked difference in their peakedness.

TABLE IX–2

Two Fictitious Distributions for Heights

Heights in Inches	Frequencies	
	Case 1	Case 2
59	1	0
61	2	2
63	5	8
65	16	20
67	52	40
69	16	20
71	5	8
73	2	2
75	1	0
Total	100	100

The measure of the kurtosis, sometimes called the *excess*, of a frequency distribution is obtained from the fourth moment, α_4. For reasons which lie beyond the scope of this book,

$$\text{Excess} = \alpha_4 - 3, \quad \text{where } \alpha_4 = \frac{\mu_4}{\sigma^4}. \tag{24}$$

For a normal distribution, α_4 can be shown to be equal to 3; hence the excess becomes zero. Other slightly differing formulas involving μ_4 are employed by various writers to define the excess or kurtosis. When the excess is positive— that is, when $\alpha_4 > 3$, the polygon is leptokurtic—that is, it is more peaked than the normal curve; when the excess is negative—that is, when $\alpha_4 < 3$—the reverse is true.

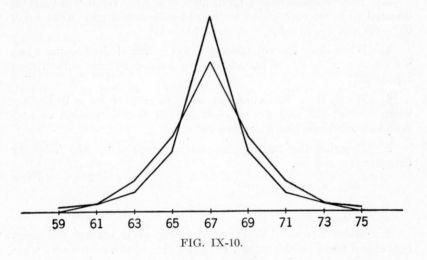

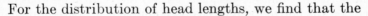

59　　61　　63　　65　　67　　69　　71　　73　　75

FIG. IX-10.

For the distribution of head lengths, we find that the

$$\text{Excess} = \alpha_4 - 3$$

$$= \frac{\mu_{4u}}{\sigma_u^4} - 3$$

$$= \frac{25.4}{(2.63)^2} - 3$$

$$= 3.67 - 3$$

$$= 0.67;$$

hence, the polygon is more peaked than normal.

It is instructive, also, to compute the values of the excess for the two distributions of Table IX–2 or Figure IX–10. In Case 1, the excess is 2.24; in Case 2, it is 0.16. Case 1, then, has much greater peakedness than normal, and Case 2 is slightly above normal.

An interesting application of the concepts of skewness and excess will be found in Reference 1, pp. 30–33.

IX—Exercises

1. The abscissa of a point is 7. What will it be when the origin is shifted (a) 3 units to the right? (b) 10 units to the right? (c) 2 units to the left? (d) 2.73 units to the right?

2. The coordinates of a point are $(-3, 8)$. What will they be, referred to new axes parallel to the old with new origin (a) at $(-3, 0)$? (b) at $(-3, -5)$? (c) at $(10, -1)$?

3. What does the equation $y = 2x^2 - 20x + 50$ become when we let $x = x' + 5$? What change in axes does this substitution represent?

4. What does the equation $x^2 - 6x + y^2 + 8y = 0$ become when $x = x' + 3$ and $y = y' - 4$? What transformation of axes does this algebraic change represent?

5. Describe the transformations represented by the following equations:

(a) $u_i = 5x_i.$ (c) $u_i = \dfrac{x_i - 2}{10}.$

(b) $u_i = \tfrac{1}{4}x_i.$ (d) $u_i = 3(x_i - 10).$

6. Make a careful freehand drawing of a normal frequency curve, and then, on the same axes, a drawing of the same curve when (a) the horizontal unit has been halved; (b) the vertical unit has been halved; (c) the horizontal unit has been doubled; (d) both units have been doubled.

* * *

Compute the uncorrected moments μ_{2x}, μ_{3x}, and μ_{4x} for the frequency distributions indicated in Exercises 7–12. Make a plan of computation similar to that of Table IX–1. Compute the skewness and the excess by means of α_3 and α_4, and comment on the results.

7. Precipitation in New York City. (Ex. IV–7.)

8. Maximum temperatures in New York City. (Ex. IV–8.)

9. Call discount rates. (Ex. IV–9.)

10. Taxation for school support. (Ex. IV–10.)

11. Brain-weight of Swedish males. (Ex. IV–11.)

12. Intelligence quotients of boys. (Ex. IV–12.)

* * *

13. Verify the value of the excess given in Section IX–13, for the data of (a) Table IX–2, Case 1; (b) Table IX–2, Case 2. Is it necessary here to employ a provisional mean and unit deviations?

14. Derive the Charlier check formula involving $\Sigma f_i(u_i + 1)^3$, Table IX–1.

15. Derive the Charlier check formula involving $\Sigma f_i(u_i + 1)^4$, Table IX–1.

16. Prove that $\dfrac{\mu_{rx}}{\sigma_x^r} = \dfrac{\mu_{ru}}{\sigma_u^r}$; hence, prove the theorem of Section IX–12.

17. What can you say about the reliability of the moments computed in Exercise 7? In Exercise 8?

CHAPTER

X

THE FREQUENCY CURVE

❖⊐||||||||||⊏⊐||||||||||⊏⊐||||||||||⊏⊐||||||||||⊏⊐||||||||||⊏⊐||||||||||⊏⊐||||||||||⊏⊐||||||||||⊏⊐||||||||||⊏⊐||||||||||⊏❖

"You boil it in sawdust: you salt it in glue:
You condense it with locusts and tape:
Still keeping one principal object in view—
To preserve its symmetrical shape."

LEWIS CARROLL, *The Hunting of the Snark.**

1. Introduction. The variation of frequency with head length was shown arithmetically in Table IV–3 and graphically in Figure IV–1. Similar variations have been exhibited throughout this book, for example, in the price of milk with the time (Section III–8) and the percentage number of acres with the percentage number of farms (Section VI–4). These are all examples of two important mathematical concepts: (1) the dependence of one variable upon another, and (2) the geometrical representation of such dependence. The fact that one variable, y, is dependent for its value upon another variable, x, is expressed in mathematics by saying that "y is a function of x."

In most of the work of elementary mathematics, a function of x is usually some "expression" in x, so that a rule for finding values of y corresponding to those of x may be given by means of an equation in x and y. Thus,

$$2x^2 - 3x + 5$$

---

* By permission of the Macmillan Company.

is a function of x.   If we set y equal to this expression, we obtain the equation:

$$y = 2x^2 - 3x + 5,$$

which constitutes the rule enabling us to find y when x is given.   Thus, if $x = 1$, $y = 4$; if $x = 2$, $y = 7$; and so on. But in some of the work of statistics, the values of y corresponding to those of x can only be given by means of a table. The price of milk, the percentage number of acres, and the frequency of certain head lengths were obtained from tabular records.   Values may also be obtained from an appropriate graph.   For example, from the ogive we may estimate values, such as the median, which are not given directly by the table. Functional relationships may exist even when pairs of related values are not available, as in the case of "all the apples in Oregon" corresponding to given dates.

Instead of representing a function of x by y, we often find it useful to use the symbol $f(x)$, read "f of x."   Thus, above we might have written:

$$f(x) = 2x^2 - 3x + 5.$$

If in the last equation we replace x by 1 and 2, respectively, we get:

$$f(1) = 2 \cdot 1^2 - 3 \cdot 1 + 5 = 4;$$
$$f(2) = 2 \cdot 2^2 - 3 \cdot 2 + 5 = 7.$$

The symbols on the left are read "f of one" and "f of two," respectively, and merely denote the values of the function when first 1 and then 2 are substituted for x.   Other functional symbols similar to $f(x)$ are employed to designate other functions.   Examples are $F(x)$, read "capital F of x," $\phi(t)$, read "phi of t," or $h(y)$, read "h of y."   Thus, we might have:

$$F(x) = 3x - 2, \quad \text{whence } F(-3) = -11,$$

$$\phi(t) = \frac{1}{\sqrt{2\pi}} e^{-\frac{t^2}{2}}, \quad \text{whence } \phi(0) = \frac{1}{\sqrt{2\pi}},$$

$$h(y) = y^3 + y^2 - 2, \quad \text{whence } h(\tfrac{1}{2}) = -1\tfrac{5}{8},$$

and so on.

It is often the task of the statistician to estimate the nature and form of a mathematical expression which best approximates an unknown function $f(x)$. The search for such formulas constitutes an important phase of statistical as well as of other scientific work. The succeeding chapters will illustrate these points more fully.

As an example of particular interest to us now take the familiar data of Table V–1. Here the functional relationship exists by virtue of the set of paired values. To a given mid-value, x_i, there corresponds a frequency, f_i; hence, the frequency f is a function of the head length x. We may write $y = f(x)$, where y, or its equivalent, $f(x)$, stands for the frequency, and x for the head length (mid-value). It happens here that f is used in a double sense, to symbolize both "frequency" and "function." Fortunately, it does no harm, and is, in fact, a happy coincidence, for we call $f(x)$ here the *frequency function*. What is the nature and form of the frequency function, $f(x)$, in this case? It is to find an answer to such questions as this that we devote the remaining work of this chapter and that of Chapter XIII.

2. The normal frequency curve. In Section IV–7, the theory underlying the concept of the frequency curve was briefly sketched. It is important that the student at this point read once more the contents of that section.

When a frequency distribution of the bell-shaped type is fairly symmetric in the region of the mean, the ideal curve corresponding to it is usually assumed to be a normal frequency curve, which we have somewhat inadequately described in geometric terms as *bell-shaped, symmetric,* and *asymptotic to the horizontal axis.* (See Figure IV–11.) The normal curve, as a type, can only be adequately defined *analytically,* that is, by means of an equation. The normal curve corresponding to a fairly symmetric frequency distribution with total frequency N, class interval k, arithmetic mean $\bar{x}$, and standard deviation σ_x can, with certain assumptions, be shown to have the equation:

$$ y = \frac{Nk}{\sigma_x \sqrt{2\pi}} e^{-\frac{1}{2}\left(\frac{x-\bar{x}}{\sigma_x}\right)^2}. \tag{1} $$

π is the familiar constant whose approximate value is

3.14159; e stands for another important constant, the base of the natural system of logarithms, whose approximate value is 2.71828. We may designate the function on the right of (1) as the frequency function, $f(x)$, so that

$$f(x) = \frac{Nk}{\sigma_x \sqrt{2\pi}} e^{-\frac{1}{2}\left(\frac{x-\bar{x}}{\sigma_x}\right)^2}. \tag{1a}$$

It is not possible, in a book of this scope, to give the full mathematical derivation of equation (1). An outline of it is given in Section XIII–13. We shall merely accept the result embodied in this equation and examine its properties and uses.

3. **Area and frequency.** The area under a frequency polygon has been shown to be equal to the area of the corresponding histogram (Section IV–4.) Moreover, with the normal frequency curve conceived to be the limiting form of a frequency polygon, we required that the area under the curve be also equal to the area, Nk, of the histogram (see Section IV–7).

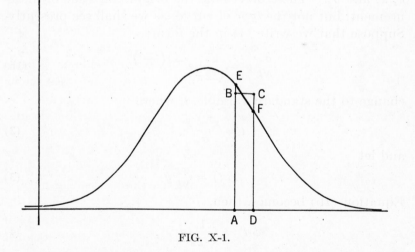

FIG. X-1.

Figure X–1 illustrates the fact that the area of a rectangle $ABCD$ of a histogram is nearly equal to the corresponding area $AEFD$ under the frequency curve. If the base of this rectangle is k and the altitude f_i, the ratio of its area, kf_i, to the total area of the histogram, Nk, is $\dfrac{kf_i}{Nk}$, or $\dfrac{f_i}{N}$, which is the *actual* relative frequency of the variates lying within the interval AD. It follows, then, that the ratio of the area $AEFD$ to the total area under the curve gives the *theoretical* relative frequency of the same variate. We must keep in mind here what was pointed out in Section IV–7, namely, that a frequency polygon represents an *actual* or *sample* distribution, and that a frequency curve represents the *ideal* distribution or universe from which the sample is imagined to be drawn. It should be fairly evident that if we wish to find the theoretical relative proportion of a group of variates lying between any two arbitrarily assigned limits, we need first to compute the area under the frequency curve between these given limits. The method of doing this will be discussed in Section 5 of this chapter.

4. The function $\phi(t)$. The size and relative proportions of the curve defined by (1) will depend upon the values of N, k, $\bar{x}$, and σ_x. These determine the origin and scale of measurement, but not the *type* of curve, as we shall see presently. Suppose that we write (1) in the form:

$$\frac{\sigma_x}{Nk}y = \frac{1}{\sqrt{2\pi}}e^{-\frac{1}{2}\left(\frac{x-\bar{x}}{\sigma_x}\right)^2}, \tag{1b}$$

change to the standard variable, t, where

$$t = \frac{x - \bar{x}}{\sigma_x}, \tag{2}$$

and let

$$\phi(t) = \frac{\sigma_x}{Nk}y. \tag{3}$$

Equation (1b) becomes, then,

$$\phi(t) = \frac{1}{\sqrt{2\pi}}e^{-\frac{1}{2}t^2}. \tag{4}$$

Equation (2) we know defines a translation and a stretching or compression. In particular, it effects a horizontal shift of origin to the mean, $\bar{x}$, and a change of horizontal scale to σ_x as a unit. Equation (3) effects a compression of the vertical or

y-scale by the constant factor, $\dfrac{\sigma_x}{Nk}$. It is a compression usu-

ally, rather than a stretching, since $\dfrac{\sigma_x}{Nk}$ is usually less than

one. It follows, then, from Section IX–3 that the curves defined by (1) and (4) are of the same type. We shall call the curve (4) the *standard form* of the normal curve. It is easier to study properties and to make applications when the standard form is employed.

The values of the ordinate, $\phi(t)$, corresponding to the variable, t, are tabulated for values of t ranging numerically from $t = 0$ to $t = 4.09$ in Table E of the Supplementary Tables.

Thus, for $\qquad\qquad t = 0, \quad \phi(t) = 0.3989,$

$\qquad$ for $\qquad\qquad t = 1.00, \phi(t) = 0.2420,$

$\qquad$ and for $\qquad\qquad t = 2.78, \phi(t) = 0.0084$, and so on.

By making use of such values, one can plot a very accurate graph of the normal curve in standard form. Other uses of the ordinate will be shown later.

5. The area under $\phi(t)$. The area under the curve (1) is Nk. What is the area under the transformed curve (4), the normal curve in standard form? The answer is easily found by examining transformations (2) and (3). Equation (2) tells us that the x-axis has been shifted $\bar{x}$ units to the right, which does not affect the area, and that the x-unit has been divided by σ_x. Equation (3) tells us that the y-unit has been

multiplied by $\dfrac{\sigma_x}{Nk}$. Thus, the area, Nk, has been multiplied

by $\dfrac{\sigma_x}{\sigma_x Nk}$; and hence, the area under the curve (4) in the new

units is exactly one, a very useful result, and, of course, in-

tended in the choice of the coefficient $\dfrac{1}{\sqrt{2\pi}}$, occurring in

the definition of $\phi(t)$.

The area under the curve (4) between two values of t, say

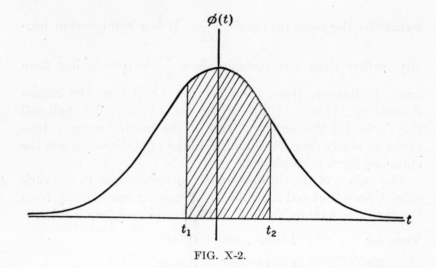

FIG. X-2.

$t = t_1$, and $t = t_2$, (Figure X–2) is designated in mathematics by the symbol:

$$\int_{t_1}^{t_2} \phi(t)dt,$$

which may be read "the area under $\phi(t)$ from t_1 to t_2."* This area will always be a number less than one. (Why?) For example, $\int_0^{t_1} \phi(t)dt$ represents the area from the origin to t_1, $\int_{-2}^{3} \phi(t)dt$ represents the area from $t = -2$ to $t = +3$, and so on.

Table F of the Supplementary Tables gives values of the areas under $\phi(t)$ from 0 to positive values of t, that is, it gives values of $\int_0^{t} \phi(t)dt$. Because of the symmetry of the curve with respect to the vertical or $\phi(t)$-axis, the area from 0 to a positive value, t_1, equals the area from $-t_1$ to 0. (Figure X–3.) Note that we express the interval for the area from the left end-point to the right end-point. If we do this, the

---

* More precisely, this symbol, borrowed from calculus, is read "the definite integral of $\phi(t)dt$ between the limits t_1 and t_2."

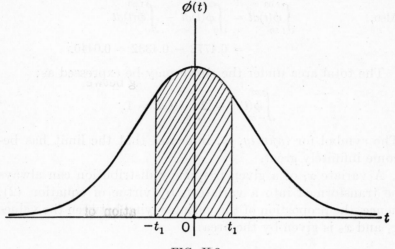

FIG. X-3.

area under $\phi(t)$ can be shown always to be a positive number. If we reverse the order, the area comes out negative.

Thus,
$$\int_{-t_1}^{0} \phi(t)dt = \int_{0}^{t_1} \phi(t)dt;$$

but
$$\int_{0}^{-t_1} \phi(t)dt = -\int_{0}^{t_1} \phi(t)dt.$$

From Table F of the Supplementary Tables, one can easily verify that

$$\int_{0}^{0.50} \phi(t)dt = 0.1915, \qquad \int_{0}^{3} \phi(t)dt = 0.4987,$$

and so on.

All areas under the curve other than those given in the table can be easily derived from them. Thus,

$$\int_{-2}^{2} \phi(t)dt = \int_{-2}^{0} \phi(t)dt + \int_{0}^{2} \phi(t)dt$$

$$= 2\int_{0}^{2} \phi(t)dt$$

$$= 2 \times 0.4772 = 0.9544.$$

Also,
$$\int_{1.50}^{2.00} \phi(t)dt = \int_0^{2.00} \phi(t)dt - \int_0^{1.50} \phi(t)dt$$

$$= 0.4772 - 0.4332 = 0.0440.$$

The total area under the curve may be expressed as:

$$\int_{-\infty}^{\infty} \phi(t)dt = 2\int_0^{\infty} \phi(t)dt = 1.$$

The symbol for *infinity*, ∞, indicates that the limit has become infinitely great.

A variate x_i of a given frequency distribution can always be transformed into a variate t_i by virtue of equation (2); hence, the proportion of the variates lying between the values x_1 and x_2 is given by the area:

$$\int_{t_1}^{t_2} \phi(t)dt,$$

where t_1 and t_2 correspond to x_1 and x_2, respectively, according to (2).

6. Properties of the standard curve. Let us set down again for convenient reference the equation of the normal frequency curve in standard form:

$$\phi(t) = \frac{1}{\sqrt{2\pi}} e^{-t^2/2}. \tag{4}$$

The following properties are of chief importance. Some of them have already been noted in connection with the theory underlying the concept of a normal distribution.

(i) *Symmetry.* The curve is symmetrical with respect to the $\phi(t)$-axis. This can be shown directly from equation (4). If t were replaced by $-t$, $\phi(t)$ would remain unchanged. In other words, the ordinate $\phi(t)$ is the same at equal distances on either side of the origin. Statistically, this means that the arithmetic mean and the median of a normal frequency distribution coincide at the center of it. $\bar{t} = 0$ corresponds to $x = \bar{x}$.

(ii) *Shape.* The exponent of e in $\phi(t)$ is negative, $-\frac{1}{2}t^2$. Hence, $\phi(t)$ is a maximum when $t = 0$; all other values of t

make $\phi(t)$ smaller, since $e^{-t^2/2} = \dfrac{1}{e^{t^2/2}}$. The maximum value of $\phi(t)$ is, therefore,

$$\phi(0) = \frac{1}{\sqrt{2\pi}} = 0.3989.$$

As t increases numerically, $e^{-t^2/2}$ decreases; and when t becomes infinite, $\phi(t)$ approaches zero. Thus, the curve is asymptotic to the t-axis in both the positive and negative directions.

The *points of inflection* of the curve are the points at which the curve changes from concave downward to concave upward. By the methods of calculus it can be shown that the points of inflection are situated at a unit's distance from the $\phi(t)$-axis. This distance can be shown to be equal to the (theoretical) standard deviation of t, so that $\sigma_t = 1$ (Figure X–4).

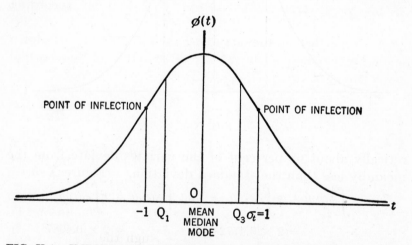

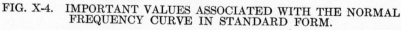

FIG. X-4.   IMPORTANT VALUES ASSOCIATED WITH THE NORMAL FREQUENCY CURVE IN STANDARD FORM.

It is clear, then, from the preceding paragraphs that the standard curve has its maximum value $\dfrac{1}{\sqrt{2\pi}}$ units above the origin, that it is concave downward until $t = \pm1$, when it becomes concave upward, and that it rapidly approaches, but never quite reaches, the t-axis. These properties determine its bell-shaped form.

(iii)   *Areas.*   The total area under the curve has already been shown to be exactly one.

The area under the curve from $t = 0$ to $t = 1$ is 0.3413, so that the area comprised within the interval −1 to +1 is 2×0.3413, or 0.6826. Statistically, this means that theo-

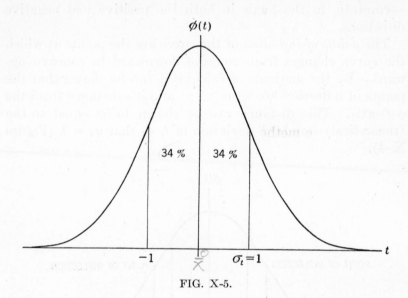

FIG. X-5.

retically about 68 per cent of the variates deviate from the mean by less than the standard deviation.   (Figure X–5.)

$$\int_{-2}^{2}\phi(t)dt = 2\int_{0}^{2}\phi(t)dt \quad \text{and} \quad \int_{-3}^{3}\phi(t)dt = 2\int_{0}^{3}\phi(t)dt$$

$$= 2 \times 0.4772 \qquad\qquad\qquad = 2 \times 0.4987$$

$$= 0.9544; \qquad\qquad\qquad\quad = 0.9974.$$

The preceding values show that although the curve extends indefinitely to the left and to the right, it approaches the t-axis so closely that over 95 per cent of the area is included between the limits −2 and +2, and over 99.7 per cent of the area is included between −3 and +3.   (Figure X–6.)

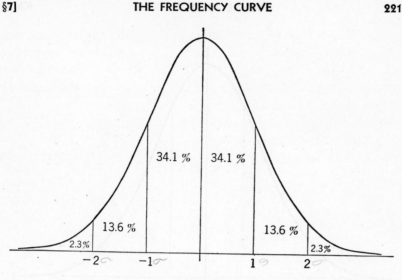

34.1 %   34.1 %

13.6 %   13.6 %

2.3%   2.3%

−2   −1   1   2

FIG. X-6.

(iv)   *Quartiles.*   The quartiles Q_1 and Q_3 of the curve are the values of t whose ordinates together with the $\phi(t)$-axis divide the area under the curve into four equal areas.   From the equation

$$\int_0^t \phi(t)dt = 0.2500$$

we can, by inverse interpolation in Table F, find the value of t corresponding to one-fourth the area.   This value of t is found to be 0.6745, and represents Q_3.   Hence, $Q_1 = -0.6745$ and $Q_3 = +0.6745$.   (Figure X–7.)

The semi-interquartile range or quartile deviation is obviously 0.6745.   Fifty per cent of the area lies between -0.6745 and $+0.6745$.

7. $\phi(t)$ **and** $f(x)$.   Comparison of equations (1a) and (4) has shown that the unit of measure along the x-axis is σ_x times as great as that along the t-axis.   In other words, σ_x itself is the unit when we employ the variable t.   That is why $\sigma_t = 1$.   This is a very useful device and enables us to express easily many of the properties just enumerated in terms of the original variable, x.   For example, abscissas of the points of inflection of the curve (1a) are $\pm \sigma_x$.   Therefore, 68 per cent of

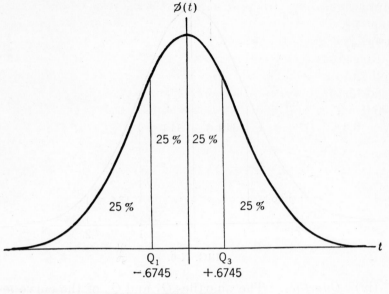

FIG. X-7.

the variates have values lying between the limits $\bar{x} + \sigma_x$ and $\bar{x} - \sigma_x$. Less than 0.3 per cent of the variates deviate from the mean by more than $3\sigma_x$. Fifty per cent of the variates lie within the limits $\bar{x} \pm 0.6745\sigma_x$.

8. Probability. The curve defined by (4) is often called the *normal probability curve* because it is based upon fundamental laws of probability. (See Chapter XIII.) It will suffice for our present purposes to note that since the area under this curve is one, any partial area, $\int_{t_1}^{t_2} \phi(t)dt$, represents the probability that a value of t selected at random from a normal distribution lies between t_1 and t_2. (Section 3.) In particular, the probability that t lies between -0.6745 and $+0.6745$ (Figure X–7), or the equivalent, that x lies between $-0.6745\sigma_x$ and $+0.6745\sigma_x$, is one-half. In other words, given a normally distributed variable x, there is a "fifty-fifty" chance that a variate x_i selected at random differs from the mean by more than 0.6745 times the standard deviation. The quantity 0.6745σ has been called the *probable error*.

More accurately, it is that value of the error or deviation corresponding to a probability of one-half. The use of "probable error" has been diminishing in recent years.

Referring to the data for head lengths, Table VIII–1, let us find the probability that a criminal chosen at random has a head length between 190.0 and 195.0 millimeters. Let $x_1 =$ 190.0 and $x_2 = 195.0$. We have found that $\bar{x} = 191.8$ and $\sigma_x = 6.48$. Hence,

$$t_1 = \frac{x_1 - \bar{x}}{\sigma_x} \qquad\qquad t_2 = \frac{x_2 - \bar{x}}{\sigma_x}$$

$$= \frac{190.0 - 191.8}{6.48} \qquad\qquad = \frac{195.0 - 191.8}{6.48}$$

$$= -0.28. \qquad\qquad = 0.49.$$

$$\int_{-0.28}^{0.49} \phi(t)dt = \int_{-0.28}^{0} \phi(t)dt + \int_{0}^{0.49} \phi(t)dt$$

$$= \int_{0}^{0.28} \phi(t)dt + \int_{0}^{0.49} \phi(t)dt$$

$$= 0.1103 + 0.1879$$

$$= 0.2982;$$

hence the probability sought is about 0.30.

As a second example, let us find the probability that a criminal chosen at random has a head length deviating, numerically, from the mean by more than 20.0 millimeters. Since $x_1 - \bar{x} = 20$, $t_1 = \dfrac{20.0}{6.48} = 3.09$. The probability for a deviation less, numerically, than 20.0 millimeters is:

$$2\int_{0}^{3.09} \phi(t)dt = 2 \times 0.4990 = 0.9980.$$

Hence, the probability for a deviation numerically more than 20.0 millimeters is $1.000 - 0.9980$, or 0.0020. Theoretically, then, about two criminals in a thousand would have such large deviations from the mean. The probability just found is represented geometrically by the two tiny shaded areas in Figure X–8.

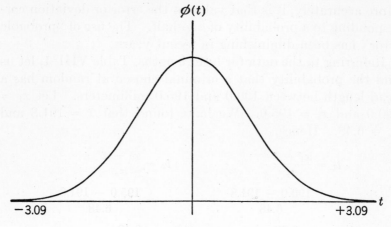

FIG. X-8.

9. Fitting a normal curve to a frequency distribution.

Given a frequency distribution of the usual bell-shaped type exhibiting fairly good symmetry in the main body of the distribution, one can construct the corresponding normal frequency curve with the aid of a table of values of $\phi(t)$. The curve is usually superposed upon the histogram so that equation (1) or (1a), which preserves the scale of the original data, is used.

$$f(x) = \frac{Nk}{\sigma_x\sqrt{2\pi}}\, e^{-\frac{1}{2}\left(\frac{x-\bar{x}}{\sigma_x}\right)^2}. \tag{1a}$$

The preceding equation defines a theoretical or ideal distribution, the distribution of an infinite population or universe from which the actual or sample distribution is conceived to be drawn. The position and scale of this curve will depend upon the mean, $\bar{x}$, the standard deviation, σ_x, and the area, Nk, under the curve, of this ideal, infinite distribution. Of course, we can never know, with certainty, what these three values should be in the ideal case; so we take as our best estimate of them the values computed from the actual distribution. We therefore assume the following three principles as those to be followed in fitting a normal curve to a given frequency distribution:

(i)   *The arithmetic mean of the ideal distribution should equal the arithmetic mean of the given frequency distribution.*

(ii)   *The standard deviation of the ideal distribution should equal the standard deviation of the given frequency distribution.*

(iii)   *The area under the normal frequency curve should equal the area of the histogram or frequency polygon.*

Some authors prefer to use different symbols to distinguish between the constants of the actual and the theoretical distribution, as, for example, $\bar{x}$ and σ_x for the former, and $\bar{x}'$ and σ_x' for the latter.   Rules (i), (ii), and (iii) above reduce, then, to the assumptions that $\bar{x} = \bar{x}'$, $\sigma_x = \sigma_x'$, and $Nk = A$ (area), respectively.   The ideal curve (1a) would then be written:

$$f(x) = \frac{A}{\sigma_x'\sqrt{2\pi}}\, e^{-\frac{1}{2}\left(\frac{x-\bar{x}'}{\sigma_x'}\right)^2}.$$

Constants such as $\bar{x}'$, σ_x', and so forth, which characterize a theoretical distribution, are often called *parameters;* the corresponding constants of an actual distribution are called *statistics.*

In the actual process of fitting a normal curve to a frequency distribution for which N and k are known, and from which $\bar{x}$ and σ_x have been computed, we obtain by means of equation (2) the values t_i, corresponding to convenient given values x_i, which may be selected as the end-values or the mid-values of the class intervals of the frequency distribution or as any other suitable equally spaced values of x.   From Table E of the Supplement we find the values of $\phi(t_i)$.   To obtain the same vertical scale, y, as that of the histogram, we make use of equation (3), from which it appears that:

$$\frac{Nk}{\sigma_x}\phi(t) = y. \tag{3a}$$

Hence, multiplying the values $\phi(t_i)$, found from Table E by $\dfrac{Nk}{\sigma_x}$, we find the ordinates y_i of the theoretical curve (1) corresponding to the values x_i.

A smooth curve, properly drawn through the points plotted from the pairs of values (x_i, y_i) will represent our best estimate of the normal frequency curve corresponding to the given distribution.

10. An example of fitting a normal curve. The preceding explanation will now be illustrated by fitting a normal curve to the distribution of head lengths. Here $N = 462$, $k = 4$, $\bar{x} = 191.8$, and $\sigma_x = 6.48$; hence, the equation of the curve sought may be written down at once:

$$y = \frac{462 \times 4}{6.48 \times \sqrt{2\pi}}\, e^{-\frac{1}{2}\left(\frac{x-191.8}{6.48}\right)^2}.$$

However, the equation itself has little practical value in the actual construction of its curve. The procedure outlined in the preceding section may be followed in Table X–1, where the mid-values, x_i, of the class intervals are used. The

TABLE X–1

COMPUTATION OF THEORETICAL ORDINATES CORRESPONDING TO MID-VALUES OF
CLASS INTERVALS, USED IN FITTING A NORMAL CURVE TO THE
FREQUENCY DISTRIBUTION OF HEAD LENGTHS

1	2	3	4	5
Mid-Value x_i	Actual Frequency f_i	$\dfrac{x_i - \bar{x}}{\sigma_x}$ t_i	$\phi\,(t_i)$	Theoretical Ordinate $\dfrac{Nk}{\sigma_x}\,\phi(t_i)$ y_i
173.5	3	−2.82	.0075	2.1
177.5	9	−2.21	.0347	9.9
181.5	29	−1.59	.1127	32.1
185.5	76	−.97	.2492	71.0
189.5	104	−.35	.3752	107.
193.5	110	.26	.3857	110.
197.5	88	.88	.2709	77.2
201.5	30	1.50	.1295	36.9
205.5	6	2.11	.0431	12.3
209.5	4	2.73	.0096	2.7
213.5	2	3.35	.0015	.4
217.5	1	3.97	.0002	.1
$(\bar{x} = 191.8)$		(0)	(.3989)	(114.)

$N = 462$ $Nk = 1848$	$\sigma_x = 6.48$		Approximate Total
$\dfrac{1}{\sigma_x} = 0.1543$	$\dfrac{Nk}{\sigma_x} = 285$		461

method of finding t_i (Column 3) was illustrated in Section 8. The last column, y_i, yields the ordinates of the curve at the mid-points of the class intervals. These theoretical ordinates may be considered theoretical frequencies to be compared with the actual frequencies. These ordinates are then used to plot points through which the normal curve is drawn. The maximum ordinate occurs when $t = 0$ and equals $\phi(0)$ or 0.3989. $t = 0$ when $x = \bar{x} = 191.8$.

Therefore,
$$y = f(\bar{x}) = \frac{Nk}{\sigma}\phi(0)$$
$$= 285 \times 0.3989$$
$$= 114.$$

It is good practice to plot the maximum point. In the case of the head lengths, the mean 191.8 is very close to the end-value, 191.8, so that the difference between the ordinates at these two points is negligible. This is not, however, the case in general.

Figure X–9 shows the normal curve corresponding to the distribution of head lengths.

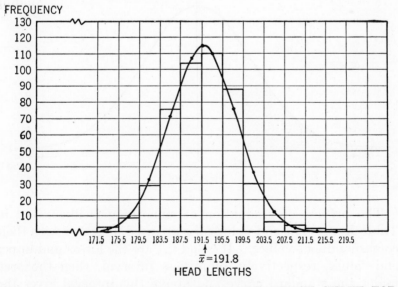

FIG. X-9. HISTOGRAM AND NORMAL FREQUENCY CURVE FOR HEAD LENGTHS.

11.   Graduation of data.   If a normal curve fits a frequency distribution well, we may feel that the curve gives a better picture of what such a distribution would be "on the average" than the particular distribution itself does.   We recall that a given distribution is conceived to be merely one sample chosen at random from infinitely many possible samples, and that these samples will exhibit variations or fluctuations from the ideal distribution.   Conclusions drawn from the ideal distribution should be better "in the long run" than those based upon the single sample alone.   Assuming the last statement to be true, we may calculate the theoretical frequencies corresponding to the actual frequencies by finding the area under the curve corresponding to that of a given rectangle of the histogram.   The remarks connected with Figure X–1 are pertinent here.   The process of calculation for the purpose of smoothing out the data to fit the curve is called *graduation.*

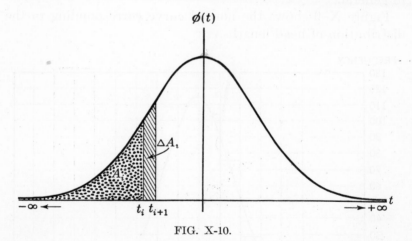

FIG. X-10.

The process of graduation or smoothing is illustrated in Table X–2.   The end-values of x are used, together with their corresponding t-values.   If t_i and t_{i+1} are the lower and upper end-values, respectively, of a class interval, then the area under the standard curve and above this interval gives the theoretical relative frequency of the class.   If we let A_i represent the "partial area" under the curve to the left of t_i (Figure X–10), so that:

$$A_i = \int_{-\infty}^{t_i} \phi(t)dt,$$

the area under the curve from the end-point t_i to the next end-point to the right, t_{i+1}, which we shall call the "difference-

TABLE X-2

COMPUTATION FOR THE GRADUATION OF HEAD LENGTHS BY
MEANS OF THE NORMAL CURVE

1	2	3	4	5	6
End-Value	Actual Frequency	$\dfrac{x_i - \bar{x}}{\sigma_x}$	Partial Area $\int_{-\infty}^{t_i} \phi(t)dt$	Difference-Area	Theoretical Frequency
x_i	f_i	t_i	A_i	ΔA_i	$N\Delta A_i$
171.5		−3.13	.0009		
	3			.0051	2.4
175.5		−2.51	.0060		
	9			.0227	10.5
179.5		−1.90	.0287		
	29			.0716	33.1
183.5		−1.28	.1003		
	76			.1543	71.3
187.5		−.66	.2546		
	104			.2255	104.2
191.5		−.05	.4801		
	110			.2356	108.8
195.5		.57	.7157		
	88			.1673	77.3
199.5		1.19	.8830		
	30			.0811	37.5
203.5		1.80	.9641		
	6			.0281	13.0
207.5		2.42	.9922		
	4			.0066	3.0
211.5		3.04	.9988		
	2			.0011	.5
215.5		3.66	.9999		
	1			.0001	.0
219.5		4.27	1.0000		
	Total = 462	$\bar{x} = 191.8$	$\sigma_x = 6.48$		Total = 461.6

area," ΔA_i (read "delta-A-sub-i"), will be found as the difference of two areas, so that:

$$\Delta A_i = A_{i+1} - A_i$$

$$= \int_{-\infty}^{t_{i+1}} \phi(t)dt - \int_{-\infty}^{t_i} \phi(t)dt$$

$$= \int_{t_i}^{t_{i+1}} \phi(t)dt.$$

(See Section 5.) ΔA_i equals the theoretical relative frequency.

The fourth column of Table X–2 gives the partial areas, A_i. These are calculated from the values of $\int_0^{t_i} \phi(t)dt$ found in Table F of the Supplement. Because of the symmetry of the curve,

$$\int_{-\infty}^{0} \phi(t)dt = \int_{0}^{\infty} \phi(t)dt = 0.5000.$$

It follows that for values of $t_i < 0$ (Figure X–10),

$$A_i = \int_{-\infty}^{t_i} \phi(t)dt = 0.5000 - \int_{t_i}^{0} \phi(t)dt$$

$$= 0.5000 - \int_{0}^{t_i} \phi(t)dt.$$

For values of $t_i > 0$ (Figure X–11),

$$A_i = \int_{-\infty}^{t_i} \phi(t)dt = 0.5000 + \int_{0}^{t_i} \phi(t)dt.$$

The values in the fourth column may be found, then, by simply subtracting from or adding to 0.5000 the values found from Table F.

The difference-areas, ΔA_i, in the fifth column are found by subtracting each value in the preceding column from the one below it. These differences or theoretical relative frequencies are converted into the theoretical frequencies by simply multiplying by the total frequency, N, in this case, 462. The second and last columns may then be compared. The discrepancies between them are called the *errors of the sample* or

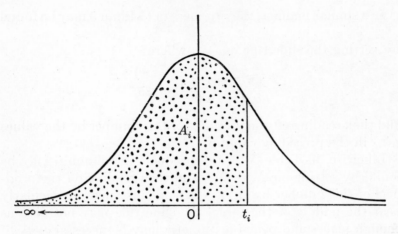

FIG. X-11.

fluctuation errors. We may call the values in the last column the *smoothed* or *graduated frequencies.*

12. **Remarks on the computation connected with curve fitting and graduation.** (i) *Slide rule computation.* Much of the computation can be done with sufficient accuracy for most purposes with a slide rule. Referring to Table X–1, to compute the values of t_i (Column 3), we first subtract the mean, 191.8, from the values x_i. For the first value,

$$x_i - \bar{x} = 173.5 - 191.8 = -18.3.$$

The remaining values of these differences, $x_i - \bar{x}$, are then found by adding successively the number 4 to the first value, -18.3, since the mid-x's, in order, differ by 4. Thus, the differences (not shown in the table) to be used in Column 3 will be -18.3, -14.3, -10.3, and so on. By using $\dfrac{1}{\sigma_x}$, where

$$\frac{1}{\sigma_x} = \frac{1}{6.48} = 0.154,$$

the slide rule may be set on this number and the products, $\dfrac{1}{\sigma_x}(x_i - \bar{x})$, of the reciprocal by the differences read off directly.*

---

* Although the successive values of t_i differ by a constant (approximately 0.62 in this case), the method here described prevents an accumulation of errors and is easy to use.

In a similar manner, the products in Column 5 may be found by setting the slide rule on $\dfrac{Nk}{\sigma}$, where

$$\frac{Nk}{\sigma} = \frac{462 \times 4}{6.48} = 285,$$

and then reading off the products of this number by the values $\phi(t_i)$ in the preceding column.

Likewise, in Table X–2, the products in column 6 may be found by setting on $N = 462$, and then reading off the products of this number by ΔA_i. In some instances, particularly near the middle of the table, the slide rule may not give us enough places and pencil arithmetic may be necessary.

(ii) *Use of a computing machine.* The usual type of computing or adding machine may be used to advantage, especially for obtaining the values of t_i. Since

$$t_i = \frac{x_i - \bar{x}}{\sigma}$$

$$= \frac{x_i - 191.8}{6.48}$$

$$= 0.154x_i - 29.6,$$

$$-t_i = 29.6 - 0.154x_i.$$

We register 29.6 on the lower dial of the machine and 0.154 on the keyboard; and then by reversing the motion of the machine (as for subtraction) so that the successive values x_i are registered on the upper dial, we subtract 0.154 x_i from 29.6. The corresponding values $-t_i$ are then read from the lower dial until all negative values of t are found.

To find the positive values of t, we use the equation:

$$t_i = 0.154x_i - 29.6.$$

The value -29.6 is registered on the lower dial (reversed motion) and 0.154 on the keyboard. Direct motion of the machine registers the successive values x_i on the upper dial, and the values t_i are read from the lower dial.

(iii) *Checking.* Gross errors in the calculation may often

be detected by watching the values of y_i (Table X–1).   Those corresponding to the mid-values should be of the same general magnitude as the respective frequencies, f_i; and their sum, Σy_i, should approximate N.   As a matter of fact, these values, y_i, constitute one form of estimate (not the best) of the theoretical frequencies.   The sum of the difference-areas, ΔA_i (Table X–2), should very nearly equal one, and the sum of the theoretical frequencies (Column 6) should very nearly equal N.

(iv)   *Use of the values,* x_i.   In constructing the normal curve, we plotted points the ordinates of which corresponded to the mid-values of the class intervals.   If we desire more points for plotting, we can employ the end-values of the class intervals also.   It is sometimes convenient to use points whose abscissas deviate from the mean, $\bar{x}$, by multiples and sub-multiples of σ_x.   Such abscissas might be $\bar{x} \pm \frac{1}{3}\sigma_x$, $\bar{x} \pm \frac{2}{3}\sigma_x$, $\bar{x} \pm \sigma_x$, $\cdots\cdot$ Of course, the process of graduating the frequencies requires the use of end-values of x.

Naturally, there is no limit to the number of values of $\phi(t)$ and of $\int_0^t \phi(t)dt$ which we may obtain if we wish, except that set by the tables available.   Every possible value of t can be converted into a value of x, and vice versa.

(v)   *Discrete data.*   The discussion thus far has assumed that the frequency distributions to which curves are fitted are composed of continuous data.   A natural question arising at this point is one pertaining to data that are discrete. (Section IV–3.)   Can one fit a frequency curve to a distribution of the number of heads appearing when six pennies are tossed (Figs. IV–2, 3), of the sizes of shoes worn by college girls, of the number of students per class in a large university, and so on?   The answer is an affirmative one, although the method involves some procedures which may seem artificial. Because of the discontinuity of the data, there are, on the horizontal axis, no end-points common to two adjacent intervals; that is to say, the upper limit of one class is not the lower limit of the next.   To remedy this, we set artificial boundary points midway between two adjacent end-points.   For example, the frequency diagram of Figure IV–2 is thus replaced by the histogram of Figure X–12. The frequency for a given number of heads is represented by the area, as well as the altitude of the appropriate rectangle the base of which is unity. Of course, numbers of heads given by the values at the end-points of the bases or at any other points save the mid-points of the bases are impossible.

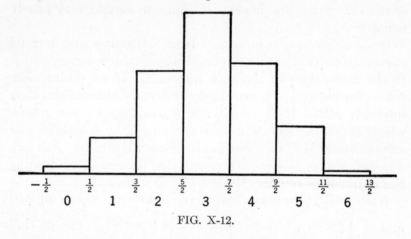

FIG. X-12.

In the case of shoe sizes (Ex. IV–13), the artificial boundaries would be $2\frac{1}{4}$, $2\frac{3}{4}$, $3\frac{1}{4}$, and so forth.

Chapter XIII will deal more adequately with problems of the type suggested here.

13. Uses of curve fitting and graduation. The process of smoothing or graduation is not restricted to the normal curve nor to the methods described in the preceding sections. It may be applied to many widely different forms of data. For example, the use of twelve-month moving averages for milk prices "ironed out" the seasonal fluctuations in the wavy curve of Figure III–9 and represents a form of graduation. Certain types of data show irregularities which tend to mislead the interpreter of the data. A classical example occurs in the case of census data, where people tend to give their ages as multiples of five. Bulges in such data occur at the ages 35, 40, 45, and so on. A proper method of graduation will increase the reliability of conclusions drawn from such records. The general subject of graduation is of considerable scope and cannot be fully treated here. Interpolation formulas based upon tables of differences (Section XI–17) are of great service in graduating data.

One use of a fitted curve is fairly obvious. It serves to replace irregularities or discontinuities in a graph, such as a frequency polygon or a histogram, by a smooth-flowing curve which aids and satisfies the eye as it traces the variations in the data. In the case of data such as head lengths, statures, intervals of time, and so forth, the smooth curve more clearly characterizes their fundamental continuity.

The fitted curve also specifies or emphasizes the statistician's assumption concerning the nature of the data itself— that it constitutes a normal distribution, a skew distribution, a linear distribution, and so on.

The graduated data also allow the statistician to draw conclusions concerning the population or universe on the basis of the limited amount of information contained within the sample itself. Estimates must be made, and smoothing of the data is one of the most satisfactory methods of making such estimates.

Practical applications of the concepts of the normal distribution, curve fitting, and graduation will be found illustrated in the exercises at the end of this chapter.

14. Probability paper. It is sometimes difficult to decide whether or not a frequency distribution is sufficiently near to the normal type to be fitted by a normal curve. A preliminary decision in a given case is largely the result of experience —of good guessing. Such a decision, however, can be reinforced by a fairly simple test involving the use of *arithmetic probability paper.*

The paper just referred to is a special type of ruled coordinate paper with a uniform (arithmetic) scale in one direction and a non-uniform scale, based on the values $\int_{-\infty}^{t} \phi(t)\,dt$, in the other (Figure X–13). It is convenient to choose the former direction as horizontal and the latter as vertical. The vertical scale is therefore based on the partial areas, A_i, under the standard curve. Since the area under the whole curve is unity, the partial areas represent the *percentage cumulative frequencies* of a normal curve. For example, if we refer to Figure X–6, we find that about 2 per cent of the normally distributed t's have values less than -2, about 16 per cent have values less than -1, 50 per cent less than 0, and so on.

We illustrate the use of the paper with the aid of Table X–3 and Figure X–13. Table X–3 contains the familiar data of

TABLE X–3

PERCENTAGE CUMULATIVE
FREQUENCIES FOR HEAD LENGTHS

Boundary	Frequency f_i	Cum f_i	% Cum f_i
171.5		0	0
	3		
175.5		3	.65
	9		
179.5		12	2.60
	29		
183.5		41	8.88
	76		
187.5		117	25.3
	104		
191.5		221	47.8
	110		
195.5		331	71.7
	88		
199.5		419	90.7
	30		
203.5		449	97.2
	6		
207.5		455	98.5
	4		
211.5		459	99.3
	2		
215.5		461	99.8
	1		
219.5		462	100.0

head lengths. Inasmuch as cumulative frequencies are of prime importance here, we are interested only in boundary values and not mid-values. The last column of values is

found from the formula $100 \times \text{cum} \dfrac{f_i}{N}$. For example, the
fifth number in the last column, 25.3, equals $100 \times \dfrac{117}{462}$.

On the probability paper (Figure X–13), we lay off the
boundary points for the classes on the uniform horizontal

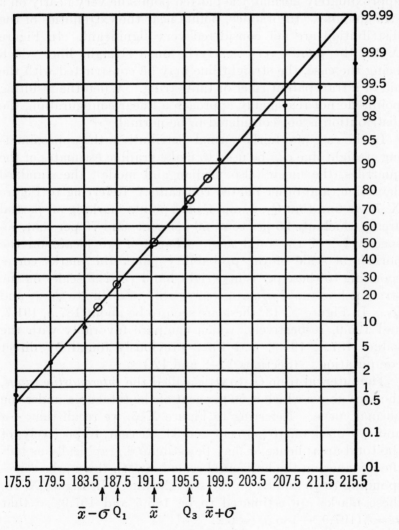

FIG. X-13.

scale. Inasmuch as the percentage cumulative frequencies 0 and 100 are of trifling importance, we omit them on the graph. The ordinates or percentage cumulative frequencies are plotted with the aid of the non-uniform vertical scale at the right. The points thus located should be clearly marked as heavy dots. If the given frequency distribution is approximately normal, the plotted points lie very nearly on a straight line. In practice, points near the extremities of the distribution are not considered very significant. In Figure X–13, the points very nearly lie on a straight line. Such being the case, the straight line may be constructed with the aid of a transparent ruler or taut string. When the resulting points do not reasonably approach a linear configuration, the distribution is not considered to be normal.

In the case of a fairly normal distribution, the approximating straight line can be used to make graphic estimates of the quartiles, the mean (also median and mode), the standard deviation, and other related constants. Referring to Figure X–7, we find that Q_1, $\bar{x}$, and Q_3 are points marking off partial areas, which are 25 per cent, 50 per cent, and 75 per cent, respectively, of the total area. Hence, if we locate on the horizontal scale of the probability paper the marks corresponding to these per cents (right-hand vertical scale) on the straight line (note circles), we are able to estimate Q_1, $\bar{x}$, and Q_3. In Figure X–13, these are seen to be about 187.5, 191.7, and 195.9, respectively, which compare favorably with the values 187.4, 191.9, and 196.2 previously found by direct computation. (Sections VI–8 and 12.)

The interval from Q_1 to Q_3 is called the *interquartile range*, the area above which is 50 per cent of the total area under the normal curve. Referring to Figure X–5, we recall that $-\sigma$ and $+\sigma$ mark off 16 per cent and 84 per cent, respectively, of the total area; hence, σ may be estimated graphically as half the distance on the horizontal scale between the marks corresponding to 16 and 84 on the straight line. In Figure X–13, these marks are estimated to be 185.5 and 197.9, so that $\sigma = \frac{1}{2}(197.9 - 185.5) = 6.2$.

Of course, the values of statistical measures obtained by

the methods just described depend upon the position of the particular line selected as the one best fitting the plotted points. Inasmuch as this is purely a matter of visual estimation, too much reliability should not be placed in the numerical results obtained. Nevertheless, probability paper furnishes us a simple, quick method of testing for normality and of getting rough estimates of the chief statistical constants. In dealing with discrete data, one must use artificial boundary values, as described in Section 12 (v).

15. The question of fit. Whether a given frequency distribution is normal or not is commonly decided by visual estimation—the frequency histogram looks fairly symmetrical, or the points plotted on arithmetic probability paper seem to lie along a straight line. It is possible to reinforce these qualitative procedures, or to supplant them, by tests which yield numerical measures.

One method requires the computation of the skewness, the excess, and a third measure called "the departure from the normal." If these values are all nearly zero, the distribution is essentially normal. This method has the advantage of suggesting types of curves other than the normal one when the distribution does not satisfy the test for normality. (See Ref. 2, Chap. 11.)

Another method tests the "goodness of fit" by means of an important criterion known as the χ^2 (read "chi-square") test. (See Section XIV–13.) The latter may be applied to many widely different kinds of distributions.

X—Exercises

1. $f(x) = 3x - 2$. Find $f(1), f(3), f(0), f(x_0)$.

2. $F(x) = x^2 - 3x + 2$. Find $F(3), F(2), F(1), F(\frac{3}{2})$.

3. $y = f(x)$, where $f(x) = 3x^2 - 5x + 2$. Find the value of y when $x = -2$; when $x = 4$; when $x = 0$.

4. If $H(t) = 2 \log_{10} t$, find $H(10), H(100), H(1)$.

5. If $P(x) = 3 \times 10^x$, find $P(0), P(1), P(3), P(-2)$.

*   *   *

By using Table E of the Supplement, find $\phi(t)$ for the values of t indicated in Exercises 6–8.

6. (a) 0.50;   (b) 0.28;   (c) −1.34;   (d) −0.83;   (e) 2.81.

7. (a) 0.66;   (b) 1.69;   (c) −2.40;   (d) 0.12;   (e) −0.21.

8. (a) 3.12;   (b) 1.04;   (c) −1.04;   (d) 1.97;   (e) −3.35.

*   *   *

By using Table F of the Supplement, find the areas indicated in Exercises 9–14.

9. (a) $\int_0^{0.50} \phi(t)dt;$ (b) $\int_{-1.10}^{0} \phi(t)dt;$ (c) $\int_0^{3.29} \phi(t)dt.$

10. (a) $\int_0^{2.71} \phi(t)dt;$ (b) $\int_{-0.77}^{0} \phi(t)dt;$ (c) $\int_0^{1.55} \phi(t)dt.$

11. (a) $\int_{0.18}^{0.45} \phi(t)dt;$ (b) $\int_{2.00}^{2.40} \phi(t)dt;$ (c) $\int_{0.25}^{1.00} \phi(t)dt.$

12. (a) $\int_{-0.27}^{1.31} \phi(t)dt;$ (b) $\int_{-0.12}^{0.12} \phi(t)dt;$ (c) $\int_{2.17}^{2.32} \phi(t)dt.$

13. (a) $\int_{-0.75}^{0.75} \phi(t)dt;$ (b) $\int_{-\infty}^{-1.20} \phi(t)dt;$ (c) $\int_{-\infty}^{0.29} \phi(t)dt.$

14. (a) $\int_{2.00}^{\infty} \phi(t)dt;$ (b) $\int_{-1.20}^{\infty} \phi(t)dt;$ (c) $\int_{-2.65}^{-1.65} \phi(t)dt.$

*   *   *

By means of inverse interpolation in Table F of the Supplement, find the values of t corresponding to the areas given in Exercises 15–17.

15. (a) $\int_0^t \phi(t)dt = 0.0616;$ (b) $\int_0^t \phi(t)dt = 0.4825.$

16. (a) $\int_{-t}^{0} \phi(t)dt = 0.2432;$ (b) $\int_{-t}^{t} \phi(t)dt = 0.9920.$

17. (a) $\int_{-t}^{0} \phi(t)dt = 0.4542;$ (b) $\int_{-t}^{t} \phi(t)dt = 0.1886.$

*   *   *

18. What per cent of the head lengths of criminals differ numerically from the mean head length by less than five millimeters? Find answers to this question by the following two ways: (1) In the given frequency distribution, employ a method of interpolation similar to that used in finding the median. Cumulative frequencies will not be necessary. The values of x involved will be $\bar{x} + 5$ and $\bar{x} - 5$ where $\bar{x} = 191.8$. (2) Use the values of $\bar{x}$ and σ_x and Table F. Explain carefully the difference in meaning of the two answers.

19. Compute the number of Swedish males (Ex. IV–11) having brain-weights between $\bar{x} - \sigma_x$ and $\bar{x} + \sigma_x$. See part (1) of the preceding exercise.

20. Compute the number of runaway boys (Ex. IV–12) having I. Q.'s (a) between $\bar{x} - \sigma_x$ and $\bar{x} + \sigma_x$; (b) differing numerically from $\bar{x}$ by more than $2\sigma_x$.

21. (a) Find the probability that a Swedish male selected from the 416 listed in Exercise IV–11 has a brain-weight between 1300 and 1500 grams. (b) Compute the probability that any adult Swedish male has a brain-weight between 1300 and 1500 grams. Note the difference between these two problems. Discuss the reliability of your answer in (b).

22. Find the probability that any adult Swedish male has a brain-weight (a) less than 1250 grams; (b) greater than 1550 grams. See the preceding exercise.

23. (a) Find the probability that a runaway boy selected at random from the 660 listed in Exercise IV–12 has an I. Q. of 100 or greater. (b) Compute the probability that any runaway boy of the type studied has an I. Q. greater than 100. Note the difference between these two problems.

24. Find the answer in (b) of the preceding exercise for an I. Q. (a) between 90 and 110; (b) less than 70.

* * *

Fit a normal curve to each of the frequency distributions in Exercises 25–28. Graduate the data as directed by your instructor.

25. Taxation for school support. (Ex. IV–10.)

26. Brain-weight of Swedish males. (Ex. IV–11.)

27. Intelligence quotients of boys. (Ex. IV–12.)

28. Sizes of shoes worn by college girls. (Ex. IV–13.)

* * *

By means of arithmetic probability paper, test the distributions in Exercises 29–35 to see if they appear to be of normal type. When they are, estimate from your graph the values of $\bar{x}$ (also the median and the mode), Q_1, Q_3, Q, and σ. Where possible, compare these values with those previously computed by other methods.

29. Maximum temperatures in New York City. (Ex. IV–8.)

30. Rate of taxation for school support. (Ex. IV–10.)

31. Brain-weight of Swedish males. (Ex. IV–11.)

32. Intelligence quotients of boys. (Ex. IV–12.)

33. Sizes of shoes worn by college girls. (Ex. IV–13.)

34. Daily wages of employees. (Ex. IV–14.)

35. Bills for electric current. (Table IV–2.)

*   *   *

36. One thousand milking records of a certain dairy showed an average per cent of fat content of 5.20, with a standard deviation of 0.60. Assuming the distribution to be normal, how many records show a fat content of less than 4.30 per cent?

37. The brushes on the generator of a certain make of automobile as found from the analysis of 900 cars, have an average life of 20 months with a standard deviation of 5 months; if an agency selling this number of cars agrees to replace, free of charge, all brushes worn out in less than a year, how many brushes should it expect to replace? How many brushes are expected to last more than three years? Interpret the word *brush* to mean *set of brushes*.

CHAPTER

XI

CURVE FITTING

❖⊐ⅢⅢⅢⅢⅢⅢⅢⅢⅢⅢⅢⅢⅢⅢⅢⅢⅢⅢⅢⅢⅢⅢⅢⅢⅢⅢⅢⅢⅢⅢⅢⅢⅢⅢⅢⅢⅢ❖

"An equation is the most serious and important thing in mathematics."

SIR OLIVER LODGE. *Easy Mathematics*, 1906.

1. Introduction. The accompanying graphs exhibit markedly different configurations of plotted points. In Figure XI–1, the points appear to lie along a straight line; in Figure XI–2, they appear to lie on or near a curve known as a *parabola;* and in Figure XI–3, they do not appear to lie along any recognizable curve. Configurations of plotted points may or may not indicate trends in the data from which they arise. It is often the duty of the statistician to discover and to measure such trends when they exist. This means that he must solve a problem in curve fitting. The preceding chapter dealt with such a problem, but there the type of curve was defined in advance by means of equation (1). From the given data, $\bar{x}$, σ_x, and the area, Nk, were computed so that the constants associated with (1) were known. There remained only the problem of actually constructing the curve.

In this chapter we are concerned with the more general problem of fitting an equation or a curve to data involving *paired values.* A frequency distribution pairing variates, x_i, with corresponding frequencies, f_i, is but one example of such data. Statistical items may be arranged in other forms. The time series (Section III–8) pairs one set of variates with

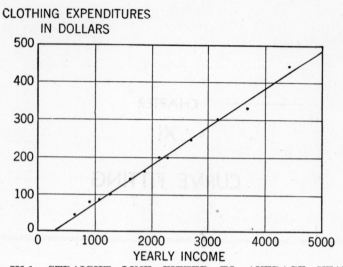

CLOTHING EXPENDITURES
IN DOLLARS

FIG. XI-1. STRAIGHT LINE FITTED TO AVERAGE YEARLY
CLOTHING EXPENDITURES AT SUCCESSIVE INCOME LEVELS FOR
WAGE EARNER FAMILIES IN CHICAGO. (A. D. H. Kaplan, "Expenditure Patterns of Urban Families," *Journal of the American Statistical Association*, March 1938, p. 90.)

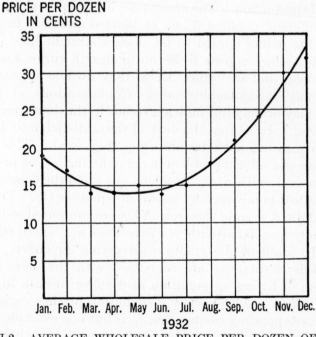

PRICE PER DOZEN
IN CENTS

FIG. XI-2. AVERAGE WHOLESALE PRICE PER DOZEN OF EGGS,
BOSTON, 1932.

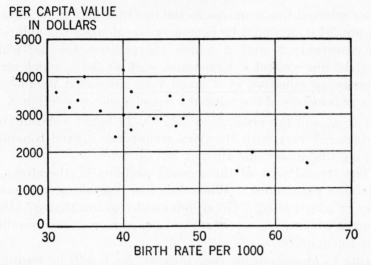

FIG. XI-3. BIRTH RATES AND PER CAPITA PROPERTY VALUE.

intervals or instants of time; the Lorenz curve (Section VI–4) pairs corresponding percentages; Figure XI–3 pairs birth rates with per capita property value.

Statistical problems centered about curve fitting may be resolved into three parts.

(i) *The statistician must decide what kind of curve to fit to the data.*. The decision is often a matter of common sense and good judgment.   The best-fitting curve is sometimes too complicated for practical use and must be replaced by a simpler one.   Perhaps one portion of the data requires one curve while the remainder demands another.   It will suffice now to say that the plotted points themselves most frequently give the clue to the type of curve required.

(ii) *The statistician must calculate the constants involved in the equation of the curve selected to fit the data.*   This equation is usually written in the form $y = f(x)$, where $f(x)$ is some function of x.

For example, the first-degree equation:

$$y = \lambda x + \beta \qquad\qquad (1)$$

defines a straight line.   (λ is read "lambda," and β, "beta".)

If we selected this equation as the one best fitting the data of Figure XI–1, it would be necessary to calculate the values of the constants λ and β which characterize the particular straight line we seek. Constants, such as these, which characterize an equation of a given type are called *parameters*. The parameters of the normal frequency curve (Section X–2) are $\bar{x}$, σ_x, and the area, $A = Nk$. $\sqrt{2\pi}$ is not a parameter; it does not vary with the data given; it is a fixed constant, having the same value always.

The second part of the general problem is, therefore, to calculate parameters. When this has been done, the curve may be constructed. Good judgment requires that we select a curve whose parameters are not too numerous nor too difficult to compute.

(iii) *The statistician may interpret the results by means of explanations, estimates, and predictions.*

There is an infinite variety of curves in mathematics; yet for the purposes of statistical curve fitting, the curves used are relatively limited in type. Fortunately for us, the straight line is the simplest and one of the most important curves used.

2. The straight line. The equation:

$$y = \lambda x + \beta \tag{1}$$

is an equation of the first degree in x and y. It can be proved to define a straight line. The function $\lambda x + \beta$ is therefore called a *linear function of x*. The difference

$$y_i - (\lambda x_i + \beta) \tag{2}$$

is zero only if point (x_i, y_i) lies on line (1). If we write

$$y' = y - \beta, \tag{3}$$

we obtain

$$y' = \lambda x. \tag{1a}$$

Geometrically, the transformation (3) defines a vertical shift of the origin, O, through a distance β to O'. β, the ordinate of O' relative to the x-axis, is called the **y-*intercept*** of the line (1).

From Figure XI–4, we can find a simple but significant

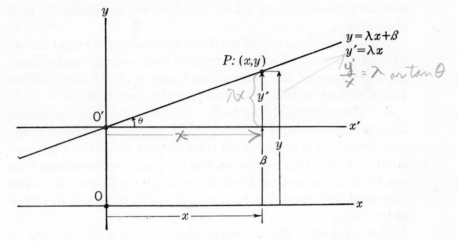

FIG. XI-4.

meaning for the parameter λ. From (1a) we find that $\lambda = \dfrac{y'}{x}$.

The quantity $\dfrac{y'}{x}$ measures the steepness of the line, for it is the ratio of the rise, y', to the horizontal distance, x. For this reason the parameter, λ, is called the *slope* of the line. From elementary trigonometry we know that, if θ is the angle made by the line with the positive x-axis, the tangent of θ equals $\dfrac{y'}{x}$. Hence, we may write, $\tan \theta = \lambda$. When the line ascends from left to right, as in Figure XI–4, y' and x are positive, and the slope, λ, is therefore positive; when the line descends from left to right, y' is negative and the slope is also.

It is important to note that any translation of axes does not affect the slope of a straight line, but a change of unit caused by a stretching or compression will.

3. Fitting a straight line. The selection of a straight line rather than some other curve to fit a set of points is usually made upon the basis of the appearance of the plotted points themselves. One would not hesitate to select a straight line for those of Figure XI–1. There are, however, occasions when we desire to find best-fitting straight lines for points

such as those of Figure XI–3.   In fact, we do this in the next
chapter.

We list here four useful methods for fitting a straight line to
a set of points.   "Fitting a straight line" usually means finding the values of the parameters λ and β of the straight line
(1) as well as actually constructing the line itself.

4.   The graphical method.   The straight line is drawn
after a careful visual estimate of its position has been made
with the aid of a transparent ruler or taut thread.   The coordinates of any two points on the line, not too near together,
are then measured and substituted in equation (1).   The
two resulting equations in λ and β are then solved for these
parameters.

This method is illustrated in Figure XI–5 with the data of
the first three columns of Table XI–1.   The mid-values of

TABLE XI–1

AVERAGE AGE OF ENTRANCE OF HARVARD FRESHMEN BY FIVE-YEAR PERIODS,
1856–1900. (*Data from President Lowell's Report for 1928–1929.*)
(See Ex. III-3, 4.)

Period	Age y_i	Time x_i	t_i	t_i^2	$t_i y_i$
1856–1860	17.9	0	−4	16	−71.6
1861–1865	18.4	5	−3	9	−55.2
1866–1870	18.4	10	−2	4	−36.8
1871–1875	18.6	15	−1	1	−18.6
1876–1880	18.8	20	0	0	0
1881–1885	19.0	25	1	1	19.0
1886–1890	19.3	30	2	4	38.6
1891–1895	19.1	35	3	9	57.3
1896–1900	19.0	40	4	16	76.0
Total	168.5			60	+8.7

the nine five-year periods have been designated for convenience as $x = 0, 5, 15, \cdot \cdot \cdot 40$.   The straight line has been
fitted by eye.   Choosing points P_1 and P_2 as two convenient points on the line, we estimate their coordinates to be
(12.5, 18.5) and (35, 19.4), respectively.   Since these coordinates must satisfy equation (1), we have:

$$18.5 = 12.5\lambda + \beta,$$
$$19.4 = 35\lambda + \beta.$$

Subtracting the upper equation from the lower,

$$0.9 = 22.5\lambda,$$
$$\lambda = 0.04. \quad \longrightarrow slope$$

or

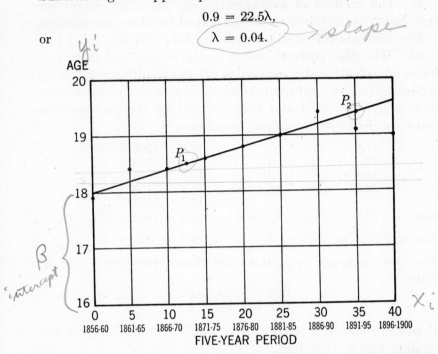

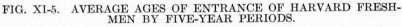

FIG. XI-5. AVERAGE AGES OF ENTRANCE OF HARVARD FRESH-MEN BY FIVE-YEAR PERIODS.

Substituting this value of λ in the upper equation,

$$18.5 = (12.5 \times 0.04) + \beta,$$

whence
$$\beta = 18.0. \quad \longrightarrow intercept$$

The equation of the straight line is, therefore:

$$y = 0.04x + 18.0.$$

The values of λ and β are easily checked from the figure. The straight line crosses the y-axis or axes of ages 18.0 units above the origin, and for a horizontal distance of 5 units the straight line rises about 0.20 units. Thus, the slope is about 0.04, and the y-intercept about 18.0.

The method described will obviously yield only approximate results and should be used when such are adequate for the purpose in hand.

5. The method of averages. Two "average" equations in λ and β are obtained and then solved for these parameters.

We illustrate this method with the data of Table XI–1 just used. The nine pairs of values in the second and third columns are substituted in expression (2), the resulting expressions separated into two approximately equal groups, the expressions in each group added and then divided by their number, in order to yield two "average" equations:

$$
\begin{array}{ll}
17.9 - (0\lambda + \beta) & 18.8 - (20\lambda + \beta) \\
18.4 - (5\lambda + \beta) & 19.0 - (25\lambda + \beta) \\
18.4 - (10\lambda + \beta) & 19.3 - (30\lambda + \beta) \\
18.6 - (15\lambda + \beta) & 19.1 - (35\lambda + \beta) \\
& 19.0 - (40\lambda + \beta)
\end{array}
$$

Sum: $\quad 73.3 - (30\lambda + 4\beta) = 0 \qquad 95.2 - (150\lambda + 5\beta) = 0$

Average: $18.4 = 7.5\lambda + \beta \qquad\qquad 19.0 = 30\lambda + \beta$

The two "average" equations are then solved for λ and β. Thus,

$$
\begin{cases}
18.4 = 7.5\lambda + \beta \\
19.0 = 30\lambda + \beta
\end{cases}
$$

yield the solution $\lambda = 0.03$, $\beta = 18.2$. The equation of the straight line is, therefore,

$$
y = 0.03\,x + 18.2.
$$

This result compares favorably with the result obtained graphically.

6. The method of least squares. This method assumes that the best-fitting line is the one for which the sum of the squares of the vertical distances of the points (x_i, y_i) from the line is a minimum. (See also Section XII–3.) It is more accurate than either of the two methods just described and is in very common use. Moreover, the fundamental principle and methods involved may be extended to more general cases. If

$$
y = \lambda x + \beta \tag{1}
$$

is the equation of this line, the ordinate of any point, Q_i, on the line vertically below a given point, P_i, can be found by substituting the abscissa, x_i, in the right-hand member of (1). The two coordinates of Q_i will be $(x_i, \lambda x_i + \beta)$ (Figure XI–6). The vertical distance, d_i, from the line of any point P_i with coordinates (x_i, y_i) will therefore be given by the equation:

$$d_i = y_i - (\lambda x_i + \beta). \tag{4}$$

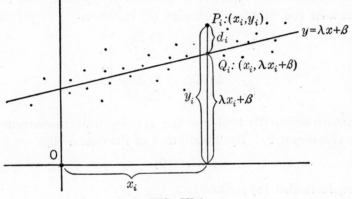

FIG. XI-6.

We may say that d_i represents the distance between the *actual* ordinate, y_i, of a point and its *theoretical* ordinate, $\lambda x_i + \beta$. The quantity d_i is often called a *residual*.

The best-fitting line is that line for which the sum of the squares, Σd_i^2, is a minimum. Our problem is to find the values of λ and β which make Σd_i^2 a minimum. It will be shown in the next section that these values are given by the formulas,

$$\left. \begin{aligned} \lambda &= \frac{N\Sigma x_i y_i - \Sigma x_i \Sigma y_i}{N\Sigma x_i^2 - (\Sigma x_i)^2} \\[2mm] \beta &= \frac{\Sigma x_i^2 \Sigma y_i - \Sigma x_i \Sigma x_i y_i}{N\Sigma x_i^2 - (\Sigma x_i)^2} \end{aligned} \right\}, \tag{5}$$

where N is the number of points (x_i, y_i). These formulas may be simplified considerably by a familiar transformation of axes. We let

$$t_i = \frac{x_i - \bar{x}}{k}, \tag{6}$$

where k is the interval between successive values of x assumed to be equally spaced. We thus place the new origin at the mean, $\bar{x}$, and compress (or stretch) the intervals to unity. We now seek the parameters λ' and β' in a new equation:

$$y = \lambda't + \beta' \tag{7}$$

of the straight line referred to the new (t, y)-axes. In terms of the new coordinates, formulas (5) become:

$$\left.\begin{aligned}\lambda' &= \frac{N\Sigma t_i y_i - \Sigma t_i \Sigma y_i}{N\Sigma t_i^2 - (\Sigma t_i)^2} \\[2mm] \beta' &= \frac{\Sigma t_i^2 \Sigma y_i - \Sigma t_i \Sigma t_i y_i}{N\Sigma t_i^2 - (\Sigma t_i)^2}\end{aligned}\right\} . \tag{8}$$

Transformation (6) replaces the x_i's by unit deviations, t_i, from the mean, $\bar{x}$. By Theorem 1 of Section V–6,

$$\Sigma t_i = 0; \tag{9}$$

hence, formulas (8) reduce to:

$$\left.\begin{aligned}\lambda' &= \frac{N\Sigma t_i y_i - 0}{N\Sigma t_i^2 - 0} \\[2mm] \beta' &= \frac{\Sigma t_i^2 \Sigma y_i - 0}{N\Sigma t_i^2 - 0}\end{aligned}\right\} ,$$

which further simplify to the convenient form:

$$\left.\begin{aligned}\lambda' &= \frac{\Sigma t_i y_i}{\Sigma t_i^2} \\[2mm] \beta' &= \frac{1}{N}\Sigma y_i = \bar{y}\end{aligned}\right\} . \tag{10}$$

These are important formulas. Their use will be illustrated with the data of Table XI–1.

The fourth column of Table XI–1 gives the values of t_i, where, by (6),

$$t_i = \frac{x_i - 20}{5}.$$

The fifth and sixth columns give the values of t_i^2 and $t_i y_i$. From formulas (10), we obtain:

$$\lambda' = \frac{\Sigma t_i y_i}{\Sigma t_i^2}$$

$$= \frac{8.7}{60} = 0.14,$$

$$\beta' = \frac{1}{N} \Sigma y_i$$

$$= \frac{168.5}{9} = 18.7;$$

whence the equation (7) of the line may be written as:

$$y = 0.14t + 18.7.$$

The more useful form of the last equation is found by replacing t by its value $\dfrac{x - 20}{5}$ in the equation just obtained:

$$y = 0.14 \left(\frac{x - 20}{5} \right) + 18.7$$

$$= 0.028x + 18.1.$$

From this form, the straight line can be actually constructed on the graph paper containing the plotted points. Any two convenient values of x, not too close together, are substituted in the equation and the corresponding values of y found. Thus, if $x = 0$,

$$y = 18.1,$$

and if $x = 30$,

$$y = (0.028 \times 30) + 18.1 = 18.9.$$

The two points $(0, 18.1)$ and $(30, 18.9)$ will then determine the line. The position of the line will vary slightly from that shown in Figure XI–5.

7. **Derivation of the values of λ and β.** In order to derive formulas (5), we first note, without proof, a few properties of the quadratic function:

$$y = ax^2 + bx + c. \tag{11}$$

The curve defined by equation (11) is called a *parabola*

(Figures XI–7 and 8). It is symmetric with respect to a vertical line passing through its highest or lowest point. If the coefficient a is positive, the parabola opens upward, as in Figure XI–7; if a is negative, it opens downward, as in Figure XI–8. For our purposes it is important to find the value of x which makes the value of y in (11) as small as possible, when $a > 0$.

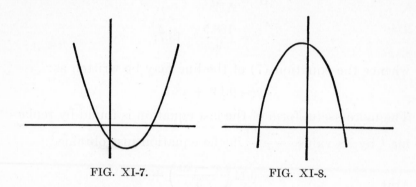

FIG. XI-7.   FIG. XI-8.

We need only consider the case where $a > 0$; that is, we need to find the value of x which makes the quadratic function (11) a minimum. We write:

$$y = ax^2 + bx + c$$

$$= a(x^2 + \frac{b}{a}x \quad) + c,$$

and complete the square within the parenthesis.

$$y = a\left[x^2 + \frac{bx}{a} + \left(\frac{b}{2a}\right)^2\right] + c - a\left(\frac{b}{2a}\right)^2$$

$$= a\left(x + \frac{b}{2a}\right)^2 - \frac{b^2 - 4ac}{4a}.$$

The quantity on the right will be as small as possible when

$$x + \frac{b}{2a} = 0,$$

that is, when

$$x = -\frac{b}{2a}. \tag{12}$$

Referring now to Section 6, we seek the values of λ and β which make Σd_i^2 a minimum. By (4):

$$\Sigma d_i^2 = \Sigma[y_i - (\lambda x_i + \beta)]^2$$
$$= \Sigma(y_i^2 + \lambda^2 x_i^2 + \beta^2 - 2\lambda x_i y_i - 2\beta y_i + 2\lambda\beta x_i)$$
$$= \Sigma y_i^2 + \lambda^2\Sigma x_i^2 + N\beta^2 - 2\lambda\Sigma x_i y_i - 2\beta\Sigma y_i + 2\lambda\beta\Sigma x_i.$$

We may express the right member as a quadratic function of λ:

$$\Sigma d_i^2 = (\Sigma x_i^2)\lambda^2 + 2(\beta\Sigma x_i - \Sigma x_i y_i)\lambda + (\Sigma y_i^2 + N\beta^2 - 2\beta\Sigma y_i); \quad (13)$$

or as a quadratic function of β:

$$\Sigma d_i^2 = N\beta^2 + 2(\lambda\Sigma x_i - \Sigma y_i)\beta + (\Sigma y_i^2 + \lambda^2\Sigma x_i^2 - 2\lambda\Sigma x_i y_i). \quad (14)$$

Hence, for a minimum value of Σd_i^2 treated as a quadratic function of λ, we have, from (12) and (13),

$$\lambda = -\frac{2(\beta\Sigma x_i - \Sigma x_i y_i)}{2\Sigma x_i^2}.$$

Also, for a minimum value of Σd_i^2 treated as a quadratic function of β, we have, from (12) and (14),

$$\beta = -\frac{2(\lambda\Sigma x_i - \Sigma y_i)}{2N}.$$

The last two equations may be written in the form:

$$\left.\begin{array}{l} (\Sigma x_i^2)\lambda + (\Sigma x_i)\beta = \Sigma x_i y_i \\ (\Sigma x_i)\lambda + N\beta = \Sigma y_i \end{array}\right\}. \quad (15)$$

These constitute two equations of the first degree in the unknowns λ and β. Solving, we get equations (5) of Section 6:

$$\left.\begin{array}{l} \lambda = \dfrac{N\Sigma x_i y_i - \Sigma x_i \Sigma y_i}{N\Sigma x_i^2 - (\Sigma x_i)^2} \\[2mm] \beta = \dfrac{\Sigma x_i^2 \Sigma y_i - \Sigma x_i \Sigma x_i y_i}{N\Sigma x_i^2 - (\Sigma x_i)^2} \end{array}\right\}. \quad (5)$$

8. The use of normal equations. When the least squares criterion of best fit is employed, a procedure different from the preceding may be applied. It has the decided advantage of being applicable to more general cases than the linear one.

Suppose we are fitting the straight line:

$$y = \lambda x + \beta \tag{1}$$

to a set of points (x_1, y_1), (x_2, y_2), $\cdots$ (x_N, y_N).

(i)   Write the N expressions* obtained by substituting the N pairs of observed values, (x_i, y_i), in the expression (2) on page 246:

$$y_1 - (\lambda x_1 + \beta)$$
$$y_2 - (\lambda x_2 + \beta)$$
$$y_3 - (\lambda x_3 + \beta)$$
$$\cdot \quad \cdot \quad \cdot$$
$$\cdot \quad \cdot \quad \cdot$$
$$\cdot \quad \cdot \quad \cdot$$
$$y_N - (\lambda x_N + \beta)$$

(ii)   Multiply each of these expressions by the coefficient, x_i, of the first parameter, λ, in the parenthesis, and add the results:

$$\Sigma x_i y_i - (\lambda \Sigma x_i^2 + \beta \Sigma x_i).$$

(iii)   Multiply each of the expressions by the coefficient, 1, of the second parameter, β, in the parenthesis, and add:

$$\Sigma y_i - (\lambda \Sigma x_i + N\beta).$$

When the two expressions thus obtained are set equal to zero, they are called *normal equations* and are identical with (15).   When solved for λ and β, they lead to formulas (5). The latter give the values of λ and β which make the sum of the squares of the residuals, Σd_i^2, a minimum.

9.   The method of moments.   A fourth method of obtaining the line of best fit admits even wider application than the method of least squares.   This method makes use of moments about the y-axis of the given set of points.

The rth moment of the points (x_1, y_1), (x_2, y_2), $\cdots$ (x_N, y_N) *about the y-axis (the value $x = 0$) is defined as* $\sum_{i=1}^{N} y_i x_i^r$.

---

* These expressions, equated to zero, are called *observation equations*, but they are not true equalities, in general. Why?

We employ as many moments as there are parameters to be found; hence, to find λ and β in (1), we make use of the zeroth and first moments, $\Sigma y_i x_i^0$ and $\Sigma y_i x_i$. The principle of moments that we assume states merely that the sum of the moments of the given points, $P_i:(x_i, y_i)$, shall be equal to the moments of the corresponding points, $Q_i:(x_i, \lambda x_i + \beta)$, on the line. Thus, for the zeroth moment,

$$\Sigma(\lambda x_i + \beta)x_i^0 = \Sigma y_i x_i^0,$$

or
$$\Sigma(\lambda x_i + \beta) = \Sigma y_i; \tag{16}$$

and for the first moment,

$$\Sigma(\lambda x_i + \beta)x_i = \Sigma y_i x_i. \tag{17}$$

Equations (16) and (17) may be solved for λ and β. They are precisely the formulas (15) with which we are familiar.

We should state, in passing, that the constants, N, $\bar{x}$, and σ_x, used in fitting a normal curve to a frequency distribution, represent the zeroth, first, and second moments of the distribution.

10. Application to time series. The data for the ages of entrance of Harvard freshmen (Table XI–1) contained equally spaced values of x. This fact simplified the subsequent calculation materially. However, all the methods and formulas discussed thus far are applicable to data for which the x-intervals are not equal.

The data just referred to also furnish an example of a time series, and in such series the time intervals are usually equal. The determination of the trend of a time series is an important procedure in statistics and deserves additional attention. We shall restrict our discussion to linear trends for which the time intervals are equal.

If we let the successive values of the time be $x_1, x_2, x_3, \cdots x_N$, we may write:

$$\bar{x} = \frac{x_1 + x_N}{2}. \tag{18}$$

In other words, the mean value of a set of numbers arranged in arithmetical progression is half the sum of the first and the last. (See Section XII–17.) The x's represent either instants of time or intervals of time. In either case, we represent x_1, x_2, x_3, $\cdots x_N$ by equally spaced points on the x-axis. $\bar{x}$ is not only the arithmetic mean; it is also a mid-value or median, which belongs to the given set of x's if N is odd, or is midway between the two middle ones if N is even. For example, in the third column of Table XI–1, the values $x = 0, 5, 10, \cdots 40$ may be interpreted to designate the mid-points of each five-year interval, since the ages given are averages for these intervals. $\bar{x} = \frac{1}{2}(0 + 40) = 20$, so that $\bar{x}$ belongs to the set of given x's and is the middle one. In the fourth column of Table XI–2, the values $x = 0, 1, 2, \cdots 35$ correspond to the fifteenth of the month. Here $\bar{x} = \frac{1}{2}(0 + 35) = 17\frac{1}{2}$, so that $\bar{x}$ does not belong to the set of x's given.

When the time series contains a fairly large number of items, the computation of λ and β by means of formulas (10) and (6) can be further simplified. We illustrate with the time series of Table XI–2. Assuming the month as the unit on the x-axis, we designate the 36 successive months given by the numbers 0, 1, 2, $\cdots$ 35. $\bar{x} = 17\frac{1}{2}$ and $k = 1$, so that the successive values of t are $-\frac{35}{2}$, $-\frac{33}{2}$, $-\frac{31}{2}$, $\cdots \frac{31}{2}, \frac{33}{2}, \frac{35}{2}$ (Column 5). We do not need to compute a column, t_i^2, in order to evaluate the denominator of λ' in (10) as we did in Table XI–1, for the second of the following two formulas is applicable here:

$$1^2 + 2^2 + 3^2 + \cdots + N^2 = \frac{N(N + 1)(2N + 1)}{6}, \qquad (19)$$

$$1^2 + 3^2 + 5^2 + \cdots + (2N - 1)^2 = \frac{N(2N - 1)(2N + 1)}{3}. \qquad (20)$$

The proofs of these formulas will not be given here, but they may be established easily by means of mathematical induction, as well as by other methods. In Column 5, we see that

$$\Sigma t_i^2 = 2[(\tfrac{1}{2})^2 + (\tfrac{3}{2})^2 + (\tfrac{5}{2})^2 + \cdots + (\tfrac{35}{2})^2],$$

or that

$$\Sigma t_i^2 = \tfrac{1}{2}[1^2 + 3^2 + 5^2 + \cdots + 35^2].$$

According to (20), the last number, $(2N - 1)$, in the series is 35:

$$2N - 1 = 35,$$

or
$$N = 18.$$

TABLE XI–2

AVERAGE PRICE OF MILK PER 100 POUNDS (*Data of Figure III–9*)

(1)	(2)	(3)	(4)	(5)	(6)
		Price		$x_i - \dfrac{35}{2}$	
Year	Month (15th)	in Dollars			
		y_i	x_i	t_i	$2t_iy_i$
1930	Jan.	2.53	0	$-35/2$	-88.55
	Feb.	2.44	1	$-33/2$	-80.52
	Mar.	2.38	2	$-31/2$	-73.78
	Apr.	2.35	3	$-29/2$	-68.15
	May	2.28	4	$-27/2$	-61.56
	June	2.22	5	$-25/2$	-55.50
	July	2.15	6	$-23/2$	-49.45
	Aug.	2.18	7	$-21/2$	-45.78
	Sept.	2.25	8	$-19/2$	-42.75
	Oct.	2.30	9	$-17/2$	-39.10
	Nov.	2.31	10	$-15/2$	-34.65
	Dec.	2.20	11	$-13/2$	-28.60
1931	Jan.	2.04	12	$-11/2$	-22.44
	Feb.	1.96	13	$-9/2$	-17.64
	Mar.	1.92	14	$-7/2$	-13.44
	Apr.	1.85	15	$-5/2$	-9.25
	May	1.73	16	$-3/2$	-5.19
	June	1.66	17	$-1/2$	-1.66
	July	1.62	18	$1/2$	1.62
	Aug.	1.64	19	$3/2$	4.92
	Sept.	1.70	20	$5/2$	8.50
	Oct.	1.72	21	$7/2$	12.04
	Nov.	1.73	22	$9/2$	15.57
	Dec.	1.67	23	$11/2$	18.37
1932	Jan.	1.56	24	$13/2$	20.28
	Feb.	1.49	25	$15/2$	22.35
	Mar.	1.43	26	$17/2$	24.31
	Apr.	1.39	27	$19/2$	26.41
	May	1.29	28	$21/2$	27.09
	June	1.17	29	$23/2$	26.91
	July	1.20	30	$25/2$	30.00
	Aug.	1.21	31	$27/2$	32.67
	Sept.	1.25	32	$29/2$	36.25
	Oct.	1.28	33	$31/2$	39.68
	Nov.	1.26	34	$33/2$	41.58
	Dec.	1.26	35	$35/2$	44.10
TOTALS		64.62			-305.36

Hence, by (20),

$$\Sigma t_i^2 = \frac{1}{2}\left(\frac{(18 \cdot 35 \cdot 37)}{3}\right),$$

or $\qquad \Sigma t_i^2 = 3885.$

To avoid carrying fractions, we place in the sixth column the values $2t_i y_i$. Then,

$$\Sigma t_i y_i = \tfrac{1}{2}\Sigma 2t_i y_i$$
$$= \tfrac{1}{2}(-305.36)$$
$$= -152.7.$$

From formulas (10), we find:

$$\lambda' = \frac{\Sigma t_i y_i}{\Sigma t_i^2}$$

$$= \frac{-152.7}{3885} = -0.0393,$$

$$\beta' = \bar{y}$$

$$= \frac{64.62}{36} = 1.80,$$

and the equation of the trend line in terms of y and t is:

$$y = -0.0393t + 1.80.$$

To obtain the equation in x and y, we substitute

$$t = x - \frac{35}{2}$$

in the last equation:

$$y = -0.0393\ (x - 17.5) + 1.80$$
$$= -0.0393x + 2.49.$$

This trend line is shown in Figure XI–9, together with the graph of the prices. The figure should be compared with Figure III–9, where the graph of moving averages is shown. It should be observed that the slope -0.0393 is negative, which indicates a downward trend.

The data of milk prices just used contained an even number of items, 36, so that formula (20) was used to shorten the computation. Table XI–1 may be used to illustrate the use of formula (19), although the odd number of items, 9, is so small as to render the use of this formula unnecessary. From this table,

$$\Sigma t_i^2 = 2(1^2 + 2^2 + 3^2 + 4^2).$$

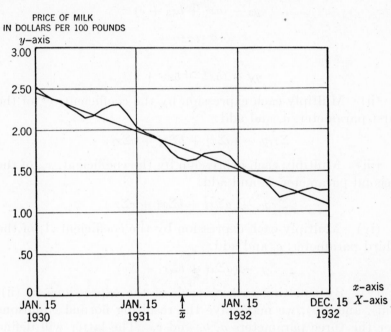

PRICE OF MILK
IN DOLLARS PER 100 POUNDS

FIG. XI-9. TREND LINE FOR MILK PRICES. (See Table XI-2.)

Here the last number, N, in the series is 4. From (19), then,

$$\Sigma t_i^2 = 2\left(\frac{4 \cdot 5 \cdot 9}{6}\right)$$
$$= 60,$$

which, of course, agrees with the sum previously found.

11. Fitting a parabola. When there are indications that a set of points exhibits a parabolic trend, as in Figure XI–2, the fitting of a quadratic function:

$$y = ax^2 + bx + c \tag{20}$$

to the data may be carried out either by the method of least squares or by the method of moments.   Using the former, we outline the work as follows:

(i)   Write the N expressions:

$$y_1 - (ax_1^2 + bx_1 + c)$$
$$y_2 - (ax_2^2 + bx_2 + c)$$
$$y_3 - (ax_3^2 + bx_3 + c)$$

$$\cdot \quad \cdot \quad \cdot$$
$$\cdot \quad \cdot \quad \cdot$$
$$\cdot \quad \cdot \quad \cdot$$

$$y_N - (ax_N^2 + bx_N + c)$$

(ii)   Multiply each expression by the coefficient, x_i^2, of the first parameter, a, and add:

$$\Sigma x_i^2 y_i - (a\Sigma x_i^4 + b\Sigma x_i^3 + c\Sigma x_i^2).$$

(iii)   Multiply each expression by the coefficient, x_i, of the second parameter, b, and add:

$$\Sigma x_i y_i - (a\Sigma x_i^3 + b\Sigma x_i^2 + c\Sigma x_i).$$

(iv)   Multiply each expression by the coefficient, 1, of the third parameter, c, and add:

$$\Sigma y_i - (a\Sigma x_i^2 + b\Sigma x_i + Nc).$$

(v)   By equating to zero each of the expressions in (ii), (iii), and (iv), we may solve the resulting normal equations for the three parameters a, b, and c.   The latter will define the best-fitting parabola (20).

In the case of a series with equispaced x's, the preceding equations can be simplified by the familiar transformation:

$$t = \frac{x - \bar{x}}{k},$$

and by the fact that:

$$\bar{x} = \tfrac{1}{2}(x_1 + x_N).$$

The parabola (20) then assumes the form:

$$y = a't^2 + b't + c'.$$

Since $\qquad\qquad\qquad\qquad \Sigma t_i = 0$

and $\qquad\qquad\qquad\qquad \Sigma t_i^3 = 0,$

the three normal equations reduce to:

$$\left.\begin{array}{l} a'\Sigma t_i^4 \quad\quad + c'\Sigma t_i^2 = \Sigma t_i^2 y_i \\ \quad\quad b'\Sigma t_i^2 \quad\quad\quad = \Sigma t_i y_i \\ a'\Sigma t_i^2 \quad\quad + c'N \quad = \Sigma y_i \end{array}\right\} . \tag{21}$$

We illustrate the method with the data of Figure XI–2 and Table XI–3, which were selected from the more extensive time series of Exercise III–24.

TABLE XI–3

(1) Month (1932)	(2) Price in Cents y_i	(3) x_i	(4) $2t_i$	(5) $(2t_i)^2$	(6) $(2t_i)^4$	(7) $2t_i\, y_i$	(8) $(2t_i)^2 y_i$
Jan.	19	0	−11	121	14,641	−209	2,299
Feb.	17	1	−9	81	6,561	−153	1,377
Mar.	14	2	−7	49	2,401	−98	686
Apr.	14	3	−5	25	625	−70	350
May	15	4	−3	9	81	−45	135
June	14	5	−1	1	1	−14	14
July	15	6	1	1	1	15	15
Aug.	18	7	3	9	81	54	162
Sept.	21	8	5	25	625	105	525
Oct.	24	9	7	49	2,401	168	1,176
Nov.	30	10	9	81	6,561	270	2,430
Dec.	32	11	11	121	14,641	352	3,872
Totals	233			572	48,620	375	13,041

It is more convenient, when the number of items is even, to use values $2t_i$, as in Column 4, in order to avoid fractions in the calculations. $\bar{x} = \frac{1}{2}(0 + 11) = 5\frac{1}{2}$ and $k = 1$, so that $t_i = x_i - 5\frac{1}{2}$.

$$\Sigma y_i = 233;$$

$$\Sigma t_i^2 = \tfrac{1}{4}\Sigma(2t_i)^2$$

$$= \frac{572}{4} = 143;$$

$$\Sigma t_i^4 = \frac{1}{16}\Sigma(2t_i)^4$$

$$= \frac{48620}{16} = 3039;$$

$$\Sigma t_i y_i = \tfrac{1}{2}\Sigma(2t_i y_i)$$

$$= \frac{375}{2} = 187.5;$$

$$\Sigma t_i^2 y_i = \tfrac{1}{4}\Sigma(2t_i)^2 y_i$$

$$= \frac{13041}{4} = 3260.$$

Equations (21) become:

$$\left\{
\begin{aligned}
3039a' \quad & + 143c' = 3260 \\
143b' \quad & = 187.5 \\
143a' \quad & + 12c' = 233;
\end{aligned}
\right.$$

whence, $$b' = \frac{187.5}{143} = 1.31.$$

The first and third equations yield:

$$a' = 0.362,$$
$$c' = 15.1.$$

The desired parabola is, therefore:

$$y = 0.362t^2 + 1.31t + 15.1.$$

To obtain the equation of the parabola in terms of x, we substitute $t = x - 5\tfrac{1}{2}$ in the last equation:

$$y = 0.362(x - 5.5)^2 + 1.31(x - 5.5) + 15.1$$
$$= 0.362x^2 - 2.67x + 18.8.$$

By assigning convenient values, such as 0, 1, $\cdots$ 11, to x, computing the corresponding values of y, and plotting the corresponding points, we may construct the parabola. This has been done in Figure XI–2.

In the case of a series of equispaced x's with a large number of items, the calculations required may be simplified by formulas analogous to (19) and (20). (See, for example, Ref. 1, p. 123.)

12. The polynomial. Linear and quadratic functions of x are merely simple cases of the more general *rational integral function of x* or *polynomial in x.*

A polynomial in x is a function of the form:

$$a_0x^n + a_1x^{n-1} + a_2x^{n-2} + \cdots + a_{n-1}x + a_n,$$

where the a's are constant coefficients and n is a positive integer. The corresponding equation is:

$$y = a_0x^n + a_1x^{n-1} + a_2x^{n-2} + \cdots + a_{n-1}x + a_n. \qquad (22)$$

If $n = 1$, the polynomial is linear; if $n = 2$, quadratic; and so on.

The method of least squares may be used in fitting a polynomial to data. The normal equations will be $n + 1$ in number, one more than the degree of the polynomial. The procedure is merely an extension of that for the quadratic function, and, of course, involves increased calculation.

13. The compound interest law of nature. It may not seem possible that a compound interest table, the shell of the chambered nautilus, a particle of radium, and the population of the United States possess a common property which is of significant interest to statisticians, yet such is the case. Each exemplifies a general law of growth or decay, a law which is inherent in the fact that certain varying magnitudes change at a rate directly proportional to the magnitude itself. The rate of increase of the compound amount (principal plus interest) of an invested sum is proportional to the amount of that sum; the rate of growth of the nautilus depends upon its size; the rate of disintegration of radium varies with its mass; a population free to multiply may do so in proportion to its number.

The compound interest law of investment may be written in the form:

$$A_n = P(1 + i)^n, \qquad (23)$$

where P is the principal, n the number of conversion periods, i the interest rate per period expressed as a decimal, and A_n the final amount due after a term of n conversion periods. Thus, if \$100 is invested at 3 per cent compounded quarterly for 7 years, the rate per quarter is $\dfrac{0.03}{4}$ or 0.0075 ($\tfrac{3}{4}\%$), and the number of periods is 7×4 or 28, so that:

$$A_n = 100 \ (1.0075)^{28}$$

$$= \$123.27.$$

The amount of 1 at $\frac{3}{4}$ per cent for 28 periods is found from Table G of the Supplement. If we imagine the number of conversion periods to increase indefinitely, so that we conceive of interest as being compounded, not quarterly, not monthly, not weekly, not daily, but instantaneously, it can be shown that formula (23) assumes the form:

$$A_n = Pe^{in}. \qquad (24)$$

Thus, if interest is added continuously at a rate always proportional to the compound amount, A_n, the compound interest law becomes the exponential law (24). Note that n need no longer be an integer; it may represent *any* period of time.

Instead of using the symbols of formula (24), let us write the more general form of this law as:

$$y = Ae^{Bx}. \qquad (25)$$

Here y and x are the variables and A and B are the parameters, just as in (24) A_n and n are the variables and P and i are assumed given. Equation (25) epitomizes the "compound interest law of nature," sometimes called the "snowball law," since a snowball rolled in the snow increases its size more rapidly as it gets larger.

The continuous growth of an organism at a rate involving the exponential law (25) is an important biological phenomenon. It has been verified for such widely different cases as the bodily growth of frogs and white rats, change of size of a hen's egg with successive layings, the change of milk production with the age of dairy cattle,* the configuration of the shell of the pearly nautilus, and so on. Population growths exhibit phases governed, in part at least, by the exponential law. This is true not only for human populations, but also for insect and bacteriological populations. Epidemics may spread "exponentially."

---

*See Raymond Pearl, *Studies in Human Biology*, Williams and Wilkins, Baltimore, 1924, pp. 561-562.

Growths in business may, for a time, be exponential, especially where the particular product involved meets a great demand and there is little competition.

It seems, then, that we are justified in considering a bit further trends which are exponential in character.

14. Exponential and logarithmic functions. Equation (25) is an exponential equation, but we may transform it by taking the logarithms of both sides:

$$\log y = \log Ae^{Bx}.$$

According to Theorem 1, Section II–12, we may write:

$$\log y = \log A + \log e^{Bx};$$

and by Theorem 3 of the same Section:

$$\log y = \log A + Bx \log e.$$

If we replace $\log y$ by Y and the constants $\log A$ and $B \log e$ by β and λ, respectively, we obtain:

$$Y = \lambda x + \beta, \tag{26}$$

which defines a straight line.

The straight line (26) may be fitted to the given set of points $(x_i,\ Y_i)$ where $Y_i = \log y_i$, by the methods discussed earlier in this chapter. Such a straight line is not the precise mathematical equivalent of the exponential curve accurately fitted to the points $(x_i,\ y_i)$, but is good enough for many purposes.

It is possible to detect an exponential trend by plotting the ordinates $(x_i,\ Y_i)$, where $Y_i = \log y_i$, with the aid of semi-logarithmic paper. The points are then joined with line segments. If the resulting graph is approximately linear, we may assume the data to exhibit an exponential trend. The student should read again at this juncture Section III–9. Of course, the graph thus plotted is not the same as a straight line fitted by standard methods. We recall that a linear configuration on semi-logarithmic paper is a criterion for constant ratios or rates, and is often called a *ratio chart*. If the observed y's corresponding to successive equally spaced x's, have reasonably constant ratios, each with the preceding, so that

$$\frac{y_2}{y_1} = \frac{y_3}{y_2} = \frac{y_4}{y_3} = \cdots = \frac{y_N}{y_{N-1}}, \text{ approximately,}$$

$$\log\left(\frac{y_2}{y_1}\right) = \log\left(\frac{y_3}{y_2}\right) = \log\left(\frac{y_4}{y_3}\right) = \cdots = \log\left(\frac{y_N}{y_{N-1}}\right).$$

By Theorem 2, Section II–12,

$$\log y_2 - \log y_1 = \log y_3 - \log y_2 = \log y_4 - \log y_3 = \cdots$$

$$= \log y_N - \log y_{N-1}$$

or $$\quad Y_2 - Y_1 = Y_3 - Y_2 = Y_4 - Y_3 = \cdots = Y_N - Y_{N-1}$$

Hence, the successive differences in the ordinates, Y_i, on the semi-logarithmic paper will be approximately constant. (Figure XI–10.)

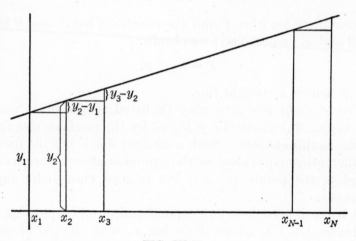

FIG. XI-10.

15. Double logarithmic paper. The equation:

$$y = Bx^\lambda \tag{27}$$

may be discussed by taking the logarithms of both sides:

$$\log y = \log Bx^\lambda$$

$$= \log B + \log x^\lambda$$

$$= \log B + \lambda \log x.$$

Let $X = \log x$, $Y = \log y$, and $\beta = \log B$.
Then,

$$Y = \lambda X + \beta. \tag{28}$$

Hence, if we employ ruled paper with logarithm scales along both axes and plot the values (X, Y), the resulting graph will be the straight line (28). There is occasional use for double logarithmic or "log-log" paper, especially in the case of income distribution, where skewness is often a strong characteristic. The Pareto curve* offers such an example.

16. Other exponential curves. The function composing the right-hand member of equation (25) may be considered a basis for the synthesis of more elaborate formulas aiming to describe data which possess certain exponential characteristics.

The *Gompertz* curve* is defined by the equation:

$$y = kg^{c^x}, \tag{29}$$

which may be written:

$$Y = K + Gc^x, \tag{30}$$

where $Y = \log y$, $K = \log k$, and $G = \log g$. This curve is valuable in describing a growth, particularly in business, which is characterized by an initially slow rate of increase, a later rapid rate, and finally a declining rate approaching stable conditions.

The *logistic* or *Pearl-Reed* curve* may be defined by an equation of the form:

$$y = \frac{1}{Ae^{Bx} + C}. \tag{31}$$

Its form is similar to the Gompertz curve. It has been used extensively to describe the growth of various biological populations.

17. The method of differences. The accompanying Table XI–4 is a *table of differences* formed for the polynomial:

$$P(x) = 2x^3 - 3x^2 + 5x - 1$$

when x assumes the values 1, 2, 3, 4, 5, and 6. Column 2 of

---

* See, for example, Ref. 2.

this table contains the computed values $P(1)$, $P(2)$, $P(3)$, $P(4)$, $P(5)$, and $P(6)$. For example,

$$P(2) = 2 \cdot 2^3 - 3 \cdot 2^2 + 5 \cdot 2 - 1$$
$$= 13.$$ (See Section X–1.)

TABLE XI-4

A TABLE OF DIFFERENCES

x	$P(x)$	Δ	Δ^2	Δ^3	Δ^4	Δ^5
1	3					
		10				
2	13		18			
		28		12		
3	41		30		0	
		58		12		0
4	99		42		0	
		100		12		
5	199		54			
		154				
6	353					

The third column, headed Δ, contains *first differences* obtained by subtracting each value of $P(x)$ from the one below. The column of *second differences*, designated Δ^2, is obtained by subtracting each first difference from the one below; and so on. It will be observed that the third differences are all equal, hence the differences of the fourth or higher order are all zero. An important theorem for our present purposes is the following. A proof may be found in Reference 1.

*The **n**th differences of a polynomial, **P**(**x**), of the **n**th degree are always constant provided the successive values of **x** form an arithmetical progression.*

Theoretically, the differences should enable us to decide what degree polynomial might be reasonably fitted to given data characterized by equally spaced x's. A column of fairly constant differences would indicate the degree to be used. Unfortunately, much data are so irregular that a test by differences alone reveals little.

However, when a properly selected curve has been fitted to given data, it may be employed to smooth or graduate the data, that is, to replace all irregular values by values following more closely the apparent general trend. For a polynomial of the nth degree, the given data may be graduated by adjusting the given ordinates so that their nth differences become approximately constant. There are many methods and formulas based on differences which may be used for graduation and interpolation. The *calculus of finite differences* forms a large and important field of mathematics with important applications in the natural sciences as well as in statistics.

The method of differences may be extended to many types of functions other than polynomials by means of transformations of variables. Thus, a set of values not having constant first differences may reveal such differences in their logarithms. Data of this type have already been discussed.

XI—Exercises

1. Find the slope of the line $y = 3x + 5$. Where does the line cross the y-axis? The x-axis? What is the value of y when $x = 10$?

2. Find the slope of the line $y = -1.15x - 2.13$. Where does the line cross the x-axis? The y-axis? What is the value of y when $x = 1.00$? When $x = -2.00$?

3. Find the slope of the line $y = 2.13x - 0.98$. Where does the line cross the y-axis? The x-axis? What is the value of y when $x = 0$? When $x = 10$? When $x = 1$?

* * *

Compute the equation of the trend line and construct the line for each of the series in Exercises 4–12, according to the method designated by your instructor.

4. Number of automobile accident claims paid by a certain insurance company:

Year................	1924	1925	1926	1927	1928	1929	1930
No. Claims...........	3612	4350	4903	5296	5775	5979	6536

5. Infant mortality rate (per 1000) in New York City:

Year.....	1926	1927	1928	1929	1930	1931	1932	1933	1934
Rate.....	67.8	55.9	65.5	58.5	57.2	55.6	50.9	58.2	52.2

6.　Average prices of 25 industrial stocks:

Year	1913	1914	1915	1916	1917	1918
Price	67	62	110	119	100	92

Year	1919	1920	1921	1922	1923	1924
Price	138	130	91	116	118	135

7.　Marriage rates per 1,000 of the population of the United States, 1887–1906.　(From *National Council of Teachers of Mathematics, Seventh Yearbook,* Teachers College, Columbia University, 1932, p. 130.)

Year	Rate	Year	Rate
1887	8.7	1897	8.9
1888	8.8	1898	8.8
1889	9.1	1899	9.0
1890	9.0	1900	9.3
1891	9.2	1901	9.6
1892	9.1	1902	9.8
1893	9.0	1903	10.1
1894	8.6	1904	9.9
1895	8.9	1905	10.0
1896	9.0	1906	10.5

8.　Revised index of physical production for all manufacturing in the United States, 1899–1926.　(From Paul H. Douglas, *Theory of Wages,* Macmillan, 1934, p. 176.)

Year	Index	Year	Index
1900	100	1914	171
1901	112	1915	187
1902	121	1916	218
1903	123	1917	219
1904	123	1918	237
1905	142	1919	210
1906	151	1920	224
1907	150	1921	181
1908	133	1922	229
1909	160	1923	260
1910	157	1924	247
1911	156	1925	274
1912	175	1926	285
1913	180		

9. Percentage of gold to stock of money in the United States, 1883–1931. (From *Statistical Abstract of the United States*, 1934, p. 218.)

Year	%	Year	%	Year	%
1883	36.9	1900	43.7	1917	56.7
1884	36.7	1901	44.8	1918	45.8
1885	38.3	1902	46.0	1919	40.5
1886	37.8	1903	46.0	1920	35.1
1887	40.1	1904	46.8	1921	40.1
1888	41.7	1905	46.5	1922	45.7
1889	41.0	1906	47.5	1923	46.5
1890	41.3	1907	46.4	1924	50.7
1891	38.5	1908	47.3	1925	52.5
1892	37.9	1909	47.6	1926	52.8
1893	34.4	1910	47.2	1927	52.9
1894	34.8	1911	48.6	1928	50.6
1895	35.0	1912	49.1	1929	50.6
1896	33.3	1913	49.5	1930	54.6
1897	36.5	1914	49.8	1931	54.6
1898	41.6	1915	49.0		
1899	44.0	1916	53.8		

10. Average yield per acre of wheat. (See Ex. III–27.)

11. Homicide rate. (See Ex. III–28.)

12. Average weekly car loadings. (See Ex. III–26.)

*   *   *

Fit parabolas to the data in Exercises 13–16.

13. The points $(-4, 0)$, $(0, 6)$, $(4, 8)$, $(8, 7)$, $(10, 3)$, $(12, 0)$.

14. Average price of eggs for 1934. (See Ex. III–24.)

15. Earnings of banks. (d) Other earnings. (See Ex. VII–6.)

16. Index numbers of prices received by farmers for cotton and cottonseed:

Year............	1921	1922	1923	1924	1925	1926
Index Number....	101	156	216	212	177	122

*   *   *

17. The rate of growth of a yeast colony has been measured by observing the rate of production of carbon dioxide. The following readings were taken:

Time (t)	Manometer Reading in cm.
0	2.05
4	3.8
5	4.4
6	5.15
9.1	8.25
9.4	8.65
10.6	10.2
10.8	10.4

Show that the rate follows an exponential law. Use two-cycle semi-logarithmic paper. (Adapted from Arthur Slator, "The Rate of Fermentation by Growing Yeast Cells," *The Biochemical Journal*, Vol. VII, p. 203.)

18. Investigation of the rate of dying of cells and organisms reveals that the curve of disappearance has a logarithmic character. The constant of decrease, Z, for man is shown in the table below, and is seen to increase rapidly with the age. Plot on three-cycle semi-logarithmic paper the value of log $(Z - 0.00110)$ against age. The law has been shown to be of the type $Z = a + e^{kx}$. (Arthur Slator, "A Note on the Lag-Phase in the Growth of Micro-organisms." *The Journal of Hygiene*, Vol. XVI, pp. 105–106.)

Age	Z
20	.00199
30	.00292
40	.00520
50	.00849
60	.0159
70	.0325
80	.0716
90	.150
100	.276

19. Construct graphs on semi-logarithmic paper for such data of Exercises III: 29–34 as were not used for this purpose earlier, as directed by your instructor. Indicate cases where the function involved does not appear to be exponential or logarithmic in character.

20. The readings of a cooling body at 20-second intervals were found to yield the following temperatures. Plot the values on semi-logarithmic paper. What can you say about the law of cooling?

Time.........	0	20	40	60	80	100	120
Temperature....	26°	23.5°	21.8°	20.8°	19.4°	17.5°	16.0°

21. Show that the method of moments applied to the fitting of the parabola (20) leads to the same equations as those in (ii), (iii), and (iv) of Section XI–11.

22. The litter size, N, and the average litter weight, W, at birth of gray Norwegian rats are given in the table below. Plot log W against log N by means of 2×2 cycle double logarithmic paper. (Adapted from Helen D. King, "Birth Weight in the Gray Norway Rat," *Anatomical Record*, Vol. 63, p. 339, and W. J. Crozier, "On the Relation between Birth Weight and Litter Size in Mice," *Journal of General Physiology*, Vol. 23, pp. 309–320.)

Litter Size (N)	Average Litter Weight (W)
1.................	5.6
2.................	11.2
3.................	16.8
4.................	22.1
5.................	27.2
6.................	32.2
7.................	37.6
8.................	42.7
9.................	47.2
10.................	51.7
11.................	56.9
12.................	58.7
13.................	66.8
15.................	73.0

CHAPTER

XII

CORRELATION

❖⫴⫴⫴❖

"It is evident that the understanding of relations is a major concern of all men and women."

CASSIUS J. KEYSER, *Mole Philosophy*.

1. Introduction. Our statistical data up to this point have, in general, consisted of sets of measurements or observations concerned with a *single* variable. Thus, we have been interested from time to time in a single characteristic of English criminals—their head lengths. Other attributes, however, might have been associated with the same group of criminals—their heights, weights, ages, shoe sizes, and so on. Occasionally, also, our attention has been engaged with the price of milk for a series of months. Other variables might also have been associated with the same series of months, such as the price of eggs, the consumption of butter, or the rainfall. Correlation may be defined as "the amount of similarity, in direction and degree, of variations in corresponding pairs of observations of two variables." The principal problem of simple correlation is that of determining the degree of association between these pairs of observations. When more than two variables or characteristics are involved, the problem belongs to the field of *multiple correlation*. As an example of the latter, we might study the interrelation of the weights,

276

heights, and ages of a group of boys.   The present chapter is
concerned mainly with simple correlation.

   2. The scatter diagram.   Consider, for example, the data
of Table XII–1.   The birth rate and the per capita property
value are given for 24 states.   What is the degree of relationship between these two characteristics of the states?   A first
approach to the problem may be made graphically.   The

TABLE XII–1

BIRTH RATES OF NATIVE-BORN WHITES PER 1,000 ENUMERATED FEMALE
POPULATION, 1920, AND PER CAPITA ESTIMATED VALUE OF
ALL PROPERTY, 1922, BY STATES (From Raymond Pearl,
The Biology of Population Growth, Knopf, 1925, p. 160.)

State	Birth Rate	Per Capita Value of All Property
Connecticut	31.2	$3614
Massachusetts	33.2	3243
New York	33.5	3436
District of Columbia	33.9	3879
California	34.7	4007
New Hampshire	37.0	3074
Vermont	39.1	2389
Oregon	39.5	4182
Ohio	39.9	3048
Washington	41.0	3600
Maine	41.3	2586
Pennsylvania	42.0	3187
Indiana	43.8	2942
Wisconsin	45.4	2887
Kansas	46.4	3493
Maryland	47.1	2665
Michigan	47.7	2899
Minnesota	48.5	3442
Nebraska	49.8	4004
Kentucky	55.1	1459
Virginia	56.7	2050
South Carolina	59.1	1385
North Carolina	64.2	1703
Utah	64.5	3247

values of the birth rate are designated by x_i and those of the
per capita property value by y_i, and the 20 points (x_i, y_i) are
plotted.   The resulting aggregate of points, called a *scatter
diagram*, is then examined for a possible trend.   Study of

Figure XII–1 or of Figure XI–3 shows that there is apparently a slight downward trend, that is, a tendency for low per capita property values to be associated with high birth rates, but the trend is by no means strongly marked in the diagram.

    3. The lines of regression. Let us assume that we have a set of N values, (x_i, y_i), with corresponding points. Let us find the equation of the trend line, defined in the preceding chapter as that line for which the sum of the squares of the

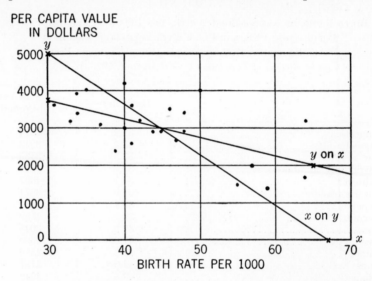

FIG. XII-1. SCATTER DIAGRAM FOR BIRTH RATES AND PER CAPITA PROPERTY VALUE. (Data of Table XII-1.)

vertical distances of the points from it is a minimum. Let

$$X_i = x_i - \bar{x}, \\ Y_i = y_i - \bar{y}. \Big\}$$

$$(1)$$

Thus, the origin, O, has been translated to a new origin, O', whose (x, y)-coordinates are $(\bar{x}, \bar{y})$. This means that the X_i's and Y_i's measure deviations from the means. (Figure XII–2.)

$$\Sigma X_i = 0; \qquad (2)$$

$$\Sigma Y_i = 0. \qquad \text{(Why?)}$$

Also,
$$\Sigma X_i^2 = N\sigma_x^2; \tag{3}$$
$$\Sigma Y_i^2 = N\sigma_y^2. \quad \text{[See (4), Section VIII–5.]}$$

Hence, equations (5) of XI–6 become:
$$\left.\begin{array}{l} \lambda' = \dfrac{\Sigma X_i Y_i}{N\sigma_x^2}; \\[2mm] \beta' = 0. \end{array}\right\} \tag{4}$$

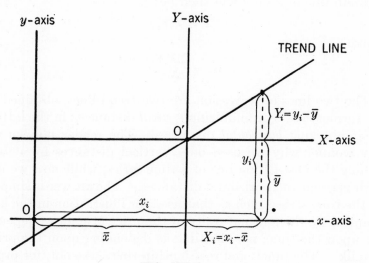

FIG. XII-2.

We shall write $\lambda_x = \lambda'$. Note that a translation of axes never affects the slope of a line. The equation of the trend line
$$y = \lambda x + \beta.$$
becomes:
$$Y = \lambda_x X, \tag{5}$$
where
$$\lambda_x = \lambda' = \frac{\Sigma X_i Y_i}{N\sigma_x^2}. \tag{6}$$

This line passes through the origin $(0, 0)$ of the (X, Y)-axes, which is the point $(\bar{x}, \bar{y})$ of the original (x, y)-axes. In the theory of correlation, this line is called the *line of regression of y on x*.

A companion line to the one just defined is the *line of regression of x on y*, which may be defined as that line for which the sum of the squares of the *horizontal* distances of the points from it is a minimum. The problem of finding the equation of this line involves nothing new. It requires merely an exchange in the roles of the x- and the y-axes. Hence, the desired equations may be obtained by replacing X by Y and Y by X in equations (5) and (6). The equation of the regression line of x on y will then be:

$$X = \lambda_y Y, \tag{7}$$

where

$$\lambda_y = \frac{\Sigma X_i Y_i}{N\sigma_y^2}. \tag{8}$$

The two lines of regression are two trend lines, obtained in the former case by minimizing *vertical* distances; in the latter, by minimizing *horizontal* distances. The reader may properly wonder why we used only vertical distances for determining the best-fitting line of a time series, while now we use both vertical and horizontal distances. The answer is simple. In the time series, such as that used for illustration in the last chapter, we thought naturally of the price of milk as depending upon the time, not the time as depending upon the price of milk. The functional relationship there was not, for practical statistical purposes, a reversible one. We sought, therefore, a line which minimized the squares of the deviations of actual milk prices from theoretical milk prices as represented by certain ordinates on the line.

In the case of birth rates and per capita valuation, we cannot say that the birth rate depends upon the per capita value any more than we can say that the per capita value depends upon the birth rate. Do people have more children when they possess less or do people possess less when they have more children? Here the functional relationship, assuming that such exists, is, from the statistical standpoint, a reversible one. For this reason, we shall study two trend or regression lines rather than one. The dependence of one variable *on* another can be described in terms of a regression line. The association *between* two variables is described by the word *correlation*, and is usually measured by a quantity known as the *coefficient of correlation*.

4.　The coefficient of correlation.　Let us define the symbol, r, to be called the coefficient of correlation, by means of the formula:

$$r = \frac{\Sigma X_i Y_i}{N \sigma_x \sigma_y}. \tag{9}$$

We note first that the formula is symmetric; that is to say, if we replace the x's by their corresponding y's and the y's by their corresponding x's, the formula remains unchanged. Thus, the reversibility of the functional relationship, the "co-relation," so to speak, is inherent in the formula.　The numerator, $\Sigma X_i Y_i$, is called the *product moment*, and sometimes the *co-variance*.

From equations (1), we see that:

$$
\begin{aligned}
r &= \frac{\Sigma X_i Y_i}{N \sigma_x \sigma_y} \\
&= \frac{1}{N} \Sigma \left(\frac{x_i - \bar{x}}{\sigma_x} \right) \left(\frac{y_i - \bar{y}}{\sigma_y} \right),
\end{aligned} \tag{9a}
$$

so that r is seen to be the arithmetic mean of the products of corresponding values of the two sets of variates expressed as standard variates.

Since

$$
\begin{cases}
\lambda_x = \dfrac{\Sigma X_i Y_i}{N \sigma_x^2} \\[2mm]
\lambda_y = \dfrac{\Sigma X_i Y_i}{N \sigma_y^2},
\end{cases}
$$

we find from formula (9) that:

$$
\left.
\begin{aligned}
\lambda_x &= r \frac{\sigma_y}{\sigma_x} \\[2mm]
\lambda_y &= r \frac{\sigma_x}{\sigma_y}
\end{aligned}
\right\}. \tag{10}
$$

Hence, the equations of the lines of regression become:

$$Y = r\frac{\sigma_y}{\sigma_x}X, \quad \text{for } y \text{ on } x,$$
$$X = r\frac{\sigma_x}{\sigma_y}Y, \quad \text{for } x \text{ on } y.$$

$$(11)$$

In terms of the original variables, these equations may be written as:

$$y - \bar{y} = r\frac{\sigma_y}{\sigma_x}(x - \bar{x}),$$
$$x - \bar{x} = r\frac{\sigma_x}{\sigma_y}(y - \bar{y});$$

$$(11a)$$

or as

$$\frac{y - \bar{y}}{\sigma_y} = r\frac{x - \bar{x}}{\sigma_x},$$
$$\frac{x - \bar{x}}{\sigma_x} = r\frac{y - \bar{y}}{\sigma_y}.$$

$$(11b)$$

5. The properties of r. The sum of the squares of the vertical distances, d_i^2, of all points, (X_i, Y_i), from the regression line, $Y = \lambda_x X$, is (Section XI–7):

$$\Sigma d_i^2 = \Sigma(Y_i - \lambda_x X_i)^2 \qquad (12)$$
$$= \Sigma Y_i^2 - 2\lambda_x \Sigma X_i Y_i + \lambda_x^2 \Sigma X_i^2.$$

From (6), we find that:

$$\lambda_x N\sigma_x^2 = \Sigma X_i Y_i;$$

hence, (12) becomes:

$$\Sigma(Y_i - \lambda_x X_i)^2 = \Sigma Y_i^2 - 2\lambda_x^2 N\sigma_x^2 + \lambda_x^2 \Sigma X_i^2. \qquad (12a)$$

Replacing λ_x by its value in (10) and ΣX_i^2 and ΣY_i^2 by their values in (3), equation (12a) becomes:

$$\Sigma(Y_i - \lambda_x X_i)^2 = N\sigma_y^2 - 2r^2 N\sigma_y^2 + r^2 N\sigma_y^2,$$

which reduces to:

$$\Sigma(Y_i - \lambda_x X_i)^2 = N\sigma_y^2(1 - r^2). \qquad (13)$$

This equation may be written as:

$$\frac{1}{N}\Sigma d_i^2 = \sigma_y^2(1 - r^2),$$

or as $$S_y^2 = \sigma_y^2(1 - r^2). \tag{13a}$$

The quantity $S_y^2 = \dfrac{1}{N}\Sigma d_i^2$ is a sort of standard deviation. S_y is called the *standard error of estimate* of the y's. It is a measure of the deviations of the observed or empirical y's from the corresponding estimated or theoretical y's, the latter being ordinates of points on the regression line.

In a similar manner, the sum of the squares of the horizontal distances of the points (X_i, Y_i) from the line $X = \lambda_y Y$ can be shown to be:

$$\Sigma(X_i - \lambda_y Y_i)^2 = N\sigma_x^2(1 - r^2). \tag{14}$$

The standard error of estimate of the x's denoted by S_x is analogously found from the formula:

$$S_x^2 = \sigma_x^2(1 - r^2). \tag{14a}$$

Since the sum of the squares on the left of both (13) and (14) cannot be negative, the value of r^2 cannot exceed 1, and hence r is restricted to the range of values running from -1 to $+1$ inclusive.

The sum of the squares in both (13) and (14) is obviously a maximum when $r = 0$. When $r = 0$, the equations (11) reduce to:

$$\begin{cases} Y = 0, \\ X = 0, \end{cases}$$

which are merely the equations of the (X, Y)-axes. It will be recalled that these axes were originally drawn through the point $(\bar{x}, \bar{y})$ as origin. When r equals either $+1$ or -1, the sum of the squares in both (13) and (14) is zero, a minimum; hence, all points must lie on both lines of regression. The only way in which this can happen is to have the lines coincide. Reference to equations (11) shows that when r equals either $+1$ or -1, the lines of regression are identical.

The slopes λ_x and λ_y depend upon r, as we see by (10). When r is positive, the slope is also, and the lines of regression ascend from the lower left-hand quadrant to the upper right-hand quadrant. [Figures XII–3 (a), (b).]   When r is negative, the slope is also, and the lines of regression descend from the upper left-hand quadrant to the lower right [Figure XII–3 (c)].   When r is numerically very small, the line of regression of y on x is close to the X-axis.   Similarly, the line of regression of x on y is close to the Y-axis.   [Figure XII–3 (a).]   When r is near ± 1, the lines very nearly coincide. [Figure XII–3 (c).]   When $r = \pm 1$, the lines coincide.   [Figure XII–3 (d).]

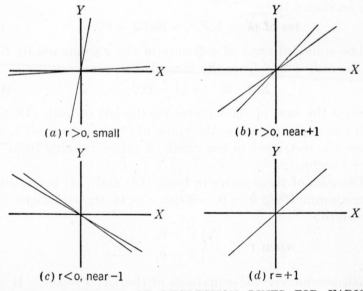

(a) r > 0, small   (b) r > 0, near +1

(c) r < 0, near −1   (d) r = +1

FIG. XII-3. POSITIONS OF REGRESSION LINES FOR VARIOUS
VALUES OF r.

Thus, as r varies from 0 to either $+1$ or -1, the lines of regression rotate from positions on the axes toward each other until they coincide.   Consequently, the amount of divergence between the two lines of regression gives a simple visual measure of the correlation.

It can be shown, from the equations (11b), *when standard variables are used,* $t_x = \dfrac{x - \bar{x}}{\sigma_x}$, $t_y = \dfrac{y - \bar{y}}{\sigma_y}$, that the two regression lines always have symmetrical positions with respect to the line bisecting the quadrants through which they pass. This means that the line of regression of y on x makes the same angle with the positive t_x-axis that the line of regression of x on y makes with the positive t_y-axis. (Figure XII–4.)

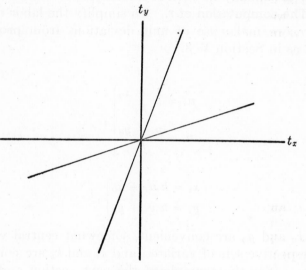

FIG. XII-4.

From (9) it is seen, since N, σ_x, and σ_y are always positive, that the sign of r is the same as the sign of the product-moment or co-variance, $\Sigma X_i Y_i$. If, in general, x and y increase together, the deviations X and Y will, in general, be of the same sign, and $\Sigma X_i Y_i$ will be positive. The points (X_i, Y_i) will be largely in the upper right-hand and lower left-hand quadrants. On the other hand, if large values of x go with small values of y, and vice versa, most of the deviations X and Y will be of opposite sign, and $\Sigma X_i Y_i$ will be negative. The points (X_i, Y_i) will lie mainly in the upper left-hand and lower right-hand quadrants. When r is positive, the lines of regression ascend from left to right; when r is negative, they descend.

From the preceding paragraphs, it appears that the closer the points lie to a line of regression, the more nearly does a simple linear equation express the association between the values of x and y. Thus, a correlation coefficient of nearly 1 (or -1) would seem to indicate a definite relationship between two given sets of values; a coefficient near zero would seem to indicate practically no such relationship.

6. The computation of r. To simplify the labor of calculating r, we make use of unit deviations from provisional means, as in Section V–3.

Let

$$\left.\begin{aligned} u_i &= \frac{x_i - x_0}{k_x} \\ v_i &= \frac{y_i - y_0}{k_y} \end{aligned}\right\}, \tag{15}$$

so that

$$\left.\begin{aligned} x_i &= k_x u_i + x_0 \\ y_i &= k_y v_i + y_0 \end{aligned}\right\}, \tag{15a}$$

where x_0 and y_0 are convenient, somewhat central values in their respective sets of variates, and k_x and k_y are convenient divisors. (See the example of the next section and also of Section 10.) According to (1c) of Section V–3,

$$\left.\begin{aligned} \bar{u} &= \frac{\bar{x} - x_0}{k_x} \\ \bar{v} &= \frac{\bar{y} - y_0}{k_y} \end{aligned}\right\}, \tag{16}$$

so that

$$\left.\begin{aligned} \bar{x} &= k_x \bar{u} + x_0 \\ \bar{y} &= k_y \bar{v} + y_0 \end{aligned}\right\}. \tag{16a}$$

Let us take the formula:

$$r = \frac{1}{N}\Sigma\left(\frac{x_i - \bar{x}}{\sigma_x}\right)\left(\frac{y_i - \bar{y}}{\sigma_y}\right) \tag{9a}$$

and substitute the values given in (15a) and (16a):

$$r = \frac{1}{N}\Sigma\left[\frac{k_x u_i + x_0 - (k_x \bar{u} + x_0)}{\sigma_x}\right]\left[\frac{k_y v_i + y_0 - (k_y \bar{v} + y_0)}{\sigma_y}\right]$$

$$= \frac{1}{N}\Sigma\left[\frac{k_x(u_i - \bar{u})}{\sigma_x}\right]\left[\frac{k_y(v_i - \bar{v})}{\sigma_y}\right].$$

But by (8) of Section VIII–7, we know that

$$\left.\begin{array}{l}\sigma_x = k_x \sigma_u \\ \sigma_y = k_y \sigma_v\end{array}\right\}; \tag{17}$$

hence, we have:

$$r = \frac{1}{N}\Sigma\left(\frac{u_i - \bar{u}}{\sigma_u}\right)\left(\frac{v_i - \bar{v}}{\sigma_v}\right)$$

$$= \frac{1}{\sigma_u \sigma_v}\left[\frac{1}{N}\Sigma u_i v_i - \bar{v}\cdot\frac{1}{N}\Sigma u_i - \bar{u}\cdot\frac{1}{N}\Sigma v_i + \bar{u}\bar{v}\right]$$

$$= \frac{1}{\sigma_u \sigma_v}\left[\frac{1}{N}\Sigma u_i v_i - \bar{v}\bar{u} - \bar{u}\bar{v} + \bar{u}\bar{v}\right]$$

$$r = \frac{\dfrac{1}{N}\Sigma u_i v_i - \bar{u}\bar{v}}{\sigma_u \sigma_v}. \tag{18}$$

If we multiply the factors following the summation sign in (9a) as we did the corresponding ones just preceding, we can show, in like manner, that:

$$r = \frac{\dfrac{1}{N}\Sigma x_i y_i - \bar{x}\bar{y}}{\sigma_x \sigma_y}. \tag{19}$$

We thus have four important formulas for r: (9), (9a), (18), and (19). Formula (18), which involves unit deviations from provisional means, will prove to be the most generally useful one in computation.

7. The computation of r for ungrouped data. Let us compute the coefficient of correlation for the birth rates and per capita property values of Table XII–1. In order to simplify the computation, we round off the given data to two significant figures, as shown in the second and third columns of Table XII–2. The steps in the computation appear in this table.   Provisional means $x_0 = 45$ and $y_0 = 3000$ are selected; $k_x = 1$ and $k_y = 100$.

TABLE XII–2

COMPUTATION OF r FOR BIRTH RATE AND PER CAPITA PROPERTY VALUE

State	Birth Rate	Per Capita Value of All Property	$x_i - 45$	$\dfrac{y_i - 3000}{100}$			
	x_i	y_i	u_i	v_i	$u_i v_i$	u_i^2	v_i^2
Conn.	31	3600	−14	6	−84	196	36
Mass.	33	3200	−12	2	−24	144	4
N. Y.	34	3400	−11	4	−44	121	16
D. C.	34	3900	−11	9	−99	121	81
Cal.	35	4000	−10	10	−100	100	100
N. H.	37	3100	−8	1	−8	64	1
Vt.	39	2400	−6	−6	36	36	36
Ore.	40	4200	−5	12	−60	25	144
Ohio	40	3000	−5	0	0	25	0
Wash.	41	3600	−4	6	−24	16	36
Me.	41	2600	−4	−4	16	16	16
Penn.	42	3200	−3	2	−6	9	4
Ind.	44	2900	−1	−1	1	1	1
Wis.	45	2900	0	−1	0	0	1
Kan.	46	3500	1	5	5	1	25
Md.	47	2700	2	−3	−6	4	9
Mich.	48	2900	3	−1	−3	9	1
Minn.	48	3400	3	4	12	9	16
Neb.	50	4000	5	10	50	25	100
Ky.	55	1500	10	−15	−150	100	225
Va.	57	2000	12	−10	−120	144	100
S. C.	59	1400	14	−16	−224	196	256
N. C.	64	1700	19	−13	−247	361	169
Utah	64	3200	19	2	38	361	4
Totals	1074	72,300	−6	3	−1041	2084	1381

$$\begin{cases} \bar{u} = -\dfrac{6}{24} = -0.250. \\[2mm] \bar{v} = \dfrac{3}{24} = 0.125. \end{cases} \begin{cases} \sigma_u = \left[\dfrac{2084}{24} - (-0.250)^2\right]^{\frac{1}{2}} = (86.7)^{1/2} = 9.31 \\[2mm] \sigma_v = \left[\dfrac{1381}{24} - (0.125)^2\right]^{\frac{1}{2}} = (57.5)^{1/2} = 7.58 \end{cases}$$

$$r = \frac{\dfrac{1}{N}\Sigma uv - \overline{uv}}{\sigma_u \sigma_v},$$

$$= \frac{-\dfrac{1041}{24} - (-0.250)(0.125)}{9.32 \times 7.58} = -0.614.$$

The value of r computed with the aid of (18) would seem to indicate a fairly high degree of correlation, the negative sign implying that high per capita property values go, in general, with low birth rates. However, the mathematical result in this case, where N is a fairly small number, does not permit such a facile conclusion. We are faced here again with a problem in sampling. Twenty-four paired items constitute a fairly small sample from which to draw conclusions concerning a supposedly larger population or universe of paired variates. At this point we shall only say that further analysis would show that we might place a fairly high degree of confidence in the interpreted result. A question somewhat beyond the power of this book to answer is the following: Are birth rates and property values directly related to the extent measured by the value, $r = -0.61$, or are both attributes really dependent upon other variables, or latent factors, not revealed by the bare data of Table XII–1? The discussion of this question may be found in the source of this table.

8. The construction and use of the lines of regression. From the values found in Table XII–2, we may compute $\bar{x}$, $\bar{y}$, σ_x, and σ_y, and then the equations of the lines of regression.

$$\bar{u} = \frac{\bar{x} - x_0}{k_x} \qquad \text{and} \qquad \bar{v} = \frac{\bar{y} - y_0}{k_y}$$

$$-0.250 = \bar{x} - 45 \qquad\qquad 0.125 = \frac{\bar{y} - 3000}{100}$$

hence, $\qquad \bar{x} = 44.8, \qquad$ and $\qquad \bar{y} = 3012.$

From Section VIII–7, we recall formulas yielding the standard deviations:

$$\sigma_u^2 = \nu_{2u} - \bar{u}^2 \qquad\qquad \text{and} \qquad \sigma_v^2 = \nu_{2v} - \bar{v}^2$$

$$= \frac{2084}{24} - (-0.250)^2 \qquad\qquad = \frac{1381}{24} - (0.125)^2$$

$$= 86.7; \qquad\qquad\qquad = 57.5;$$

$$\sigma_x = k_x \sigma_u \qquad\qquad \text{and} \qquad \sigma_y = k_y \sigma_v$$

$$= (86.7)^{\frac{1}{2}} \qquad\qquad\qquad = 100(57.5)^{\frac{1}{2}}$$

$$= 9.31; \qquad\qquad\qquad = 758.$$

The equations of the lines of regression may now be written [See (11)]:

$$Y = r\frac{\sigma_y}{\sigma_x}X \qquad\qquad X = r\frac{\sigma_x}{\sigma_y}Y$$

$$Y = -0.614\left(\frac{758}{9.31}\right)X \qquad X = -0.614\left(\frac{9.31}{758}\right)Y$$

$$Y = -50.0X, \qquad\qquad X = -0.00754Y.$$

From (11a),
$$\begin{cases} y - 3012 = -50.0(x - 44.8) \\ x - 44.8 = -0.00754(y - 3012). \end{cases}$$

The last equations may be simplified a bit and written in the form:

$$\begin{cases} y = -50.0x + 5252 \\ x = -0.00754y + 67.5. \end{cases}$$

The regression lines are plotted in Figure XII–1, where the crosses indicate convenient points used to determine the lines. A check on the work is found by estimating the coordinates of the point of intersection of the lines. These should be $(\bar{x}, \bar{y})$ or (44.8, 3012).

The first of these equations may be interpreted thus: Given a birth rate for a state, the corresponding per capita property value, expressed in hundreds of dollars, is, *on an average*, estimated to be equal to minus 50.0 times the birth rate, plus 5252. The second of these equations may be similarly interpreted. Given a per capita property value, the corresponding birth rate is, *on an average*, estimated to be equal to minus 0.00754 times the given property value, plus 67.5. Thus, if a certain state has a birth rate of 36, its per capita property value is, on an average, about \$3452, for

$$\begin{aligned} y &= (-50.0 \times 36) + 5252 \\ &= 3452. \end{aligned}$$

The question of the reliability of these estimates in view of the values $r = -0.61$ and $N = 24$ will not be discussed here.

9. The correlation table. When the total number of paired values, N, is large, the method of computing r involves the classification of the data by means of a double-frequency

distribution or correlation table.   This consists of a rectangular array of squares or *cells* containing frequencies.   The frequency recorded in a given cell represents the number of items
belonging to a certain x-class and to a certain y-class simultaneously.   In Table XII–3, each cell frequency represents
the number of women students having simultaneously a certain weight and a certain height.   For example, there were
twelve students weighing from 110 to 120 pounds (class mark,
115), and ranging in height from 62.5 to 63.5 inches (class
mark, 63).   The first step in measuring the correlation between height and weight is to construct the correlation table
proper, which, in Table XII–3, consists of that portion
bounded by heavy lines.   If each cell frequency is replaced
by an appropriate number of dots, a scatter diagram results.
Whether we do this or not (and it is usually unnecessary), it
is generally possible to decide whether the assumption that
the trend is linear is a reasonable one or not.   In the example
under discussion, it appears that increasing height is associated with fairly steadily increasing weight, so that we may
safely assume the trend to be linear.   That is to say, we
assume that we may use "lines" of regression rather than
"curves" of regression.   (See Section XII–14.)

10.   The computation of r from a correlation table.   Table
XII–3 illustrates the method of calculating r when the total
frequency, N, is large enough to justify the use of a correlation table.   We designate the class marks (mid-values) for
the weights by x_i, and for the heights by y_j.   The class intervals are 10 (pounds) and 1 (inch), respectively; the provisional means are selected as 125 (pounds) and 64 (inches).
Then, by (15),

$$\begin{cases} u_i = \dfrac{x_i - 125}{10}, \\ v_i = y_i - 64. \end{cases}$$

The column headed f_y gives the frequencies or *marginal
totals* for the heights, y_j.   These are obtained by adding the
cell frequencies in each row.   The row labeled f_x yields the
frequencies or marginal totals for the weights, x_i.   These are

TABLE XII-3

Correlation Table for the Weights and Heights of 285 Boston University Women Students (*Original data.*)

Weights in Pounds

$x \rightarrow$ $y \downarrow$	85	95	105	115	125	135	145	155	165	175	185	195	205	f_v	v_j	$f_y v$	$f_y v^2$	$v_j \sum_i u$
57										1				1	−7	−7	49	−35
58														0	−6	0	0	0
59	1	3	4	2										7	−5	−35	175	70
60		3	8	1	5	3		1						13	−4	−52	208	92
61	1	3	2	4	11	3	2							18	−3	−54	162	54
62			7	8	13	6	1	1				1		34	−2	−68	136	48
63			7	12	14	10	6	2			1			41	−1	−41	41	8
64			8	8	15	11	4			1				49	0	0	0	0
65			1	10	10	6	5	2		1				42	1	42	42	12
66		1	2	9	4	8	5	3		1			1	36	2	72	144	22
67				2	2	2	2	1	1					24	3	72	216	114
68				1		4	1	1	1					9	4	36	144	48
69										1				7	5	35	175	65
70					1						1			1	6	6	36	30
71						1								2	7	14	98	42
72														1	8	8	64	8
f_x	2	10	39	57	75	54	26	11	2	5	2	1	1	285		28	1690	578
u_i	−4	−3	−2	−1	0	1	2	3	4	5	6	7	8					
$f_x u$	−8	−30	−78	−57	0	54	52	33	8	25	12	7	8	26				
$f_x u^2$	32	90	156	57	0	54	104	99	32	125	72	49	64	934				
$u_i \sum_i v$	32	75	148	16	0	62	74	51	36	25	42	−7	24	578				

Heights in Inches

292

$$\begin{cases} \bar{u} = \dfrac{26}{285} = 0.091. \\[2ex] \bar{v} = \dfrac{28}{285} = 0.098. \end{cases} \qquad \begin{cases} \sigma_u = \left[\dfrac{934}{285} - (0.091)^2\right]^{\frac{1}{2}} = 1.81. \\[2ex] \sigma_v = \left[\dfrac{1690}{285} - (0.098)^2\right]^{\frac{1}{2}} = 2.43. \end{cases}$$

$$\begin{cases} \bar{x} = 10(0.091) + 125 = 125.9. \\ \bar{y} = 0.098 + 64 = 64.1. \end{cases} \qquad \begin{cases} \sigma_x = 10 \times 1.81 = 18.1. \\ \sigma_y = 2.43. \end{cases}$$

$$r = \frac{\dfrac{578}{285} - (0.091)(0.098)}{1.81 \times 2.43} = 0.44.$$

obtained by adding the cell frequencies in each column. These two frequency distributions may be used for calculations already familiar. The total frequency, 285, may be obtained by either a horizontal addition of the values, f_x, or a vertical addition of the values, f_y. The two sums together give a valuable check on N. The column headed v_j and the row labeled u_i contain the unit deviations from the provisional means. The next two columns and the next two rows are used to compute the means and the standard deviation, as shown after the table. Only the last column and the last row offer unfamiliar calculations. The last column, headed $v_j\sum_j u$, is used to obtain $\sum uv$. Each product in this column is found by multiplying a v_j by the sum of the products of the various u's by the row frequencies corresponding to v_j. Thus, in the fifth row, $j = 5$, $y_5 = 61$; hence, $v_5 = -3$. The sum of the products of the u's in the jth row by their frequencies will be denoted by $\sum u$, where the subscript j under $\sum$ specifies the sum of the u's in the jth row, each u occurring the number of times indicated by the corresponding frequency.

$$\sum_5 u = (1 \times -4) + (3 \times -3) + (2 \times -2) + (4 \times -1) + (5 \times 0) + (3 \times 1) = -18.$$

Hence, for this row, $v_5\sum_5 u = (-3) \times (-18) = 54$. The sum of all products $v_j\sum_j u$ in the last column gives 578. This number is exactly the quantity $\sum uv$, which is theoretically obtained by multiplying a u by its paired v and then multiplying the product uv by its proper cell frequency. However, when products uv for which v is constant (in each row) are selected, the common factor v_j simplifies the arithmetical work considerably.

Similar methods and remarks apply in obtaining the last row, $u_i\underset{i}{\Sigma}v$. For example, the total, 51, obtained at the foot of the 155-pound column is obtained by multiplying the frequencies in this column by their corresponding v's, adding, and then multiplying the sum by the value $u_8 = 3$. Thus,

$$3\,[(1 \times -4) + (1 \times -1) + (2 \times 0) + (2 \times 2) + (3 \times 3) + (1 \times 4)$$
$$+ (1 \times 5)] = 51.$$

Since $v_j\underset{j}{\Sigma}u = u_i\underset{i}{\Sigma}v = 578$, we have again a valuable check on our computation. Formula (18) yields $r = 0.44$, as shown after Table XII–3. This value indicates a moderate degree of correlation, so that we may say that the tendency for the weights and heights of women students to increase together seems to be fairly well indicated. This conclusion can be verified to be valid, since the number N in the sample is large, 285. (See Section XIV–8.)

11. Remarks on the computation of r. (i) *Significant digits.* Data used in correlation problems usually involve not more than three significant digits and generally contain but two. From the hard practical standpoint, figures beyond the second decimal place in the value of r have little significance. A good working rule, therefore, is to use three significant figures in the computation and to round off r to the second decimal place.

(ii) *Grouping errors.* No exact rule can be stated concerning the values of N for which data should be grouped into a correlation table. When N is small, say below 100, or better, below 50, the direct method without a correlation table is generally advised.

In computing r from Table XII–3, we did not use the Sheppard's corrections for σ_x and σ_y. [Section VIII–8(v).] If we had, we should have found that σ_x (corrected) = 1.79, and that σ_y (corrected) = 2.41. These values would have changed r by 0.01 to 0.45, an unimportant correction. The correlation table used consists of 16 rows and 13 columns. We call this a 16×13 table. It has been shown that as long as a table has dimensions greater than 10×10, the error in r due to the grouping of the data into classes is not very large (about 4 per cent), and this error may be somewhat reduced by applying Sheppard's corrections to the standard deviations as illustrated above. It is doubtful if these corrections are worth while for N less than 1,000. When the table is reduced below the 10×10 requirement, the error in r increases and, in fact, may become so serious as to vitiate the result. Rather than apply cumbersome corrections to correlation tables of less than 10×10 dimensions, it is generally better to compute r without grouping the data, or else to apply, where feasible, other methods as yet not discussed.

Table XII–4 was formed from Table XII–3 by enlarging the class intervals from 10 to 20 pounds and from 1 inch to 3 inches. This gives us a 7×6 table. The value of r is thus changed from 0.44 to a less accurate value, 0.39. (See Ex. XII–11.)

TABLE XII–4

REDUCED CORRELATION TABLE FOR WEIGHTS AND HEIGHTS OF
WOMEN STUDENTS (*Data of Table* XII–3.)

Weights in Pounds

		90	110	130	150	170	190	210
	57					1		
	60	8	21	8	1			
Heights in Inches	63	3	50	57	12		2	
	66	1	24	54	19	3		1
	69		1	8	5	3		
	72			2			1	

(iii) *Calculating machines.* Improvements in the modern computing machine now permit the simultaneous calculation of the quantities Σx, Σy, Σx^2, $2\Sigma xy$, and Σy^2 from ungrouped data. Such a procedure eliminates the necessity for making correlation tables and avoids errors due to grouping. (See, for example, P. S. Dwyer, "The Calculation of Correlation Coefficients from Ungrouped Data with Modern Calculating Machines," *Journal of the American Statistical Association,* December, 1940.)

There are other methods of measuring correlation which will be mentioned later. (See Sections XII: 15–19.) The choice of method depends largely on the value of the total frequency, N, the form of the data, and the objective of the particular statistical investigation.

12. The interpretation of r. It is very easy for the beginner in statistics to place too much confidence in the value of r as an immediate valid measure of the degree of association between two variables. In particular, when N is small, say below 100, one must be careful not to place too much confidence in the value of r. The reason for this statement springs from the fact previously stated (Section IV–7), that the given data constitute a *random sample* assumed to be selected from a much larger, potentially infinite group. Characteristics associated with such samples fluctuate considerably. The smaller the samples, the more likely one is to obtain characteristics widely different from the general characteristics of the larger group. The larger the sample, the more nearly, on an average, does it reflect the characteristics of the larger group. Consequently, when N is small, all values of r should be regarded with suspicion, at least until further analysis of the sampling errors involved is completed.

A fairly recently developed theory of the reliability of estimates makes it possible to enunciate precise statements about values of r obtained from samples of varying sizes. These statements, based on probability, are concerned with so-called *levels of significance.* (See Sections XIV–5, 8.)

13. The correlation surface. The graphical representation of a frequency distribution by means of a histogram or frequency polygon (Section IV–4) and the idealization of the latter into a frequency curve (Section IV–7) are already familiar. Similar processes are employed in the case of a *bivariate* distribution represented by a correlation table.   Let each cell in the table be the base of a solid rectangular column whose height is proportional to the frequency of the cell. The aggregate of columns thus constructed forms a solid histogram, a sort of modernistic building (Figure XII–5).   If

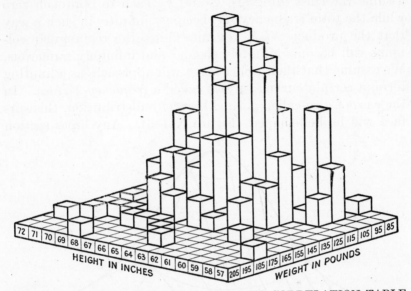

FIG. XII-5. SOLID HISTOGRAM FOR THE CORRELATION TABLE XII-3, OF HEIGHTS AND WEIGHTS OF 285 BOSTON UNIVERSITY WOMEN STUDENTS.

the dimensions of each cell are k_x and k_y (the class intervals for x and y, respectively), and the total frequency is N, then the volume of this solid histogram will be Nk_xk_y.   If the class intervals are reduced to unity, the volume becomes equal to N.

The concept of the solid histogram is not without its practical applications.   For example, a certain well-known shoe store in Boston uses an effective form of it.   The lengths of men's shoes from 4 to 12 and the widths from AAA to E constitute a double array of sizes.   Upon each cell, for example, that for size $7\frac{1}{2}$ C, is erected a vertical rod upon which uniform washers of constant thickness can be strung.   For each pair of shoes sold, a washer is dropped upon the appropriate rod.   The number of washers built up on each rod represents the frequency.   After a period of time, say a week, the aggregate of cylindrical columns formed by the washers on the rod yields a form of solid histogram which records the distributions of shoe sales by lengths and widths. Orders for new stocks of shoes can be constructed accordingly.

Returning to the discussion of the first paragraph, if we assume the class intervals, k_x and k_y, each to approach zero while the total frequency, N, becomes infinite, in such a way that the product Nk_xk_y remains finite, the rectangular columns will become infinitely slender and infinitely numerous. We assume that their upper bases will approach, as a limiting form, a certain curved surface called a *frequency surface*. In the case of a so-called normal bivariate distribution, this surface will be bell-shaped (Figure XII–6). Any cross section

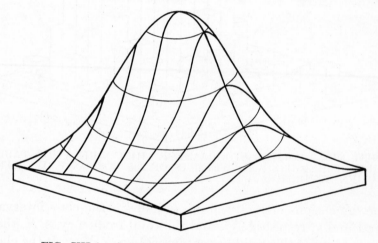

FIG. XII-6. A NORMAL FREQUENCY SURFACE.

parallel to the (x, y)-plane upon which the array of cells is situated will be an ellipse or circle. The centers of all such ellipses will lie upon the vertical line through the "mean point," $(\bar{x}, \bar{y})$; the axes of these ellipses will lie in two vertical planes perpendicular each to each. We shall call these the *axial planes* of the frequency surface. If r is numerically near 1, the ellipses will be slender ones, that is, the *major axis* will be much greater than the *minor axis*. If r is numerically near 0, the ellipses will be nearly circular, that is, the major and minor axes will be nearly equal.   Any vertical cross section parallel to an axis or to any direction whatsoever will yield a normal curve.   The surface will be asymptotic to the base, that is, it will approach infinitely near the base as it extends to infinity in all directions.   If we place the origin of the (x, y)-axes at $(\bar{x}, \bar{y})$, and change to standard variables t_x and t_y, where, as before,

$$\begin{cases} t_x = \dfrac{x - \bar{x}}{\sigma_x} \\[2mm] t_y = \dfrac{y - \bar{y}}{\sigma_y}, \end{cases}$$

and let $\Phi(t_x, t_y)$ represent the vertical distance from the (x, y)- or (t_x, t_y)-plane of a point on the surface, the equation of the surface can be shown to be:

$$\Phi(t_x, t_y) = \frac{N}{2\pi\sigma_x\sigma_y(1 - r^2)^{1/2}}\, e^{-\frac{1}{2(1-r^2)}\,(t_x^2 - 2rt_xt_y + t_y^2)}. \qquad (20)$$

The detailed study of the normal frequency surface defined by equation (20) must be left to a more advanced course.   At this point, however, we call attention to two important aspects of the correlation table and its associated surface. These are best explained by referring to correlation Table XII–3.

In the first place, we observe that the main body of this table may be enclosed in an ellipse whose longer axis slopes diagonally downward from the upper left-hand region of the table, and whose shorter axis slopes diagonally upward.   The nearer we approach these axes, the greater, generally, do the frequencies become.   These axes lie close to the axes associated with the ideal frequency surface.   (Figure XII–6.)

An interesting application of this elliptical distribution is found in gunnery.   If a gun is fired at a flat target, the distribution of the shots will exhibit two kinds of errors, one along the direction of fire (longitudinal), the other at right angles to it (latitudinal).   Shots which fall short of or exceed the required longitudinal distance will have a greater range of dispersion than shots which fall too far to the right or to the left (latitudinal dispersion).   If we imagine each shot to leave a hole in the ground about the target, the aggregate of holes will tend to form an elliptical scatter diagram whose longer axis is in the direction of fire. We assume here that the gun and its operator are behaving "normally" (Figure XII–7). If the ground about the target is ruled off into squares whose sides are parallel to and perpendicular to the line of fire, the number of shots falling in each square or cell gives a cell frequency.

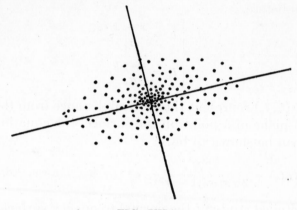

FIG. XII-7.

Returning to Table XII–3, we may state, in the second place, that it is possible to find, for each column representing a weight class, the average height of students belonging to that class. Similarly, for each row representing a height class, one may compute the average weight of students belonging to that class. For example, the average height of the 54 students belonging to the 135-pound class is 65.1 inches, and the average weight of the 13 students in the 60-inch class is 107.3 pounds. Let us denote the average of the y's, the heights, corresponding to a given weight class, x_i, by the symbol $\bar{y}_i$; and the average of the x's, the weights, corresponding to a given height class, y_j, by the symbol, $\bar{x}_j$. In what follows, the variable subscript i will refer always to the x's, and the variable subscript j to the y's. Let us plot $\bar{y}_i$ against x_i, and then $\bar{x}_j$ against y_j, as in Figure XII–8. The crosses represent the points $(x_i, \bar{y}_i)$, and the circles the points $(\bar{x}_j, y_j)$. It can be shown that the line best fitting the set of crosses is precisely the line of regression of y on x; the line best fitting

the set of circles is the line of regression of x on y. For best
fit, we weight the means according to the frequencies they
represent, and employ vertical distances in the former case
and horizontal distances in the latter. Passing to the ideal
double-frequency distribution as represented by a frequency
surface, it can be proved that if the surface is normal, the
crosses and circles will lie precisely on straight lines, the *ideal*
lines of regression. These facts are important in certain
phases of the work on correlation.

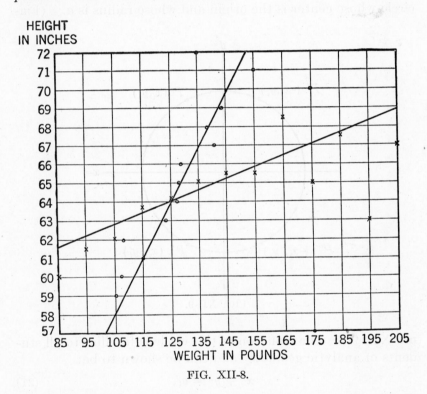

HEIGHT
IN INCHES

WEIGHT IN POUNDS

FIG. XII-8.

14. Non-linear regression. The theory of correlation as
discussed up to this point has been based upon the notion of
a straight line best fitting an array of points in a plane. As
long as the data given exhibit a fairly linear trend, no serious
difficulties ensue. However, if the points seem to lie along a
curve, other methods should be used. A bivariate universe

which is not normal is represented by a frequency surface which is not normal. It can be shown that the two ideal "lines" of regression associated with non-normal distributions are not ordinarily both straight lines: one or both may be curved lines. Grossly misleading results may be obtained by computing r upon the hypothesis of a linear trend when the trend is curvilinear.

A simple but striking example of this may be given by considering a number of points lying on the circumference of a circle whose center is the origin and whose radius is a. (Fig-

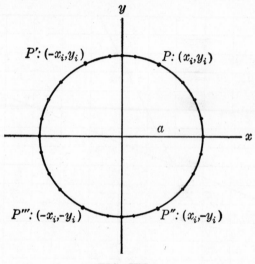

FIG. XII-9.

ure XII-9.) The equation of this circle is familiar to all students of analytic geometry and can be shown to be:

$$x^2 + y^2 = a^2. \tag{21}$$

If we assume these points to be distributed symmetrically with respect to both the x-axis and the y-axis, so that every point, such as $P:(x_i, y_i)$, has a corresponding symmetric point, $P':(-x_i, y_i)$, on the opposite side of the y-axis, and a symmetric point $P'':(x_i, -y_i)$, on the opposite side of the x-axis, it can easily be verified that $\bar{x} = 0$, $\bar{y} = 0$, and $\Sigma x_i y_i = 0$, so that by (19), $r = 0$. This would seem to indicate a complete absence of correlation between the pairs of values (x_i, y_i) corresponding to the points. This result is false, for the correlation is really perfect. The reason is that equation (21) is a mathematical law, a second-degree equation, associating values of x with corresponding values of y. Formula (19) involves the assumption that the law connecting x and y is a probable or an approximate law expressed by means of a first-degree equation, the equation of a straight line. The straight lines of regression are easily shown to be the coordinate axes $x = 0$ and $y = 0$, and these fit the points not only equally well but equally badly. It is clear that we should employ a *curve* best fitting the points, that this curve should be a circle, and that this circle fits the points perfectly.

The particular example just discussed is an artificial one, one that would not arise in practical statistical work, but it illustrates the danger of making direct measurements of correlation by standard formulas based on linear trends before the character of the distribution is investigated by means of a scatter diagram or other method. The assumption of a linear trend when a pronouncedly curvilinear trend is present is apt to lead to serious errors in the results sought. The scatter diagram, or its equivalent for large values of N, the correlation table, will often indicate the trends but cannot wholly be relied upon. A second method, quite simple and familiar, involves the use of probability paper. The x-distribution and the y-distribution are tested separately by the method described in Section X–14. For example, in Table XII–3, the distribution of weights alone forms the x-distribution; the distribution of heights forms the y-distribution. If each distribution is approximately normal, as shown by a reasonably linear configuration of points on arithmetic probability paper, it is usually safe to assume that the trend is linear for y on x and for x on y. In Table XII–3, the heights are distributed quite symmetrically; the weights are slightly skewed, but are symmetric enough about the mean to cause no difficulty.

15. The correlation ratio. We have denoted by $\bar{y}_i$ the mean height of students of weight class, x_i, that is, the mean of the heights occurring in the ith column.   Let the variance of these heights referred to $\bar{y}_i$ be denoted by $\sigma_y^{(i)\,2}$ and the corresponding total frequency in the ith column by $N^{(i)}$.   The mean of the variances, $\sigma_y^{(i)\,2}$, of all the columns, denoted by $S_y'^2$, is found by weighting each variance according to its corresponding total frequency.   Hence, by Section V–8,

$$S_y'^2 = \frac{1}{N}\Sigma N^{(i)}\sigma_y^{(i)2}, \text{ where } N = \Sigma N^{(i)}. \tag{22}$$

Thus, S_y' is a measure of the average deviation of the columnar values from their respective means, $\bar{y}_i$.   If S_y' is divided by σ_y, it becomes independent of the units employed.   For a reason which will appear presently, we square the resulting coefficient.   Then $\dfrac{S_y'^2}{\sigma_y^2}$ is also a pure number.

Consider the quantity η_{yx} ("eta sub-yx"), defined by the equation:

$$\eta_{yx}^2 = 1 - \frac{S_y'^2}{\sigma_y^2}. \tag{23}$$

When S_y' is very small, the dots of the scatter diagram corresponding to the correlation table are closely clustered about their columnar means.   In such a case, η_{yx}^2 is very nearly 1. If, on the other hand, S_y' is nearly equal to σ_y, $\dfrac{S_y'^2}{\sigma_y^2}$ is nearly unity, η_{yx}^2 is close to zero, and the various $\bar{y}_i$'s must be near $\bar{y}$. Furthermore, S_y' can never exceed σ_y.   This should be apparent from Theorem 2, Section VIII–6.   Hence, η_{yx}^2 ranges in value from 0 to 1, and measures the tendency of the dots to gather into a narrow band, straight or curved, which passes through the $\bar{y}_i$'s. η_{yx} is called the *correlation ratio of y on x*, and is analogous to the coefficient of correlation, r, in that it measures the fit of a line to the dots of the scatter diagram. The important fact is that this line may be curved, whereas in the case of r, the argument is based on the assumption that the line of best fit is a straight line.   For the *curve of regression of y on x,* η_{yx} measures the fit in terms of vertical distances.

In like manner, we define η_{xy} by means of the equation:

$$\eta_{xy}^2 = 1 - \frac{S_x'^2}{\sigma_x^2}. \tag{24}$$

η_{xy} is the *correlation ratio of x on y.*

In the case of linear regression, we found (Section XII–5) that the sum of the squares of the vertical distances of all points from the line of regression of y on x was $N\sigma_y^2(1 - r^2)$. The mean of this sum is $\sigma_y^2(1 - r^2)$, which we denoted by S_y^2. We shall not stop here to prove that the two values S_y^2 and $S_y'^2$ are equivalent, when the regression is precisely linear, but shall assume it to be established. Solving equation (13a) of Section XII–5,

$$S_y^2 = \sigma_y^2(1 - r^2),$$

for r^2, we obtain:

$$r^2 = 1 - \frac{S_y^2}{\sigma_y^2},$$

so that in perfect linear regression, r and η_{yx} are the same.

Before computing r, the student should be careful to ascertain whether or not he has data which yield linear regression. As has been shown, it is quite possible to obtain a small value of r from data which actually possess high correlation.

We shall not attempt to describe the practical methods of computing correlation ratios and constructing curves of regression, but shall mention the fact that tests for linearity of regression of y on x are based on the difference between r^2 and η_{yx}^2.

16. Tetrachoric correlation. Table XII–5 shows the division of a certain group of men into those physically strong or weak and those having a good standard of living or a poor one. The division of a group into two portions, one of which contains individuals possessing a certain attribute and the other those not possessing it, is called a *dichotomy.* Table XII–5 is dichotomous in two ways: it divides the 754 men into groups physically strong and weak, and into groups having good standards of living and poor ones. We seek a measure of the association between physique and standard of living.   Correlation based on such a 2 × 2 table is said to be *tetrachoric*.

TABLE XII–5

Standard of Living Physique	Good	Poor	Totals
Strong	302	58	360
Weak	347	47	394
Totals	649	105	754

We conceive of men as possessing physiques ranging from very frail to exceedingly robust, and having standards of living varying from abject poverty to great luxury.   Although these physical and economic characteristics may be given in a qualitative manner, we imagine them to be normally distributed.   In other words, we assume the 754 men to be a sample chosen from a bivariate universe whose correlation surface is a normal one.   This surface is conceived to be divided into four sections by vertical planes at right angles to each other in such a manner that the relative frequencies corresponding to the four portions of this theoretical distribution will be equal, respectively, to the relative frequencies of the four portions of the given table.   The fundamental shape of a correlation surface is given by its horizontal elliptical cross sections (Section XII–13), and depends upon the value of r.   Our problem, then, in tetrachoric correlation is to find the value of r which yields a correlation surface for which the desired "quartering" is possible.   In other words, the r we seek is the r which characterizes a correlation surface exactly fitting the given data.   It is unique.

The determination of tetrachoric r is not always easy, but the construction of useful tables and the employment of certain devices have facilitated the required computation, especially when approximations to tetrachoric r are sufficient.

The student may find more complete discussions of this subject in References 1, 31, and 32.

In Table XII–5, the value of tetrachoric r can be found to be about -0.14, which indicates slight negative correlation. One should also note that any correlation table can be reduced arbitrarily to a 2×2 table. Thus, Table XII–3 may lead to a classification of women students as tall or short, and heavy or light. Students less than 120 pounds in weight might be called light, and those with statures less than 64 inches might be called short. All others would be heavy and tall.

17. The correlation of ranked data. *Method of ranking.* It is often desirable to arrange variates according to rank. Thus, the following scores in a history test would be assigned ranks as indicated:

Score........	72	79	93	55	84	67	76	81	61	82
Rank........	7	5	1	10	2	8	6	4	9	3

The highest score, 93, is assigned the rank of 1; the next highest, 84, the rank of 2; and so on. When two or more variates are equal, it is customary to indicate the tie in rank by assigning to each the arithmetic mean of the rank which these items would have if they were in the same relative position with respect to the other items but not equal to one another. Thus, the following scores would be ranked as shown:

Score........	70	76	57	70	76	83	84	76	94	62
Rank........	$7\frac{1}{2}$	5	10	$7\frac{1}{2}$	5	3	2	5	1	9

In this illustration, the ranks 4, 5, and 6 are divided among the three variates 76, 76, and 76 by giving each a rank of $\frac{1}{3}(4 + 5 + 6)$, or 5. Similarly, the rank assigned to each of the two values 70 and 70 is $\frac{1}{2}(7 + 8)$, or $7\frac{1}{2}$.

The arithmetic mean of ranks. We recall from elementary algebra that the sum, S, of N terms of an arithmetic progression,

$$a + (a + d) + (a + 2d) + \cdots + [a + (N - 1)d],$$

where a is the first term and d the common difference, is given by the formula:

$$S = \frac{N}{2}(a + l),$$

where l is the Nth or last term, $a + (N - 1)d$. It follows, then, that the sum of the first N integers 1, 2, 3, $\cdots$ N is merely $\frac{N}{2}(1 + N)$. The mean value, $\overline{R}$, of a set of non-duplicate ranks 1, 2, 3, $\cdots$ N is merely $\frac{1}{N}$th their sum, so that

$$\overline{R} = \frac{1}{N}\left[\frac{N}{2}(1 + N)\right]$$

$$= \tfrac{1}{2}(N + 1). \tag{25}$$

Obviously, the arithmetic mean of the integers from 1 to 19 is 10, and of the integers from 1 to 20 is $10\frac{1}{2}$. It should be observed that the presence of duplicate ranks will not affect the value of the mean as given by (25). Why?

The standard deviation of ranks. According to formula (7), Section VIII–7,

$$\sigma_u^2 = v_{2u} - \bar{u}^2,$$

where u_i represents a unit deviation with respect to a convenient value, x_0, and where v_{2u} represents the second moment of the u's with respect to $u = 0$. Since the ranks 1, 2, 3, $\cdots$ N may be treated as u's, it follows that:

$$\sigma_u^2 = \frac{1}{N}\sum_{u=1}^{N} u^2 - \bar{u}^2. \tag{26}$$

From formula (19), Section XI–10, and from formula (26) just derived, if we let σ_R represent the standard deviation of ranks,

$$\sigma_R^2 = \frac{(N + 1)(2N + 1)}{6} - \frac{(N + 1)^2}{4}$$

$$= \frac{N^2 - 1}{12}. \tag{27}$$

Hence, the standard deviation of N non-duplicate ranks is $\left(\dfrac{N^2 - 1}{12}\right)^{\frac{1}{2}}$. The presence of tied ranks will introduce some error into the formula (27), but this will be slight if only a few duplicates are present.

Correlation of ranked data. The amount of association between two sets of paired ranks is measured by making use of the squared differences in rank. If d_i denotes the difference, $x_i - y_i$, between two paired ranks, we have, by formula (4), Section VIII–5:

$$\sigma_d^2 = \frac{1}{N}\Sigma(d_i - \bar{d})^2$$

$$= \frac{1}{N}\Sigma[(x_i - y_i) - (\bar{x} - \bar{y})]^2$$

$$= \frac{1}{N}\Sigma[(x_i - \bar{x}) - (y_i - \bar{y})]^2$$

$$= \frac{1}{N}\Sigma(x_i - \bar{x})^2 - \frac{2}{N}\Sigma(x_i - \bar{x})(y_i - \bar{y}) + \frac{1}{N}\Sigma(y_i - \bar{y})^2.$$

From (9a) of Section XII–4 it follows that

$$r\sigma_x\sigma_y = \frac{1}{N}\Sigma(x_i - \bar{x})(y_i - \bar{y}).$$

Substituting this result above, we get:

$$\sigma_d^2 = \sigma_x^2 - 2r\sigma_x\sigma_y + \sigma_y^2.$$

Solving this last equation for r, we obtain:

$$r = \frac{\sigma_x^2 + \sigma_y^2 - \sigma_d^2}{2\sigma_x\sigma_y}. \tag{28}$$

If the x's and y's represent ranks, then both the ordered sets $x_1, x_2, x_3, \cdots x_N$ and $y_1, y_2, y_3, \cdots y_N$ are the same as the integers $1, 2, 3, \cdots N$. Thus, by (27),

$$\sigma_R^2 = \sigma_x^2 = \sigma_y^2$$

$$= \frac{N^2 - 1}{12}.$$

Also

$$\sigma_d^2 = \frac{1}{N}\Sigma(d_i - \bar{d})^2$$

$$= \frac{1}{N}\Sigma[(x_i - y_i) - (\bar{x} - \bar{y})]^2.$$

But for the two sets of identical ranks, $\bar{x} = \bar{y}$; hence,

$$\sigma_d^2 = \frac{1}{N}\Sigma(x_i - y_i)^2.$$

We may now write (28) as:

$$r = \frac{2\sigma_k^2 - \sigma_d^2}{2\sigma_k^2}$$

$$= \frac{2\left(\dfrac{N^2 - 1}{12}\right) - \dfrac{1}{N}\Sigma(x_i - y_i)^2}{2\left(\dfrac{N^2 - 1}{12}\right)},$$

whence

$$\rho = 1 - \frac{6\Sigma d_i^2}{N(N^2 - 1)}. \tag{29}$$

The symbol ρ (rho) is used in place of r to indicate the co-efficient of correlation from *ranks*. The last formula is known as the *Spearman formula** for rank correlation.

Since ρ is merely a form of r for a special set of x's and y's, its value will be restricted to the interval from -1 to $+1$. When the two sets of corresponding ranks are identical, each $d_i = 0$, the correlation is perfect, and $\rho = 1$. When high ranks are generally associated with low ranks, ρ is negative.

We illustrate the use of the formula with the data of Table XII–1, ranked as shown in Table XII–6.

---

* This is not the same as Spearman's "foot-rule," $\rho = 1 - \dfrac{6\Sigma\,|\,x_i - y_i\,|}{N^2 - 1}$, which is, on the whole, a less desirable formula.

TABLE XII–6

	Birth Rate Rank x_i	Property Value Rank y_i	$d_i = x_i - y_i$	d_i^2
Conn.	1	20	−19	361
Mass.	2	14	−12	144
N. Y.	3	16	−13	169
D. C.	4	21	−17	289
Cal.	5	23	−18	324
N. H.	6	12	−6	36
Vt.	7	5	2	4
Ore.	8	24	−16	256
O.	9	11	−2	4
Wash.	10	19	−9	81
Me.	11	6	5	25
Penn.	12	13	−1	1
Ind.	13	10	3	9
Wis.	14	8	6	36
Kan.	15	18	−3	9
Md.	16	7	9	81
Mich.	17	9	8	64
Minn.	18	17	1	1
Neb.	19	22	−3	9
Ky.	20	2	18	324
Va.	21	4	17	289
S. C.	22	1	21	441
N. C.	23	3	20	400
Utah	24	15	9	81
				3438

$$\rho = 1 - \frac{6(3438)}{24(576 - 1)}$$

$$= -0.49.$$

The value of ρ just found, −0.49, is considerably different from the value of r found in Section XII–7, namely, −0.61. If the variates are normally distributed, the formula:

$$r = 2\sin\left(\frac{\pi}{6}\rho\right) \tag{30}$$

can be shown to hold. For the data of the illustration,

$$r = 2\sin\left[\frac{3.14}{6}(-0.49)\right]$$

$$= 2\sin(-0.25)$$

$$= 2(-0.248)$$

$$= -0.50.$$

Note that the angle -0.25 is expressed in radian measure, and that this value of r is not in agreement with the value of r found previously. We have no evidence that birth rates and per capita property values are normally distributed, so we should not be surprised at the lack of agreement between r and ρ.

Spearman's formula (29) is usually considered inaccurate for values of N less than 15 or 20, and may lead to laborious computation if N is too large, say $N > 30$. The use of ranks is advantageous when the variates cannot be assigned definite numerical magnitudes but may be assigned positions in an ordered series. See, for example, Exercise XII-20. It is a safe procedure to treat ρ merely as a rough estimate of correlation.

18. Multiple correlation. Simple correlation deals with the degree of association between two variables, such as weight and height. Multiple correlation deals with the degree of interrelationship among three or more variables. Weight may depend not only upon height but upon age as well, particularly in the case of growing children. Rents may depend upon tax rates as well as upon building costs, and probably upon other variables also. General intelligence in school may be related to grades in mathematics and grades in English.

For simplicity, let us confine our brief discussion to three variables only. Instead of a bivariate distribution, we are considering a *trivariate* distribution. A sample of the former was defined in terms of a two-dimensional array of cells with assigned frequencies. A sample of the latter may be defined in terms of a three-dimensional array of cells, a rectangular parallelepiped subdivided into smaller parallelepipeds with frequencies assigned to many of them. We may visualize such a configuration as an egg-crate, the cells or individual egg receptacles of which lie in horizontal layers, each layer with its cell frequencies corresponding to an ordinary correlation table. The means of the vertical columns of the egg-box determine a three-dimensional configuration of points to which a *regression plane of z on xy* may be fitted by minimizing vertical distances. The equation of this plane, of the first degree in X, Y, and Z, may be shown to have the form:

$$Z = \lambda_x X + \lambda_y Y, \tag{31}$$

where X, Y, and Z represent deviations from the mean, that is, $X = x - \bar{x}$, $Y = y - \bar{y}$, and $Z = z - \bar{z}$, where λ_x and λ_y may be evaluated in terms of the standard deviations σ_x, σ_y, and σ_z and the ordinary coefficients of correlation, r_{xy}, r_{xz}, r_{yz}, where the subscripts indicate the pairs of variables involved.

Corresponding to a given pair of values (X, Y) there will be always two values of Z: an actual value, Z, given by the data, and an estimated value, Z', obtained by substituting the given values (X, Y) in equation (31). Then the correlation coefficient for the pairs of values of Z and Z' is called the *multiple correlation coefficient* of Z on XY and is denoted by $r_{z.xy}$. Thus,

$$r_{z.xy} = \frac{\Sigma Z Z'}{N\sigma_z \sigma_z'}. \tag{32}$$

In a similar manner, we may define multiple correlation coefficients of x on yz and of y on xz, symbolized by $r_{x.yz}$ and $r_{y.xz}$, respectively. These may all be computed in terms of the simple correlation coefficients r_{xy}, r_{xz}, and r_{yz}.

For further discussions of the general subject of multiple correlation involving not only three but more than three variables, the reader should consult other works. (See, for example, Refs. 1, 3, and 7.)

19. Partial correlation. In the case of a three-way distribution, one of the "egg-crate" type, it is, of course, possible to study the association between x and y for a given value of

z, that is to say, the association existing between values of x and y in any given layer of the egg-box or, as it is sometimes called, a slice or a slab of the trivariate distribution. For example, we may measure the correlation between the heights and weights of American schoolboys of age 16, or the correlation between grades in mathematics and grades in English for high-school boys having intelligence quotients of 95.

The symbol $r_{xy.z}$ represents the *partial correlation coefficient* between x and y for a fixed value of z. There are many cases where we wish to study the degree of association between two variables for various values of a third variable.

20. The uses and misuses of correlation. The general subject of correlation is a vast one, and one which cannot be comprehensively treated here. Nevertheless, enough has been said about simple, multiple, and partial correlation to enable the critical student to avoid some of the pitfalls besetting one who attempts to employ correlation methods and to interpret the results. It should be useful, at this point, to make certain remarks and to summarize certain facts concerning the general problem of measuring degree of association.

In the first place, there should be some intelligent basis for proceeding with a proposed study of correlation. It is possible to pair the most disparate pair of variables and grind out corresponding useless values of r. The height of the morning tide and the number of shares sold at the New York Stock Exchange would form an extreme example.

In the second place, if we are proceeding with an investigation of simple correlation, we should be reasonably sure that the suspected association exists essentially by itself and is not a result of some other latent factor or factors. Any possible correlation between school ability in, say, Latin and mathematics, might be due more fundamentally to the degrees of general native intelligence of the students than to fancied common elements in the two disciplines. If other factors are plausibly involved, it is safer, perhaps, to compute partial correlation coefficients in order to see how much, if any, contribution is made by other factors.

In the third place, the confidence we can place in a correlation coefficient varies significantly with the size, N, of the sample used, and with the size of the coefficient, r, itself. (See Section XIV–8.)   Mention has been made elsewhere concerning the errors of sampling.   The general subject of sampling is, from certain points of view, one of the most important in statistics.   The next two chapters will give some indications of the mode of approach to sampling problems, but a satisfactory discussion of them must be left to a more advanced course.   For the present, we must warn the student about appraising too highly the value of r or of similar correlation coefficients for small values of N.   It may be safe to say for the present that samples less than 100 in number yield results that should be regarded with suspicion until subjected to more refined tests of reliability.

XII—Exercises

Construct a scatter diagram for each of the sets of paired values in Exercises 1–5.   Find r by using either formula (9a) or (19).   Find the equations of the lines of regression and construct these lines on your scatter diagram.   Interpret the value of r.

1. x	y		2. x	y		3. x	y
3	1		-5	1		2	8
4	1		-3	1		2	6
5	3		-1	5		4	5
8	3		1	4		5	7
10	4		3	5		5	4
12	6		5	8		6	5
						6	7
						8	5
						10	2
						12	1

4. x	-17	-15	-15	-12	-13	-8	-5	-4	-3	2	0	0	4	6	5
y	-8	-2	3	-7	-2	4	0	-4	3	0	2	8	3	5	10

5.   In a certain school the salaries and years of service of a staff of twelve teachers were as follows:

Salaries	1800	1500	1600	2400	1300	2100
Years	5	2	4	8	3	8

Salaries	1800	1900	2300	1700	2700	1700
Years	5	4	9	1	8	3

* * *

Construct a scatter diagram for each set of data in Exercises 6–9. Compute the value of r according to the method of Section XII–7. Find the equations of the lines of regression and construct them on the scatter diagram. Interpret the value of r.

6. Average hourly earnings and average hours per week in 17 industries in 1890. (From Paul H. Douglas, *The Theory of Wages*, Macmillan, 1934, p. 527.)

	Industry	Earnings in Cents	Hours
1.	Cotton	10	63
2.	Woolen	12	60
3.	Shoes	17	59
4.	Clothing	14	56
5.	Hosiery, Knitting	11	61
6.	Lumber	15	65
7.	Iron, Steel	23	67
8.	Meat Packing	17	60
9.	Machine Shops	32	54
10.	Building Trades	34	51
11.	Stone	40	49
12.	Printing	29	56
13.	Newspaper	45	49
14.	Planing Mills	29	53
15.	Baking	20	64
16.	Coal (Bituminous)	18	60
17.	Unskilled	15	60

7. Average grades in freshman algebra and number of absences for a given semester. (Original data.) (Table continued on page 317.)

Grade	75	98	83	79	77	51	84	74	93	70	92	92	86	58	74
Absences	8	0	1	4	2	3	0	3	0	2	0	0	1	1	0

Grade............	75	88	78	88	85	55	84	65	71	94	79	77	48	78
Absences..........	0	1	0	0	0	10	0	0	0	0	0	3	2	0

8. Average grades in home work and quizzes of 24 college freshmen in mathematics.   (Original data.)

Home Work...	63	87	90	95	95	82	77	83	74	82	81	82
Quizzes.......	65	79	78	82	75	83	83	82	70	75	43	70

Home Work...	82	81	79	76	93	82	83	68	50	84	91	44
Quizzes.......	55	70	58	87	50	75	55	30	45	33	93	68

9. Retail Price Per Quart of Milk, Standard or Grade B, Delivered to Family Trade in Cities, 1930.

	Population 1930	Price
Boston.................	780,000	15.3
New York..............	6,930,000	15.7
Philadelphia............	1,950,000	13.0
Pittsburgh..............	670,000	13.3
Cleveland..............	900,000	12.1
Indianapolis............	360,000	11.9
Chicago................	3,380,000	14.0
Detroit.................	1,570,000	13.1
Milwaukee.............	580,000	11.4
Minneapolis............	460,000	11.0
St. Louis...............	820,000	12.9
Kansas City, Mo.........	400,000	13.2
Washington, D. C........	490,000	14.5
Jacksonville............	130,000	18.5
Louisville...............	310,000	12.4
Birmingham.............	260,000	16.0
New Orleans............	460,000	14.0
Dallas.................	260,000	13.0
Denver.................	290,000	11.0
Salt Lake City..........	140,000	10.0
Seattle.................	370,000	11.0
Portland, Ore...........	300,000	12.6
Los Angeles.............	1,240,000	14.6
San Francisco...........	630,000	14.0

*   *   *

COMMERCIAL FAILURES—NUMBER AND LIABILITIES (*Statistical Abstract of the United States*, 1934, p. 280.)

	1923	1924	1925	1926	1927	1928	1929	1930	1931	1932	1933
Number of failures:											
Jan.	2126	2108	2317	2296	2465	2643	2535	2759	3316	3458	2919
Feb.	1508	1730	1793	1801	2035	2176	1965	2262	2563	2732	2378
Mar.	1682	1817	1859	1984	2143	2236	1987	2347	2604	2951	1948
Apr.	1520	1707	1939	1957	1968	1818	2021	2198	2383	2816	1921
May	1530	1816	1767	1730	1852	2008	1897	2179	2248	2788	1909
June	1358	1607	1745	1708	1833	1947	1767	2026	1993	2688	1648
July	1231	1615	1685	1605	1756	1723	1752	2028	1983	2596	1421
Aug.	1319	1520	1513	1593	1708	1852	1762	1913	1944	2796	1472
Sept.	1226	1306	1465	1437	1573	1635	1568	1963	1936	2182	1116
Oct.	1673	1696	1581	1763	1787	2023	1822	2124	2362	2273	1206
Nov.	1704	1653	1672	1830	1864	1838	1796	2031	2195	2073	1237
Dec.	1841	2040	1878	2069	2162	1943	2037	2525	2758	2469	1132
Liabilities (per $1,000):											
Jan.	49	51	54	44	51	48	54	61	95	97	79
Feb.	41	36	40	34	47	45	34	51	60	85	66
Mar.	48	98	34	31	58	55	36	57	60	94	49
Apr.	51	49	37	38	53	38	35	49	51	101	51
May	41	37	37	34	38	36	41	56	53	84	48
June	29	34	37	29	34	30	31	63	52	77	35
July	36	37	35	30	43	30	32	40	61	87	27
Aug.	34	55	37	28	39	58	34	49	53	77	43
Sept.	29	34	31	30	33	34	34	47	47	56	22
Oct.	79	36	30	33	36	35	31	56	71	53	31
Nov.	50	31	36	33	36	41	52	55	61	54	25
Dec.	52	45	37	46	51	41	67	84	73	64	27

10. Make a correlation table for the number of failures and liabilities given on page 318. Let the intervals for the former be 1000–1199, 1200–1399, and so forth; and for the latter, 20–24, 25–29, and so forth. What conclusions can you draw from the table?

11. Compute r for the data of Table XII–4 and verify the result given in Section XII–11.

12. Derive formula (14) (Section XII–5).

13. Derive formula (19) (Section XII–6).

14. Derive the following formula for r:

$$r = \frac{\Sigma X_i Y_i}{\sqrt{\Sigma X_i^2}\sqrt{\Sigma Y_i^2}}, \text{ where } X_i = x_i - \bar{x}, \ Y_i = y_i - \bar{y}.$$

*   *   *

Compute the value of r for each of the correlation tables given in Exercises 15 and 16, and interpret the result. Find the equations of the lines of regression as directed by your instructor.

15. Grades of medical students in Anatomy (x) and Biology (y). Numerical equivalents for the letter grades are indicated. (Original data.)

y	x	A	A−	B+	B	B−	C+	C	C−	D+	D	D−	F
		5	4	3	2	1	0	−1	−2	−3	−4	−5	−6
A	5	1		2	10	5	3	6		1		1	
A−	4	1	1	4	5	6	7	5	3	1			
B+	3	3	4		12	14	12	7	2		3		1
B	2	3	1	11	36	20	31	28	10	2	4		2
B−	1	2	2	5	6	11	30	18	9	1	4		2
C+	0	2	2	3	8	10	24	26	16	1	7	1	2
C	−1	2	1	2	13	18	17	30	10	1	7	3	3
C−	−2			1	4	2	3	9	6	2	3	2	2
D+	−3			1		2	2	4	1		1		
D	−4					1	1	2	1	1	2		

16. Average price (x) per pound of shorn wool and average price (y) in dollars per 100 pounds of sheep received by producers.

x / y	8.5	11.5	14.5	17.5	20.5	23.5	26.5	29.5	32.5	35.5	38.5	41.5	44.5
2.25	10	2	.	1	2	3							
2.75	1	4	3	1	5	4							
3.25		1	2				1						
3.75			1	1	2	1	2						
4.25			2	2	2								
4.75					1								
5.25													
5.75					2								
6.25					1								
6.75						1	3	4	3				
7.25								7	8	2	4		
7.75								2	4	9	6	1	
8.25									2	2	2	1	2

*   *   *

17. Find the means of the rows and the columns of the table in Exercise 15. Fit lines of regression to the plotted points $(x_i, \bar{y}_i)$ and $(\bar{x}_j, y_j)$ by using a transparent rule or taut thread.

18. The following correlation coefficients have been obtained from actual data. Assuming the samples involved to be large, how would you interpret each result?

    (a)   The weights and lengths of babies: $r = 0.62$ to 0.64.

    (b)   Right and left first joint of the ring finger: $r = 0.93$.

    (c)   Strength of pull and stature: $r = 0.22$ to 0.30.

    (d)   Number of children and per cent of desertions:
         $r = -0.92$.

19. Assume that the scores of a class of students in a mathematics and in a physics test are as shown below. Compute ρ by means of Spearman's formula. Note the tied ranks, but neglect their influence on the value of ρ.

| Mathematics.... | 92 | 76 | 62 | 85 | 74 | 52 | 83 | 79 |
| Physics........ | 90 | 80 | 68 | 71 | 64 | 63 | 95 | 83 |

| Mathematics.... | 75 | 84 | 68 | 51 | 73 | 77 | 66 |
| Physics........ | 77 | 73 | 65 | 55 | 72 | 80 | 60 |

20. A group of students were ranked according to general school ability and according to personality. Compute ρ by means of Spearman's formula.

| Ability....... | 1 | 2 | 3 | 4 | 5 | 6 | 7 | 8 | 9 | 10 |
| Personality... | 4 | 17 | 8 | 19 | 11 | 10 | 15 | 9 | 12 | 2 |

| Ability....... | 11 | 12 | 13 | 14 | 15 | 16 | 17 | 18 | 19 | 20 |
| Personality... | 1 | 7 | 5 | 14 | 20 | 18 | 13 | 6 | 3 | 16 |

* * *

Compute ρ by means of Spearman's formula for the data in Exercises 21–23.

21. Hourly earnings and hours per week in 17 industries. (Ex. 6.) Comment on the reliability of your result.

22. Grades in home work and quizzes. (Ex. 8.) Comment on the reliability of this result.

23. Population and price of milk. (Ex. 9.)

CHAPTER

XIII

THE BINOMIAL DISTRIBUTION

❖❘❘❘❘❘❘❘❘❘❘❘❘❚❂❘❘❘❘❘❘❘❘❘❘❘❘❚❂❘❘❘❘❘❘❘❘❘❘❘❘❚❂❘❘❘❘❘❘❘❘❘❘❘❘❚❂❘❘❘❘❘❘❘❘❘❘❘❘❚❂❘❘❘❘❘❘❘❘❘❘❘❘❚❂❘❘❘❘❘❘❘❘❘❘❘❘❚❂❘❘❘❘❘❘❘❘❘❘❘❘❚❂❘❘❘❘❘❘❘❘❘❘❘❘❚❂❘❘❘❘❘❘❘❘❘❘❘❘❚❂❘❘❘❘❘❘❘❘❘❘❘❘❖

> "And I believe that the Binomial Theorem and a Bach Fugue are,
> in the long run, more important than all the battles of history.
> "I believe in the wisdom of often saying 'probably' and 'perhaps.' "
>
> JAMES HILTON, *This Week Magazine*.*

1. Introduction. It was stated in the opening chapter of this book that modern statistics could trace its ancestry in part to that activity of questionable value, gambling. The solution of a certain problem in a game of chance has indeed furnished us with a powerful tool for studying frequency distributions of an important kind. The fundamental theory is fairly simple if we eliminate the technical details of rigorous proofs. It will be the aim of this chapter to study this tool and its wide applications. To this end, we introduce certain preliminary and fundamental notions upon which we may build an appreciation of the role of probability in modern statistics. We begin with a brief survey of *permutations* and *combinations*.

2. A fundamental theorem. The following theorem may be considered so obviously true that it requires no formal proof.

*If a thing can be done in **m** different ways, and if, after it is done in one of these ways, a second thing can be done in **n** differ-*

---

ent ways, then the two things together can be done in **mn** different ways in the order named.

For example, if a student may elect any one of five courses at nine o'clock, and any one of three courses at ten o'clock, he may choose a combination of two courses in fifteen different ways.

3. Factorials. We define *factorial N*, symbolized by $N!$, as $N(N-1)(N-2) \cdots 3 \cdot 2 \cdot 1$. N is assumed to be a positive integer. Thus, $4! = 4 \cdot 3 \cdot 2 \cdot 1 = 24$ and $7! = 7 \cdot 6 \cdot 5 \cdot 4 \cdot 3 \cdot 2 \cdot 1 = 5040$. It follows that:

$$4! = 4 \cdot 3!$$
$$3! = 3 \cdot 2!$$
$$2! = 2 \cdot 1!$$

If we carry this process forward in a mechanical manner, we should write:

$$1! = 1 \cdot 0!$$

In order for the symbol $0!$ to have meaning, it would seem that we should let $0! = \dfrac{1!}{1} = 1$. We shall therefore define the symbol $0!$ as equal to 1.

4. Permutations and combinations. Each different arrangement of a group of things is called a *permutation*. A group of things considered without reference to their order within the group is called a *combination*.

Consider, for example, the following groups of letters: *abc*, *acb*, *bac*, *bca*, *cab*, and *cba*. Each of the six groups contains the same combination of letters, but each has a different arrangement from any other. There are represented, therefore, six different permutations of three letters, but only one combination of three.

On the other hand, if from the three letters *abc* we choose two letters at a time, we can make at most six permutations; namely, *ab*, *ba*, *ac*, *ca*, *bc*, and *cb*. But the groups *ab* and *ba* constitute the same combination of letters; likewise for *ac* and *ca*, and for *bc* and *cb*. Therefore, only three combinations are possible, taking only two at a time.

5. A fundamental theorem on permutations. *The number of permutations of N different things taken r at a time, often denoted by $P(N, r)$ (or $_NP_r$) is given by the formula:*

$$P(N, r) = \frac{N!}{(N - r)!}. \tag{1}$$

Proof: We can choose the first thing in N ways; having chosen it in a given way, we can choose the second thing in the remaining $(N - 1)$ ways. By the Fundamental Theorem, we can, then, choose the first two things in $N(N - 1)$ ways. Having chosen the first two things, there are $(N - 2)$ left from which to choose the third. Hence, by the Fundamental Theorem, we may choose the first three things in $N(N - 1)(N - 2)$ ways. Continuing in this manner until r things have been chosen, we find that they may be selected in

$$N(N - 1)(N - 2) \cdots (N - \overline{r - 1})$$

ways. Since the next factor in order in this product would be $N - r$, we multiply this product by $\dfrac{(N - r)!}{(N - r)!}$ to obtain:

$$\frac{N(N - 1)(N - 2) \cdots (N - \overline{r - 1})(N - r)!}{(N - r)!}.$$

But the numerator is equivalent to $N!$; hence,

$$P(N, r) = \frac{N!}{(N - r)!}. \tag{1}$$

EXAMPLE. Signals are made by flying vertically three flags at a time. If there are five flags of different colors from which to choose, how many different signals can be made?

Solution: Here a change of order among any three flags produces a different signal; hence, we have a problem in permutations. $N = 5$ and $r = 3$; hence, applying formula (1),

$$P(5, 3) = \frac{5!}{2!}$$

$$= 60.$$

Therefore, 60 different signals may be made.

As a corollary to this theorem, we state the following:

The number of permutations of N different things taken all at a time is N!. The proof appears when we set $r = N$ in $(N - r)!$ to obtain 0! or 1 as the denominator in (1) above.

6. A fundamental theorem on combinations. *The number of combinations of N things taken r at a time, often denoted by $C(N, r)$ (or $_NC_r$) is given by the formula:*

$$C(N, r) = \frac{N!}{(N - r)!r!}. \tag{2}$$

Proof: By the preceding corollary, any given combination of r different things is susceptible to $r!$ permutations; hence, if each combination is multiplied by $r!$, we obtain the total number of permutations, $P(N, r)$. Thus,

$$P(N, r) = C(N, r)r!;$$

whence, $$C(N, r) = \frac{P(N, r)}{r!} = \frac{N!}{(N - r)!r!}.$$

EXAMPLE. A committee of 5 is to be chosen from a club of 12 members. In how many ways may the committee be chosen?

Solution: Since a different arrangement or order of a given group of 5 does not constitute a different committee, the problem is that of finding the number of combinations of 5 people at a time selected from 12. Using formula (2), we have:

$$C(12, 5) = \frac{12!}{5!\ 7!}$$

$$= 792.$$

7. Mutually exclusive events. It will be recalled from Section IV–9 that the probability, p, for the favorable issue of an event may be defined as:

$$p = \frac{f}{N},$$

where N is the number of ways for an event to happen, and f is the number of favorable ways it can happen.

Two events are said to be mutually exclusive if both cannot happen simultaneously. Thus, if a coin is tossed once and heads appear, tails obviously cannot appear.

THEOREM. *If p_1 and p_2 are the probabilities for success of two mutually exclusive events, the probability that either one or the other event happens equals $p_1 + p_2$.*

Proof: Let N be the number of different ways an event can happen, f_1 the number of ways favorable to the first event, and f_2 the number of ways favorable to the second event. The number of ways favorable to either one or the other event is, therefore, $f_1 + f_2$. The probability that either one or the other event happens is, by definition:

$$\frac{f_1 + f_2}{N} = \frac{f_1}{N} + \frac{f_2}{N}.$$

But $p_1 = \dfrac{f_1}{N}$ and $p_2 = \dfrac{f_2}{N}$; hence, the total probability is $p_1 + p_2$.

EXAMPLE. What is the probability that the throw of two dice will be 7 or 11?

Solution: Let us designate the dice as #1 and #2. Die #1 may appear in 6 different ways, and die #2 may appear in 6 different ways also. Then, by the Fundamental Theorem, the two dice together may appear in 6×6 or 36 different ways. Hence, $N = 36$. The sum 7 may appear as $1 + 6$, $6 + 1$, $2 + 5$, $5 + 2$, $3 + 4$, or $4 + 3$; or in 6 different ways. Thus, $f_1 = 6$ and $p_1 = \dfrac{6}{36} = \dfrac{1}{6}$. Likewise, the sum 11 may appear as $5 + 6$ or as $6 + 5$, or in two different ways. Thus, $f_2 = 2$, and $p_2 = \dfrac{2}{36} = \dfrac{1}{18}$. Therefore, the probability for either 7 or 11 is $\dfrac{1}{6} + \dfrac{1}{18}$, or $\dfrac{2}{9}$.

8. Mutually independent events. *Two events are said to be mutually independent if the probability for one to happen is the same whether the other event happens or not.* For example, when two coins are tossed, the probability for heads on one coin is unaffected by the result of the toss on the other coin.

THEOREM. *If two events with probabilities p_1 and p_2 are mutually independent, the probability that both of them happen equals $p_1 p_2$.*

Proof: Suppose the first event can happen in f_1 ways favorably out of N_1 possible ways, and suppose that the second event can occur f_2 times favorably out of N_2 possible ways; then, by the Fundamental Theorem, the total number of ways that both events can happen favorably is $f_1 f_2$ out of $N_1 N_2$ possible ways. Hence, the probability that both events happen is:

$$\frac{f_1 f_2}{N_1 N_2} = \frac{f_1}{N_1} \cdot \frac{f_2}{N_2} = p_1 p_2.$$

EXAMPLE. Two dice are thrown twice. What is the probability that the first throw is 7 and the second throw is 11?

Solution. The probability for 7 has just been shown to be $\frac{1}{6}$; that for 11, to be $\frac{1}{18}$. Therefore, the probability for the first throw to be 7 and the second to be 11 is:

$$\frac{1}{6} \times \frac{1}{18}, \text{ or } \frac{1}{108}.$$

9. An important problem. Assume that an event can happen in two different ways called favorable and unfavorable. A favorable result will be called a success; an unfavorable one, a failure. Let p be the probability for a success, q the probability for a failure. Suppose, next, that an event is repeated N times under essentially the same conditions. What is the probability for exactly k successes?

The probability that success results in each of the first k trials is p^k, and that failure results in each of the remaining $(N - k)$ trials is q^{N-k}; hence, the probability that the first k trials are successful and that the last $N - k$ trials are failures is $p^k q^{N-k}$. But this is the probability associated with one particular order of successes and failures. Exactly k successes in N trials can happen in $\dfrac{N!}{k!(N - k)!}$ different combinations of order; hence, the probability for exactly k successes in N trials is:

$$\frac{N!}{k!(N-k)!}\,p^k q^{N-k}. \tag{3}$$

EXAMPLE 1.   The probability that exactly two heads appear when six pennies are tossed is:

$$\frac{6!}{2!\,4!}\left(\frac{1}{2}\right)^2\left(\frac{1}{2}\right)^4 = \frac{15}{64},$$

for $p = q = \frac{1}{2}$, $N = 6$, and $k = 2$.   Note that the tossing of six pennies at once is experimentally equivalent to the tossing of one penny six times in succession.

EXAMPLE 2.   A box contains 10 balls alike in every respect save color.   Seven are white and three are black.   A blindfolded person selects a ball at random and the color is then noted.   Then the ball is replaced and all balls thoroughly mixed again.   A second ball is withdrawn and followed by the same procedure, until 5 drawings have been made.   What is the probability that three balls drawn were white and two black?

The probability, p, for drawing a white ball is $\dfrac{7}{10}$; the probability, q, of drawing a black one is $\dfrac{3}{10}$.   The number of trials, N, is 5, and $k = 3$.   Then the desired probability is:

$$\frac{5!}{3!\,2!}\left(\frac{7}{10}\right)^3\left(\frac{3}{10}\right)^2 = 0.3087.$$

10.   The binomial frequency distribution.   The binomial theorem is not unfamiliar to students of high-school algebra. In its elementary form, it may be written as the equation:

$$(q + p)^N = q^N + \frac{N!}{1!(N-1)!}q^{N-1}p + \frac{N!}{2!(N-2)!}q^{N-2}p^2$$
$$+ \frac{N!}{3!(N-3)!}q^{N-3}p^3 + \cdots + \frac{N!}{k!(N-k)!}q^{N-k}p^k + \cdots + p^N, \tag{4}$$

where N is a positive integer.   The $(k+1)$th term, or general term of the expansion, is seen to be identical with formula

(3), which represents the probability for exactly k successes in N trials. Therefore, the terms of the binomial expansion in the right member of (4) represent, in order, the probabilities for exactly 0, 1, 2, 3, $\cdots$ N successes in N trials. If in formula (4) we let $q = p = \frac{1}{2}$ and $N = 6$, we obtain:

$$\left(\frac{1}{2} + \frac{1}{2}\right)^6 = \left(\frac{1}{2}\right)^6 + \frac{6!}{1!5!}\left(\frac{1}{2}\right)^5\left(\frac{1}{2}\right) + \frac{6!}{2!4!}\left(\frac{1}{2}\right)^4\left(\frac{1}{2}\right)^2 + \frac{6!}{3!3!}\left(\frac{1}{2}\right)^3\left(\frac{1}{2}\right)^3$$

$$+ \frac{6!}{4!2!}\left(\frac{1}{2}\right)^2\left(\frac{1}{2}\right)^4 + \frac{6!}{5!1!}\left(\frac{1}{2}\right)\left(\frac{1}{2}\right)^5 + \left(\frac{1}{2}\right)^6$$

$$= \frac{1}{64} + \frac{6}{64} + \frac{15}{64} + \frac{20}{64} + \frac{15}{64} + \frac{6}{64} + \frac{1}{64}.$$

The seven fractions above are those shown in Table IV–7, where they represented the probabilities for just 0, 1, 2, $\cdots$ 6 heads to appear when 6 pennies are tossed.

We define a *binomial frequency distribution* as one for which the frequencies are proportional to the successive terms of the binomial expansion (4). The name *Bernoulli distribution* is also employed, in honor of James Bernoulli (1654–1705), who first discovered it. A portion of Table IV–7 is

TABLE XIII–1

A Binomial Distribution. The Theoretical Number of Heads Appearing When Six Pennies Are Tossed 64 Times

No. of Heads	Theoretical Frequency
0.........	1
1.........	6
2.........	15
3.........	20
4.........	15
5.........	6
6.........	1
Total.........64	

reproduced here. The binomial distribution is theoretical, and may be used as a standard for comparison with certain kinds of distributions arising in practice.   Let us take a concrete case.

Suppose that on an average only ten per cent of the candidates applying for a certain branch of the aviation service pass the qualifying test.   If a group of 12 men take this test, what is the probability (a) that just five of them pass?   (b) that at least 5 fail?

(a)   Here $p = \dfrac{1}{10}$, $q = \dfrac{9}{10}$, $N = 12$, and $k = 5$; hence, the desired probability is:

$$\frac{12!}{5!7!}\left(\frac{9}{10}\right)^7\left(\frac{1}{10}\right)^5 = 0.00379.$$

(b)   The probability that at least 5 fail may be more easily computed by subtracting from 1 the sum of the probabilities that exactly 0, 1, 2, 3, and 4, respectively, fail.   This sum is:

$$\left(\frac{1}{10}\right)^{12} + \frac{12!}{1!11!}\left(\frac{1}{10}\right)^{11}\left(\frac{9}{10}\right) + \frac{12!}{2!10!}\left(\frac{1}{10}\right)^{10}\left(\frac{9}{10}\right)^2 + \frac{12!}{3!9!}\left(\frac{1}{10}\right)^{9}\left(\frac{9}{10}\right)^3$$

$$+ \frac{12!}{4!8!}\left(\frac{1}{10}\right)^{8}\left(\frac{9}{10}\right)^4,$$

or 0.00000341.   Subtracting this sum from 1, we obtain 0.99999659 as the probability that 5 or more fail.   This probability value is practically equivalent to certainty.

Let us imagine that 1,000 groups of 20 candidates each from a certain region have been examined.   In some of the groups of 20, none might have passed; in other groups, only 1; in other groups, 2; in other groups, 3; and so on up to 20.   The frequency distribution of 1,000 groups with class values ranging from 0 to 20 successful candidates would be expected to be binomial in type, and to approximate the frequencies obtained by expanding $1{,}000\left(\dfrac{9}{10} + \dfrac{1}{10}\right)^{20}$.   Any serious deviation from this standard might be accounted for by the fact that in the particular region from which the men came $p = \dfrac{1}{10}$ is an inaccurate measure; that is, that the region provides unusual candidates.

11. The arithmetic mean of a binomial distribution. If an event is repeated N times with the probability for k successes defined by (3), the theoretical mean value or the *expected number* of successes can be shown to be Np. For example, the expected number of heads when a penny is tossed 100 times is $100 \times \frac{1}{2}$, or 50. This means that in a long series of tosses of 100 pennies, we expect the number of heads to average 50, although the occurrence of exactly 50 might be rare. The number 50 is a theoretical mean based on the known probability, $\frac{1}{2}$, of getting a head when a penny is tossed.

We may take a second illustration from the last paragraph of the preceding section. The expected number of successful candidates in a group of 20 would be $20 \times \dfrac{1}{10} = 2$. The theoretical mean, 2, gives us the information that, "in the long run," an average of 2 candidates out of 20 would pass the examination.

The proof that Np is the theoretical mean makes use of the familiar method of computing the mean from a frequency distribution (Table XIII–2). The class values are the numbers, k, ranging from 0 to N. Ordinarily, we would multiply each k by its frequency, f, and divide the sum of the products by the frequency, N, so that

$$\bar{k} = \frac{1}{N}\Sigma fk.$$

Instead, we multiply each k by its relative frequency, $\dfrac{f}{N}$, and add: $\bar{k} = \Sigma\left(\dfrac{f}{N}\right)k$. The products, $\left(\dfrac{f}{N}\right)k$, have the common factor Np, which when removed reveals the remaining factors, in order, as the successive terms of the binomial expansion $(q + p)^{N-1}$. But $q + p = 1$; hence, the theoretical mean value reduces to Np.

12. The standard deviation of a binomial distribution If k is the actual number of successes in N trials with probability of success p, then Np is the (theoretical) mean and

TABLE XIII–2

COMPUTATION OF THE THEORETICAL ARITHMETIC MEAN OF A BINOMIAL
DISTRIBUTION

Number of Successes k	Relative Frequency $\dfrac{f}{N}$	Product $\left(\dfrac{f}{N}\right)k$
0	q^N	$q^N \cdot 0 \qquad\qquad = 0$
1	$\dfrac{N!}{1!(N-1)!}\, q^{N-1}p$	$\dfrac{N!}{1!(N-1)!}\, q^{N-1}\, p \cdot 1 \;= Np \cdot q^{N-1}$
2	$\dfrac{N!}{2!(N-2)!}\, q^{N-2}p^2$	$\dfrac{N!}{2!(N-2)!}\, q^{N-2}\, p^2 \cdot 2 \;= Np \cdot \dfrac{(N-1)!}{1!(N-2)!}q^{N-2}p$
3	$\dfrac{N!}{3!(N-3)!}\, q^{N-3}p^3$	$\dfrac{N!}{3!(N-3)!}\, q^{N-3}p^3 \cdot 3 = Np \cdot \dfrac{(N-1)!}{2!(N-3)!}\, q^{N-3}p^2$
.	.	.
.	.	.
.	.	.
N	p^N	$p^N \cdot N \qquad\qquad = Np \cdot p^{N-1}$
Total	$(q+p)^N$	$Np(q+p)^{N-1}$

$k - Np$ the deviation. The square of the *theoretical standard deviation*, σ^2, is defined as the mean of the squares of the deviations, $(k - Np)^2$. This might also be called the theoretical variance, the expected value of the square of the deviation, or the second moment about the mean. It can be shown that:

$$\sigma^2 = Npq;$$
whence, $\qquad\qquad \sigma \;= \sqrt{Npq}. \qquad\qquad\qquad (5)$

The proof that $\sigma^2 = Npq$ will not be given here, but it follows the general pattern of Table XIII–2. The square of each deviation from the mean, $(k - Np)^2$, is multiplied by its relative frequency, $\dfrac{f}{N}$. The products may be obtained in a convenient form for summing by writing $(k - Np)^2 = k^2 - 2kNp + N^2p^2$, and then letting

$$k^2 = k + k(k - 1).$$

The sum of the products, $\left(\dfrac{f}{N}\right)k$, has been shown to be

$Np(q + p)^{N-1}$, or Np.   The sum of the products $\dfrac{f}{N} \cdot k(k-1)$ can

be shown in similar fashion to be $N(N - 1)p^2(q + p)^{N-2}$ or

$N(N - 1)p^2$.   The sum of the products $\dfrac{f}{N}(-2kNp)$, writ-

ten as $-2Np\left(\dfrac{f}{N}\right)k$, is shown to be $-2Np(Np)$, and the sum

of the products $\dfrac{f}{N} \cdot N^2p^2$ is N^2p^2. Note that in all these

products the variable of summation is k.   All these sums reduce to:

$$Np + N(N - 1)p^2 - 2N^2p^2 + N^2p^2 = Np - Np^2$$
$$= Np(1 - p)$$
$$= Npq.$$

If a penny is tossed 100 times, or if 100 pennies are tossed once, the theoretical standard deviation will be $\sqrt{100 \times \frac{1}{2} \times \frac{1}{2}}$, or 5.   This means that "in the long run," when 100 pennies are tossed, the average deviation of the number of heads from the expected value, 50, as measured by σ, will be 5.

Similarly, for 20 candidates taking an examination with a probability, $\frac{1}{10}$, of passing, the theoretical standard deviation would be $\sqrt{20 \times \frac{1}{10} \times \frac{9}{10}} = 1.34$.   On an average, the number of candidates passing per group of 20 would differ from the mean value, 2, by 1.34.

13.   The derivation of the normal frequency curve.   Let us represent the terms of the binomial expansion (4) by a histogram whose rectangles have altitudes $y_0, y_1, y_2, \cdots y_N$, equal to the theoretical relative frequencies given by these terms. Thus,

$$y_k = \frac{N!}{k!(N-k)!}q^{N-k}p^k. \tag{6}$$

Let the rectangles have unit bases for which the successive mid-points are 0, 1, 2, $\cdots$ N. Then the area of the rectangle with altitude y_k represents the probability for exactly k successes, or the relative frequency of k. Obviously, the total area of the histogram is 1.

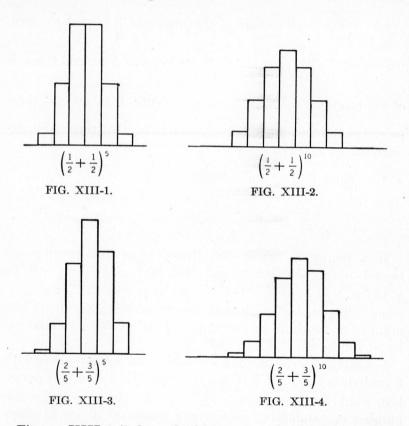

$$\left(\frac{1}{2}+\frac{1}{2}\right)^5$$

FIG. XIII-1.

$$\left(\frac{1}{2}+\frac{1}{2}\right)^{10}$$

FIG. XIII-2.

$$\left(\frac{2}{5}+\frac{3}{5}\right)^5$$

FIG. XIII-3.

$$\left(\frac{2}{5}+\frac{3}{5}\right)^{10}$$

FIG. XIII-4.

Figures XIII 1–7 show the histograms obtained for various values of p, q, and N. It should be observed from these figures that the histogram is perfectly symmetrical when $p = q = \frac{1}{2}$, but becomes more asymmetrical as the difference between p and q increases.   However, if N be increased, the histogram, at least in its main portion, tends to become symmetrical.

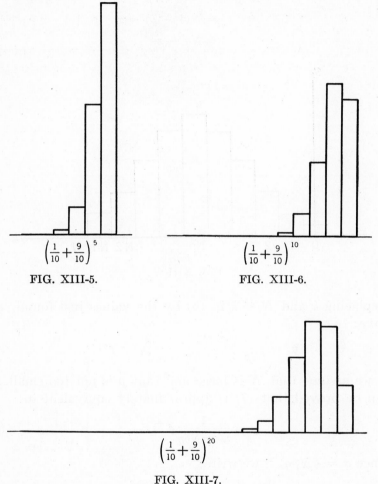

$$\left(\frac{1}{10}+\frac{9}{10}\right)^5$$

FIG. XIII-5.

$$\left(\frac{1}{10}+\frac{9}{10}\right)^{10}$$

FIG. XIII-6.

$$\left(\frac{1}{10}+\frac{9}{10}\right)^{20}$$

FIG. XIII-7.

Figure XIII-8 represents a histogram for the general case. Let us shift the origin to the point on the horizontal axis corresponding to the mean, Np, and let the new abscissa be x.   Then,

$$x = k - Np$$

and is an integer representing a deviation from the mean. Hence,

$$k = Np + x.$$
$$N - k = N - (Np + x)$$
$$= N(1 - p) - x$$
$$= Nq - x.$$

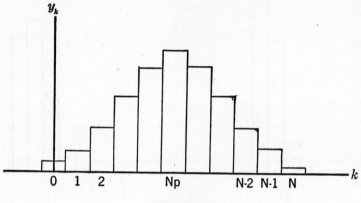

FIG. XIII-8.

Replacing k and $N - k$ in (6) by the values just found, we have:

$$y_x = \frac{N!}{(Np + x)!(Nq - x)!}q^{Nq-x}p^{Np+x}. \tag{7}$$

If we assume that N is large and that p is not too small, it can be proved that (7) is approximately equivalent to:

$$y = \frac{1}{\sqrt{2\pi Npq}}e^{-\frac{x^2}{2Npq}}. \tag{8}$$

Since $\sigma = (Npq)^{\frac{1}{2}}$, we write:

$$y = \frac{1}{\sigma\sqrt{2\pi}}e^{-\frac{1}{2}\left(\frac{x}{\sigma}\right)^2}. \tag{9}$$

The y_x of equation (7) is a probability for a deviation, x, from the mean, Np, since $x = k - Np$, and is represented by the area (or the altitude) of a rectangle of unit base the mid-point of which is x. The probability that the number of successes, k, does not differ from the expected value, Np, by more than d is given by the sum of the areas of the rectangles within the interval from $-d - \frac{1}{2}$ to $d + \frac{1}{2}$ (Figure XIII-9).

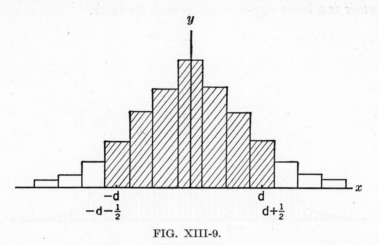

FIG. XIII-9.

When N is large and p is not too small, equation (9) is regarded as defining a curve best fitting the mid-points of the upper bases of the rectangles. In this case, the probability, P_d, for a deviation not exceeding d in numerical value is given approximately by the area under the curve from $-d - \frac{1}{2}$ to $d + \frac{1}{2}$, that is, by the definite integral:

$$P_d = \frac{1}{\sigma\sqrt{2\pi}} \int_{-d-\frac{1}{2}}^{d+\frac{1}{2}} e^{-\frac{x^2}{2\sigma^2}}\, dx. \tag{10}$$

(See Section X-5.)

When N is very large we consider the area from $-d$ to $+d$ to be a sufficiently accurate approximation, and so set:

$$P_d = \frac{1}{\sigma\sqrt{2\pi}} \int_{-d}^{d} e^{-\frac{x^2}{2\sigma^2}}\, dx. \tag{11}$$

(See Figure XIII-10.) The results thus obtained are of the highest importance and are embodied in the fundamental *De Moivre-Laplace Theorem:*

If p is the probability of success in each of N trials, where N is a large number, and p is not too small, the probability that the *deviation of the number of successes,* **k**, *from the expected value,* **Np**, *will not be greater numerically than a positive number,* **d**, *is given approximately by integrals* (10) *and* (11), *where the former is a better approximation than the latter.*

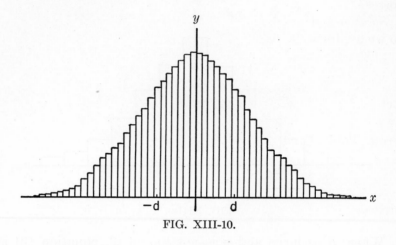

FIG. XIII-10.

14.   Applications.   Useful changes of variable are effected as follows: Let

$$t = \frac{x}{\sigma}, \qquad d' = \frac{d}{\sigma}.$$

The former is familiar.   (Section X-4.)   Under this transformation, the probability $P_{d'}$ can be shown to be given by the integral (11):

$$P_{d'} = \frac{1}{\sqrt{2\pi}} \int_{-d'}^{d'} e^{-\frac{t^2}{2}} dt$$

$$= \int_{-d'}^{d'} \phi(t) dt.$$

Because of the symmetry of the curve (See Section X–5),

$$P_{d'} = 2 \int_{0}^{d'} \phi(t) dt. \tag{12}$$

Table F of the Supplementary Tables enables one to find values of $P_{d'}$.   The use of this table was described in Section X-5.

EXAMPLE 1.   A coin was tossed 100 times and came up heads 53 times.   Since the expected number of heads is 50, there was a discrepancy of 3.   What is the probability of getting a deviation numerically not greater than 3 on 100 tosses?

Solution.   Here N is only moderately large and $p = q = \frac{1}{2}$, so we use formula (10).

$$\sigma = \sqrt{Npq} = \sqrt{100 \times \tfrac{1}{2} \times \tfrac{1}{2}} = 5.$$

Let
$$d' = \frac{d + \frac{1}{2}}{\sigma} = \frac{3.5}{5} = 0.7.$$

From Table F we find that corresponding to $t = d' = 0.7$,

$$\int_0^{0.7} \phi(t)dt = 0.2580.$$

Hence,

$$P_{d'} = 2 \times 0.2580 = 0.5160.$$

There is, therefore, a probability of about 0.52 of getting a deviation numerically not greater than 3.   This fact may be stated in another manner as follows.   In 100 experiments of tossing 100 pennies, we expect 52 of these experiments to show differences from the mean not greater than 3.

EXAMPLE 2.   According to the mortality table, Table K, of 74,173 persons alive on their 45th birthday, 64,563 will be alive on their 55th birthday.   If 10,000 businessmen 45 years of age, selected from a certain city, are found to have sustained 1,368 deaths during the next decade, what conclusions may be drawn?

Solution.   The probability that a man of the given age dies within ten years is estimated as:

$$p = \frac{74{,}173 - 64{,}563}{74{,}173} = \frac{9{,}610}{74{,}173} = 0.1296.$$

The expected number of deaths in the group of 10,000 is:

$$Np = 10{,}000 \times 0.1296 = 1{,}296.$$

The deviation from the expected value is:

$$d = 1{,}368 - 1{,}296 = 72;$$

$$\sigma = (10{,}000 \times 0.1296 \times 0.8704)^{1/2} = 33.6;$$

$$d' = \frac{72}{33.6} = 2.14;$$

$$P_{d'} = 2\int_0^{2.14} \phi(t)dt = 2 \times 0.4838 = 0.9676.$$

The probability for deviations as great as or greater than 72 is $1 - 0.9676 = 0.0324$, or approximately 0.03. We say, then, that in only about 3 per cent of samples of 10,000 persons each would we expect a discrepancy from the theoretical mean, 1,296, of as many as or more than 72. This unusual result might indicate that this group of businessmen has a mortality rate different from that of the population as a whole.

Note that in this problem p is fairly small, being equal to about 0.13, but that N is very large, so we feel justified in using the normal probability function.

EXAMPLE 3. In making 26 cuts with a pack of playing cards, what is the probability of cutting a black ace three times or more?

Solution. Here N is not very large and p is quite small, so that we may suspect that the approximation (10) is not valid. The probabilities for cutting a black ace 0, 1, 2, 3, $\cdots$, 26 times are given by the successive terms of the binomial expansion,

$$\left(\frac{25}{26} + \frac{1}{26}\right)^{26} = \left(\frac{25}{26}\right)^{26} + \frac{26!}{1!\,25!}\left(\frac{25}{26}\right)^{25}\left(\frac{1}{26}\right)$$

$$+ \frac{26!}{2!\,24!}\left(\frac{25}{26}\right)^{24}\left(\frac{1}{26}\right)^2 + \cdots + \left(\frac{1}{26}\right)^{26}.$$

It is fairly evident that the histogram determined by the terms of this expansion is far from symmetrical because the first few terms of the binomial are relatively large compared with the later ones. There is, therefore, no justification for assuming that a normal curve can be approximately fitted to the histogram. The values of the first three terms above are 0.361, 0.375, and 0.188, so that the probability for cutting a black ace less than three times is their sum, 0.924.   Hence, the probability of cutting a black ace three times or more is $1 - 0.924$, or 0.076.

15. Probable error. The illustrative problems of the preceding section were all reduced to the following type. Given a value, $t = d'$, what is the corresponding value of the probability, $P_{d'}$? But the inverse problem is also possible. Given a value, $P_{d'}$, what must the associated value, d', be? To a value of the probability, $P_{d'} = \frac{1}{2}$, given by (12), there corresponds a value, d'.

If

$$\frac{1}{2} = 2 \int_0^t \phi(t)dt,$$

$$0.25 = \int_0^t \phi(t)dt.$$

The value t or d' which corresponds to $P = 0.25$ is found by inverse interpolation in Table F to be 0.6745.   Since $d' = \dfrac{d}{\sigma}$,

$$d = d'\sigma$$

$$= 0.6745\sigma.$$

Thus, for a value taken at random from a normally distributed population, there is a probability of $\frac{1}{2}$ that the deviation, d', is not numerically greater than 0.6745σ.   This value of d' is called the *probable error*, and is often designated by the abbreviation P. E.   The notion of the probable error used to be considered an important one, but it is now gradually diminishing in use.

EXAMPLE.   A penny is tossed 1,000 times.   What is the probable error in the number of heads?

Solution.

$$\sigma = \sqrt{Npq} = \sqrt{1000 \times \tfrac{1}{2} \times \tfrac{1}{2}} = 15.8.$$

P. E. $= 0.6745 \times 15.8 = 11$, approximately.   Hence, in 1,000 tosses there is an even chance of obtaining a discrepancy numerically less than 11 between the expected number, 500, and the actual number.

16. Other properties of the binomial distribution. The mean and the standard deviation of the distribution defined by $(q + p)^N$ are but two important measures associated with the binomial distribution. It may be shown that the most probable number of successes or the theoretical mode is the positive integer, k, determined by the double inequality:

$$Np - q \leqq k \leqq Np + p.$$

Since p and q are positive fractions having a sum unity, it follows that the most probable value, to within a proper fraction, is Np. In case $Np - q$ and $Np + p$ are integers, the equality signs hold in (3), and there will be two equal adjacent modal values.

As one illustration, consider the most probable number of black balls drawn when 10 drawings with replacements are made from a box containing 2 black and 4 white balls. Here $N = 10$, $p = \frac{1}{3}$, $q = \frac{2}{3}$; k is the integer determined by the inequality:

$$\frac{10}{3} - \frac{2}{3} \leqq k \leqq \frac{10}{3} + \frac{1}{3}.$$

Hence, $k = 3$.

As a second illustration, we find the most probable number, when 20 drawings are made, to be the integer k such that:

$$\frac{20}{3} - \frac{2}{3} \leqq k \leqq \frac{20}{3} + \frac{1}{3},$$

so that k may be either 6 or 7.

The third, fourth, and other higher moments of this important distribution may also be found. In fact,

$$\alpha_3 = \frac{q - p}{(Npq)^{1/2}}; \tag{13}$$

$$\alpha_4 = \frac{1}{Npq} - \frac{6}{N} + 3. \tag{14}$$

It will be recalled (Section IX-12) that α_3 measures the skewness of a distribution. Note that in (13) α_3 approaches zero as N becomes infinite. Likewise, α_4 (Section IX-13) measures the kurtosis. In fact, we defined the excess as equal to α_3 -3. In (14), if N becomes infinite, α_4 approaches 3; hence, the excess approaches zero, as it should in a normal distribution.

17. The Poisson distribution. In deriving formula (9), we assumed that p was not very small. If the probability, p, for an event to happen, is excessively small, the approximation is poor and a better formula must be sought. In this case, the event may be termed rare. Examples of rare events are drawing the ace of diamonds from a pack of cards, throwing a double six with a pair of dice, or contracting a case of scurvy in Boston. Under appropriate assumptions, it may be proved that the probability for exactly k occurrences of the rare event in N trials is given by the formula:

$$P_k = \frac{m^k}{k!}e^{-m}, \tag{15}$$

where the expected value or theoretical mean

$$m = Np. \tag{16}$$

The expression on the right of (15) is called the *Poisson exponential function*. The values of P_k for values of m from 0 to 37 have been computed and are readily obtained from Fisher's Tables (Ref. 28). The histogram or polygon constructed from values of P_k will be very skew and is often of the J-type.

The question as to what constitutes a small value of p is not easily answered, since the value of N also influences the shape of the distribution. It has been suggested that the Poisson formula should be employed when p is less than 0.03.

XIII—Exercises

Permutations and Combinations

1. If there are three roads leading from Smithville to Whiteside, and two roads from Whiteside to Jonesport, in how many ways can a person go from Smithville to Jonesport?

2. If a club has three candidates for president, two for vice-president, and four for secretary-treasurer, in how many ways may the officers be elected?

3. How many different arrangements can be made from the letters of the word *distance* by taking five at a time?

4. Find the number of permutations which can be made from the letters a, b, c, d, e taken (a) four at a time; (b) all at a time?

5. If a president, vice-president, secretary, and treasurer are to be elected from a club of 11 members, in how many ways may the election result?

6. A witness to a bank robbery said that the license number of the criminals' automobile was a six-figure number of which the first three figures were 487. He did not recall the last three figures, but was positive that all three were different. How many automobile license numbers must the police check?

7. A football team consists of seven line men and four backs. There are twelve candidates for the line and seven for the backfield. In how many different ways may a team be "lined up"?

8. In an examination paper, any three questions may be omitted from the ten questions given. In how many ways may selections be made?

9. In how many ways may a committee of four be chosen from a club of nine members?

10. (a) In how many ways may an assignment of five problems be made from a group of twelve problems?

(b) How many times will the most difficult problem be assigned?

11. In how many ways may a committee consisting of five men and four women be chosen from ten men and seven women?

12. In how many ways may a party of five men be chosen from a company of nine men? In how many of these parties will a particular man, Mr. Smith, be included?

13. How many different sums of money can be formed from a cent, a nickel, a dime, a half-dollar, and a dollar bill?

14. If five pennies are tossed, in how many ways may just two of them show heads?

15. If seven pennies are tossed, in how many ways may just four of them show tails?

Simple Probability

16. If three dice are thrown, what is the probability of obtaining the sum 17?

17. The probability that A wins a race is $\frac{1}{3}$; that B wins a different race, is $\frac{1}{4}$. What is the probability that: (a) both win? (b) neither wins? (c) A loses, B wins? (d) A wins, B loses?

18. If 7 pennies are tossed, what is the probability that just 5 are heads?

19. If 10 pennies are tossed, what is the probability that exactly 7 come up heads?

20. A bag contains 7 black balls and 3 white balls. After each drawing, the ball drawn is replaced. Find the probability of getting exactly 3 black balls and 2 white balls in 5 drawings.

21. A small, regular tetrahedron has 3 faces painted black and 1 red. If 7 such tetrahedrons are tossed, what is the probability that just 2 stand on the red face? that just 3 stand on a black face?

22. What is the probability of obtaining (a) exactly 3 heads when 7 pennies are tossed? (b) at least 3 heads?

The Binomial Distribution

23. A penny is tossed 64 times. Find (a) the expected number of heads; (b) the theoretical standard deviation.

24. A pair of dice is thrown 60 times. Find (a) the expected number of times that the sum 10 appears; (b) the expected value of the square of the deviation.

25. William Shanks (1812–1882) computed the number π to 707 decimal places. How many times would you expect him to have found the digit 0?

26. In tossing a coin 400 times, what is the probability that the number of heads appearing (a) exceeds the expected number by at least 25? (b) falls short of the expected number by less than 10?

27. The chance of guessing a certain card correctly is $\frac{1}{5}$. In 800 trials, there were 207 correct guesses. Was this an unusual result? Why?

28. Compute to three decimal places the probability of obtaining less than four heads when a penny is tossed 10 times.

29. If two guinea pigs, one of pure black race and the other of pure white race, are mated, the probability that an offspring of the second generation is pure white is $\frac{1}{4}$. What is the probability that among 400 such offspring more than 115 are pure white?

30. The probability of winning a game of "craps" is 0.495. If a player won 27 games out of 50, what could you say about this result?

31. According to the American Experience Mortality Table, about 17 per cent of persons 50 years of age die before reaching 60 years. What might you conclude about a group of 1,000 persons of age 50 of whom 140 died before reaching their sixtieth birthday?

32. The probability of cutting an "honor" card is $\frac{5}{13}$. If 13 cuts are made, what is the probability of cutting fewer than four "honor" cards?

33. What is the probability of obtaining a value in a given sample (assumed to have normal distribution) which differs numerically from the expected value by more than the standard deviation?

34. How many times must you toss a penny in order that the chance of getting a deviation from the mean value of more than 10 is $\frac{2}{5}$?

35. A pair of dice is tossed 70 times. What is the most probable number of times that the sum of 10 appears?

36. In a certain unfair game of chance, the probability that a certain man wins is $\frac{3}{5}$. If he makes 100 bets of one dollar each, what is the probability that his profit is at least ten dollars?

37. Referring to Exercise 21, find the most probable number of times that red does not appear in 27 tosses of a single tetrahedron.

38. On an average, 32 people out of 100 afflicted with a certain malady die. If under a new treatment 47 out of 200 die, what might you say about the new treatment?

MEASURES OF RELIABILITY; THE CHI SQUARE TEST

❖⫶⫶⫶❖

> "Everywhere one observes the unfortunate habit of generalizing, without demonstration, from special cases."
>
> NIELS ABEL, 1826.

1. Sample and universe. It was stated in the opening chapter that statistical analysis might be divided into two broad types, empirical and theoretical. The former type has been the major concern of this book. Succinct but adequate descriptions of the chief aspects of data obtained by observation or experiment have been discussed. As yet little in drawing conclusions about a universe or population of variates from a single sample selected at random from it has been attempted. It will be the object of this chapter to describe briefly the mode of approach to this seemingly difficult problem and to state some of the most illuminating and useful results.

2. Some basic assumptions. Suppose we wished to investigate the statures of American college freshmen. We could proceed by taking a random sample composed of a large number of such individuals, say 500. By a random sample we mean, not 500 freshmen drawn in haphazard fashion from one college or from one particular state or region, but a group of 500 individuals each one of whom appears as the result of a selection made by pure chance from all freshmen everywhere in the country. We could compute the arithmetic mean, the standard deviation, the median, and so on, of such a sample group. We might feel that these statistical constants were fairly representative of the indefinitely large population of college freshmen as a whole, yet we could not be certain that the sample selected was truly typical of all freshmen any more than we could be sure that a single throw of ten pennies with seven heads appearing is typical of all throws of ten pennies. If we could select, however, a large number of samples of approximately equal numbers of freshmen and could compute the desired averages for each, we should then have available a frequency distribution for each statistical average computed. To be specific, suppose we had 1,000 samples of 500 freshmen each. We could then form a frequency distribution of the 1,000 arithmetic mean heights. This frequency distribution would yield an arithmetic mean of means, a standard deviation of means, a median of means, and so on. Similarly, we could form frequency distributions of the 1,000 standard deviations, of the 1,000 medians, and so on. In the case of the arithmetic mean of means, we would probably feel such confidence in this average that we would accept it as a highly accurate measure of the true mean height of college freshmen. Similarly, the standard deviation of the 1,000 means would form an excellent measure of the variability of the means among the samples.

That the procedure described above is too laborious, if not in many cases impossible, is evident, yet the underlying theory will serve as a guide in studying the reliability of a given sample. Our problem, then, is to find some index of accuracy of the results obtained from a single random sample.

We are well aware that in a sample toss of 500 pennies we may obtain any number of heads from 0 to 500. Suppose that we record the results for 1,000 such sample tosses. The number of heads obtained yields a frequency distribution of 1,000 results whose arithmetic mean will be in the neighborhood of the expected number, 250. One may note the following characteristics of the distribution: (1) that the probability for heads remains the same for each penny, (2) that the result obtained in a sample is not influenced by results in other samples, and (3) that the samples are all of the same type.

Now, in the case of the 1,000 samples of 500 freshman heights, we may assume, for our present purposes, in like manner, (1) that there is an underlying constant probability, determined in some unknown way by biological conditions, let us say, that the height of a freshman lies within a given interval; (2) that the resulting statistic obtained from any sample is independent of that obtained in other samples; and (3) that the samples are all essentially of the same type. Under these hypotheses we may treat, for example, the distribution of the 1,000 arithmetic means as binomial in character and study the characteristics of a single sample as compared with the general characteristics of not merely 1,000 samples, but of an infinite number of them. In other words, we may pass from the finite, discrete binomial distribution to the infinite, continuous normal distribution. We may ask questions like the following: How does the arithmetic mean, $\bar{x}$, of this random sample compare with the true arithmetic mean, $\bar{\bar{x}}$ (read, "x double-bar"), of the population? Is the difference between $\bar{x}$ and $\bar{\bar{x}}$ so great that we must consider $\bar{x}$ to be an unusual rather than a usual value?

With these considerations in mind, we proceed to a discussion of variations or fluctuations in random samples.

3. Standard error. We have seen that, for a large number of samples, each *statistic*, such as the arithmetic mean, the standard deviation, the median, and so forth, will have its own arithmetic mean and standard deviation. Thus, there will be an arithmetic mean of means and a standard deviation of means, an arithmetic mean of standard deviations and a standard deviation of standard deviations, and so on. *The standard deviation of any statistic is called the* **standard error** *of that statistic.* There will be, then, a standard error of the mean, a standard error of the median, a standard error of the standard deviation, and so forth. An important problem set for the statistician is that of finding the best estimate of the standard error from the results given by a single sample.

We have seen that a set of variates, x_1, x_2, x_3, $\cdot$ $\cdot$ $\cdot$ x_N, commonly arises from a normally distributed population. The so-called normal function, $f(x)$, has been derived. (See Section XIII-13.) $\bar{x}$ is a function of these variates; in fact, it is $\dfrac{1}{N}$th their sum:

$$\bar{x} = \frac{1}{N}(x_1 + x_2 + x_3 + \cdot \cdot \cdot + x_N).$$

The question then arising is this: If a set of variates is normally distributed, how will $\dfrac{1}{N}$th their sum be distributed? Mathematical statistics has shown that the mean, $\bar{x}$, will be normally distributed also.

Again, the second moment, ν_{2x}, is a function of these same variates; in fact, it is $\dfrac{1}{N}$th the sum of their squares:

$$\nu_{2x} = \frac{1}{N}(x_1^2 + x_2^2 + x_3^2 + \cdot \cdot \cdot + x_N^2).$$

(See Section IX-8.) How, then, will ν_{2x}, a function of the sum of the squares of normally distributed variates, be distributed? The answer to this question has to do with the distribution function of σ_x. Questions such as these, phrased not only for a normal population, but also for non-normal populations, have stimulated mathematical statistics to a remarkable degree in recent years. They have led to results of far-reaching importance and have pointed the way to other unsolved problems.

The mathematical logic whereby certain useful formulas for the standard error are derived will have to be dispensed with here, but we can, nevertheless, enjoy the results. The standard error of a given statistic is usually symbolized by σ with an appropriate subscript. Thus, $\sigma_{\bar{x}}$ denotes the standard error of the mean, $\bar{x}$; σ_σ, the standard error of the standard deviation; and so forth.

4. Standard error of the mean. It is natural to expect that the frequency distribution, $F(\bar{x})$, of the means, $\bar{x}$, of a set of samples will show much less variability or dispersion with respect to the true or population mean, $\bar{\bar{x}}$, than the frequency distribution, $f(x)$, of the variates, x, obtained from the population itself. This fact is illustrated in Figure XIV-1. In fact, we should expect the average deviation of the $\bar{x}$'s from $\bar{\bar{x}}$ to diminish as the number, N, in each sample

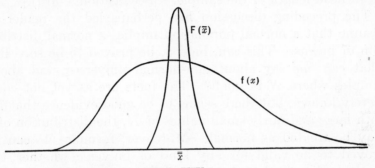

FIG. XIV-1.

increased; and this, upon investigation, is found to be the case. The theoretical standard deviation of the arithmetic means of all samples—in other words, the standard error of the mean, $\sigma_{\bar{x}}$—is estimated to be approximately equal to $\dfrac{\sigma_x}{\sqrt{N}}$, where σ_x is the standard deviation of a given sample and N is the number in the sample. Hence, we write:

$$\sigma_{\bar{x}} = \frac{\sigma_x}{\sqrt{N}}. \tag{1}$$

$\sigma_{\bar{x}}$ is, therefore, a measure of the variability or the reliability of the mean, $\bar{x}$, of a sample. The variability decreases or the reliability increases as $\sqrt{N}$, but is obviously dependent upon the value of the standard deviation, σ_x, of the single sample. When N is small, a better estimate is obtained by replacing $\sqrt{N}$ by $\sqrt{N-1}$.

For the head lengths of English criminals, $\bar{x} = 191.8$, $\sigma_x = 6.48$, and $N = 462$; hence,

$$\sigma_{\bar{x}} = \frac{6.48}{\sqrt{462}}$$

$$= 0.301$$

We may interpret this result roughly as follows. The mean head length of a sample of 462 criminals deviates some 68 per cent of the time from the true mean not more than about 0.3 millimeters. [See Section X-6 (iii).] For this reason, we do not feel justified in considering more than four digits as significant when we write 191.8 as the computed mean head length of the sample. [See Section V-5(ii).]

The preceding discussion has perhaps led the reader to assume that a normal population implies a normal distribution of means. This can, indeed, be proved to be so. But what can one say about non-normal universes, and about samples where N is small? The facts are as yet not completely known, but there seems to be good evidence that for both large and fairly small values of N, the distribution of $\bar{x}$ may be treated as normal. Moreover, formula (1) can be proved to be valid for any kind of universe whether the resulting distribution of $\bar{x}$ is normal or not, provided that the σ_x in the numerator of (1) is interpreted as the standard deviation of the universe and not of the sample.

5. Confidence or fiducial limits. Suppose that we wish to make the best possible estimate of the true value of the mean head length, $\bar{\bar{x}}$, of *all* English criminals, this estimate to be based only on the data given in our single sample of 462 criminals. We would like to find two values, $\bar{x}_1$ and $\bar{x}_2$, such that we may assert that $\bar{\bar{x}}$ lies between them; and in making such an assertion, we wish our probability of being correct to be, let us say, 0.98. The two values, $\bar{x}_1$ and $\bar{x}_2$, as yet unknown, constitute the 98 per cent *confidence* or *fiducial limits* for $\bar{\bar{x}}$. To find $\bar{x}_1$ and $\bar{x}_2$, we proceed in a manner not wholly unfamiliar. Recall that the standard variable, t, was defined as $\dfrac{x - \bar{x}}{\sigma_x}$ and that a transformation from the original variable, x, to the standard variable, t, enabled us to employ advantageously the table of values associated with $\phi(t)$. We therefore set up an analogous expression, $\dfrac{\bar{x} - \bar{\bar{x}}}{\sigma_{\bar{x}}}$, where $\sigma_{\bar{x}}$ is given by (1). We recall that a probability,

P, less than $\frac{1}{2}$, can always be interpreted as the area under the curve of $\phi(t)$ from the origin to a given positive value of t. This area is expressed as $\int_0^t \phi(t)dt$ and can be found in Table F of the Supplement. A probability of 0.98 can be expressed as approximately twice the area under the curve from the origin to the value $t = 2.33$. The value of t corresponding to a probability of $\frac{1}{2}$ (0.98), or 0.49, is found by solving t in the equation:

$$0.49 = \int_0^t \phi(t)dt.$$

We merely employ Table F in an inverse manner. Corresponding to the area 0.4900, we find that t is practically equal to 2.33. We seek, therefore, the value $\bar{x}$ such that the probability is 0.98 that *any* mean of a sample differs numerically from $\bar{x}$ by less than our particular mean, 191.8, does. Since $t = 2.33$ corresponds to a probability 0.4900, we write:

$$\frac{|191.8 - \bar{x}|}{\sigma_{\bar{x}}} < 2.33.$$

But since $\sigma_{\bar{x}}$ was found by means of (1) to be equal to 0.301, we have:

$$\frac{|191.8 - \bar{x}|}{0.301} < 2.33,$$

or $$|191.8 - \bar{x}| < 0.702.$$

Hence, $$191.8 - 0.702 < \bar{x} < 191.8 + .702,$$

or $$191.1 < \bar{x} < 192.5.$$

Hence, we may state that the mean head length of *all* English criminals lies between 191.1 and 192.5 millimeters, and our probability of being correct in making this statement is 0.98; that is, we expect to be correct 98 per cent of the time. The two numbers 191.1 and 192.5 are called the 98 per cent confidence or fiducial limits for the mean head length.

It should be noted that the discussion of this section is valid only for samples in which N is considerably greater than 30, say for $N > 100$. For $N \leq 30$, the assumption that $t = \dfrac{\bar{x} - \bar{\bar{x}}}{\sigma_{\bar{x}}}$ constitutes a normal distribution is not valid. Use must be made of *Fisher's t-Distribution*. For values of N between 30 and 100, we may use the variable $t = \dfrac{\bar{x} - \bar{\bar{x}}}{\sigma'_{\bar{x}}}$, where $\sigma'_{\bar{x}} = \dfrac{\sigma_x}{\sqrt{N - 3}}$, for t will then be normally distributed.

6. Standard error of the median. Provided the population sampled is normally distributed, the standard error of the median, σ_m, can be shown to be given by the formula:

$$\sigma_m = \frac{1.2533\,\sigma_x}{\sqrt{N}}, \tag{2}$$

which may be written in the less precise but more easily remembered form:

$$\sigma_m = \frac{5}{4} \frac{\sigma_x}{\sqrt{N}}. \tag{2a}$$

Since the standard error of the median is about 25 per cent greater than that of the mean, it follows that the mean is a more reliable average than the median, and this despite the fact that the median and mean coincide in a normal distribution.

7. Other standard errors. The standard errors for a very large number of statistical measures have been calculated. Some of the more important ones are listed below.

Standard Error of the Standard Deviation (Normal Population):

$$\sigma_\sigma = \frac{\sigma_x}{\sqrt{2N}}. \tag{3}$$

Standard Error of a Quartile (Normal Population):

$$\sigma_{Q_1} = \sigma_{Q_3} = \frac{1.3626\,\sigma_x}{\sqrt{N}}. \tag{4}$$

Standard Error of the Semi-interquartile Range (Normal Population):

$$\sigma_Q = \frac{0.7867\,\sigma_x}{\sqrt{N}}, \tag{5}$$

$$= \frac{1.6495Q}{\sqrt{2N}}. \tag{5a}$$

It should be borne in mind that these formulas are valid for reasonably large values of N, say $N > 100$. Special procedures for small samples are generally more complicated.

8.   Standard error of the coefficient of correlation. When the universe may be represented by a normal frequency surface, we may write:

$$\sigma_r = \frac{1 - r^2}{\sqrt{N}}. \tag{6}$$

This formula is reasonably valid under the following conditions:

$r \leqq 0.5$, and N at least 100;

$0.5 < r < 0.8$, and N at least 400.

For values of $r \geqq 0.8$, special handling is usually necessary.

Let us apply formula (6) to the data for the heights and weights of college girls (Table XII-3). $N = 285$, $r = 0.44$; so that the formula is applicable.

$$\sigma_r = \frac{1 - (0.44)^2}{\sqrt{285}}$$

$$= 0.048.$$

Roughly, this means that we might expect an average deviation of about 0.05 in values of r from the true value. More careful statements about the interval within which r probably lies could be made by establishing fiducial limits.

9.   Probable error. The term *probable error* was mentioned in Section XIII-15.   The probable error of any statistic can be obtained by multiplying its standard error by the quantity 0.6745.

10.   The reliability of a sample. We have discussed briefly the reliability of an individual statistic such as the mean, the median, the quartile deviation, and so forth, but we have not yet touched upon the reliability of the whole sample itself. This is an important concept and worthy of our attention.

The normal function of distribution, $\phi(t) = \dfrac{1}{\sqrt{2\pi}} e^{-\frac{t^2}{2}}$, has been seen to be a dominating one in most of the statistical discussions up to this point, but there are other functions defining distributions of variates which become centers of interest in other portions of statistical study. Many of these arise from a consideration of the problem of small samples, a problem which belongs primarily to a more advanced field of statistics. Among such functions we may cite the χ^2-function (read "Chi-square"), to which we now turn our attention. Its distribution is defined by the formula:

$$y = \frac{1}{K} e^{-\frac{\chi^2}{2}} (\chi^2)^{\frac{m}{2} - 1},\tag{7}$$

where

$$K = 2^{\frac{m}{2}} \left(\frac{m}{2} - 1 \right)!,$$

and where m, the number of degrees of freedom, will be explained presently.

11. An example. The data of Table IV-8 will serve to illustrate one form of application of the χ^2-test. These data represent the actual frequency distribution which resulted when six pennies were tossed 128 times as compared with the theoretical distribution. We reproduce in Table XIV-1 the data, slightly altered in form for a reason to be explained later.

TABLE XIV-1

No. of Heads	Theoretical	Actual
0 or 1........	14	12
2........	30	28
3........	40	44
4........	30	30
5 or 6........	14	14
Total.......	128	128

If p_i is the probability for a given number of heads when six pennies are tossed, the expected number (Section XIII-11) of successes or the theoretical frequency in N trials is Np_i. Let f_i be the corresponding actual frequency; then $f_i - Np_i$ represents the discrepancy between the two. We now define the quantity Chi-square by the formula:

$$\chi^2 = \sum_{i=1}^{n} \left[\frac{(f_i - Np_i)^2}{Np_i} \right], \tag{8}$$

where n is the number of frequencies. For the data above,

$$\chi^2 = \frac{(-2)^2}{14} + \frac{(-2)^2}{30} + \frac{4^2}{40} + \frac{0^2}{30} + \frac{0^2}{14}$$

$$= 0.82.$$

It is clear that if $\chi^2 = 0$, the agreement between the theoretical and the actual frequencies will be perfect. As χ^2 increases, the disparity between the two sets of values increases also. The question which then arises is the following: What is the probability that in a given sample the discrepancy between the actual values and the theoretical will be as large as or larger than χ^2? In the case of the data cited above, what is the probability that the deviations between actual frequencies and theoretical will be as great as 0.82?

The answer to this question depends upon the manner in which χ^2 is distributed, and this has been found to be governed by the function (7). However, this function contains a *parameter*, that is to say, a constant, m, the value of which changes with each set of data. The "variable constant," m, is always equal to the *number of degrees of freedom* which the variates enjoy. Let us explain this phrase. The total number of classes listed in Table XIV-1 is 5. Let us call each class or compartment of division a *cell*. Theoretically, the actual frequencies or *cell frequencies* resulting in an experiment or sample set of 128 tosses could follow any pattern of distribution whatsoever, subject to just one restriction—as soon as four cell frequencies had been allocated, the fifth would be automatically determined, since the total frequency, N, is given, 128. Thus, the number of degrees of freedom which the cell frequencies possess is 4, one less than the number of cells, 5.

Values of χ^2 corresponding to different values of m and to convenient values of the probability are listed in Table J of the Supplement. In using this table, we seek in the row corresponding to the appropriate m the value of χ^2 found from the given sample. The value of the corresponding probability, P, gives us the chance for discrepancies as large as χ^2. P will usually have to be estimated by rough inverse interpolation, as the exact value of χ^2 will hardly ever be found in the table. In the data for tossing pennies, $m = 4$ and $\chi^2 = 0.82$; hence, P exceeds 0.90. Apparently, then, the probability for a sample to deviate by at least as much as 0.82 is close to unity, and we say that the actual frequencies are in close agreement with the theoretical. This problem, however, cannot be disposed of in such a summary fashion. If we ask, what is the probability for a value of χ^2 as small as or smaller than 0.82, we get a very small value for $1 - P$. It is just as unusual to obtain very close agreement with theory as it is to obtain a wide deviation from it. Thus, when we toss 100 pennies, we really do not "expect" to get the expected number of heads, 50. A result of just 50 heads should surprise us. To refer back to our illustrative exercise, the actual results were surprisingly close, but not impossible.

Inasmuch as the conclusions drawn from our single example might confuse the reader, we shall presently give other examples. But before doing so, it will be well to call attention to various restrictions surrounding the use of the χ^2-test.

12. **Remarks on the χ^2-test.** (a) The total frequency, N, should be fairly large, say $N > 50$.

(b) Each cell frequency, f, should exceed 5 at least, and should preferably be much larger. When cell frequencies are too small, they may be grouped together. This was done in forming Table XIV-1 from Table IV-8.

(c) The number of classes or cells should not be too large. It is safer to have fewer than 20.

(d) The conditions imposed on the cell frequencies from which the number of degrees of freedom was computed must be expressible as equations of the first degree. Thus, in the example of the text, $f_1 + f_2 + f_3 + f_4 + f_5 = 128$.

(e) Values of P near unity as well as those near zero excite suspicion concerning the character of the sample.

If $P < 0.02$, the sample is usually considered not to be a random one. It is highly improbable that such a divergence from the expected result would occur. If $0.02 < P < 0.05$, the sample deserves, at least, our suspicion.

13. Goodness of fit. The χ^2-test may be applied advantageously to graduated data. Consider, for example, the graduated frequency distribution of head lengths shown in Table X-2 and reproduced here in altered form. In Table XIV-2, certain frequencies near the extremities of the table have been combined.

TABLE XIV-2

COMPUTATION OF χ^2 FOR THE FREQUENCY DISTRIBUTION OF
HEAD LENGTHS

Class Intervals	Actual Frequency f_i	Graduated Frequency f_i'	$f_i - f_i'$	$(f_i - f_i')^2$	$\dfrac{(f_i - f_i')^2}{f_i'}$
171.5–179.5	12	12.9	−.9	.81	.06
179.5–183.5	29	33.1	−4.1	16.81	.51
183.5–187.5	76	71.3	4.7	22.09	.31
187.5–191.5	104	104.2	−.2	.04	.00
191.5–195.5	110	108.8	1.2	1.44	.01
195.5–199.5	88	77.3	10.7	114.49	1.48
199.5–203.5	30	37.5	−7.5	56.25	1.50
203.5–219.5	13	16.5	−3.5	12.25	.74
Total	462	461.6			4.61

The value of χ^2 is seen to be 4.61. The number of cells is 8, but the number of degrees of freedom is not *one* less, but *three* less than 8, or 5. The reason for this is the fact that the fitted normal curve is determined by means of three parameters or statistical measures, N, $\bar{x}$, and σ_x. In other words, three conditions were imposed upon the set of variates composing the frequency distribution. Since, then, $m = 5$, we find from Table J that P is in the neighborhood of 0.47. This means that in only about 47 cases out of 100 we should expect a fit as poor as this or poorer. Thus, the hypothesis that head lengths of criminals form a normal distribution seems to be a tenable one, since the probability, 0.47, for as wide a fluctuation is reasonably large.

14. Applications to problems in association. Table XII-5 was constructed with the purpose of discovering what degree of association existed between *standards of living* and *physique*. Suppose that we arbitrarily set up the hypothesis that there is no connection between these two characteristics. Is this hypothesis valid? The Chi-square test will aid us in answering this question, one which is typical of many similar questions raised in the fields of biology and psychology in particular. Referring to the data of Table XII-5, we may say that $\frac{649}{754}$, or 86.1 per cent, of the entire group had *good* standards of living, while 13.9 per cent had *poor*. If physique and living standard were utterly independent of each other, 86.1 per cent of the 360 strong individuals, or 310, should, on the average, have good standards of living and the remaining 50 should be poor. Likewise, 86.1 per cent of the 394 weak

TABLE XIV-3

Physique	Standard of Living		Totals
	Good	Poor	
Strong.........................	$f_1 = 302$ $f_1' = 310$	$f_2 = 58$ $f_2' = 50$	360
Weak..........................	$f_3 = 347$ $f_3' = 339$	$f_4 = 47$ $f_4' = 55$	394
	649	105	754

individuals, or 339, should, on the average, have good standards and 55 poor standards. In Table XIV-3, the actual frequencies are denoted by f_1, f_2, f_3, and f_4, and the theoretical by the corresponding f_1', f_2', f_3', and f_4'. Using formula (8), where f_i' replaces Np_i, we have:

$$\chi^2 = \Sigma \frac{(f_i - f_i')^2}{f_i'}$$

$$= \frac{(-8)^2}{310} + \frac{8^2}{50} + \frac{8^2}{339} + \frac{(-8)^2}{55}$$

$$= 2.84.$$

To determine m, the number of degrees of freedom, we observe that there are 2×2, or 4, cell frequencies given, subject to the restrictions set by the marginal totals. Each row and column of two cells each must have the appropriate marginal total; also, if we know two adjacent marginal totals and one other, we know all four, for the complete total is the sum of two adjacent ones. Thus, there are really only three restrictions, and $m = 4 - 3 = 1$. Another way of determining m is to note that any single cell frequency may be assigned at will, and then the remaining three are determined by the marginal totals.

For $\chi^2 = 2.84$ and $m = 1$, we find from Table J that $P = 0.09$, approximately. The hypothesis, therefore, is not disproved, for the probability of as large a divergence from theory is about 0.09, and this is not small enough to discredit the assumption. On the other hand, this value of P does not support our hypothesis either. As a rule, values of P less than 0.02 are assumed to discredit the hypothesis. Notice that the conclusion of Section XII-16 is in accord with this, for r was found equal to -0.14.

Problems of the type just discussed can be generalized to include tables consisting of p rows of q cells each, or pq cells in all. In a $p \times q$ table, the number of conditions can be shown to be $p + q - 1$; hence, the number of degrees of freedom will be $pq - (p + q - 1) = (p - 1)(q - 1)$.

XIV—Exercises

Find the standard error of the mean for the data given in Exercises 1–6. It is suggested that exercises be selected for which $\bar{x}$ and σ_x have previously been computed. Find the standard errors for other averages as requested by your instructor.

1.   Precipitation in New York City.   (Ex. IV–7.)

2.   Maximum daily temperatures in New York City.   (Ex. IV–8.)

3.   Call discount rates.   (Ex. IV–9.)

4.   Brain-weight of Swedish males.   (Ex. IV–11.)

5.   Intelligence quotients of runaway boys.   (Ex. IV–12.)

6.   Wages of male employees.   (Ex. IV–14.)

*   *   *

7.   Find 98% fiducial limits for the arithmetic means of the distributions specified above, as requested by your instructor.

8.   Find 95% fiducial limits as in the preceding exercise.

9.   Find 99% fiducial limits as in Exercise 7.

10.   Find the standard error of the coefficient of correlation for the grades of students in anatomy and biology.   (Ex. XII–15.)

11.   Could you apply the formula for the standard error of r (a) to the data of Table XII–2?   Why? (b) To the data of Exercise XII–16?   Why?

12.   In tossing five pennies 320 times, the following results were obtained:

No. Heads	Frequency
0.	12
1.	60
2.	110
3.	75
4.	48
5.	15

Would you say that the pennies were tossed each time with equal randomness?

13.   Two pennies were tossed 1,000 times with the following results: No head—273 times; one head—451 times; two heads—276 times.   What would you say about this sample?

14.   In assigning grades to students, a teacher tries, in the long run, to distribute them as follows: A's—10%; B's—20%; C's—40%; D's—20%; F's—10%.   In a certain class of 100 students, he found that he had distributed the grades as follows: A's—8%; B's—22%; C's—46%; D's—10%; F's—14%.   Is this class a usual one?

15. A company has operated a fleet of 250 taxicabs for a good many years and has found that it has had to replace tires according to the schedule below. The company then used a new brand of tire with the results shown. What does the experience with the new brand show?

Miles of Service	No. of Tires (Experience)	No. of Tires (New Brand)
Under 16,000	20	15
16,000–18,000	70	60
18,000–20,000	110	125
20,000–22,000	210	110
22,000–24,000	240	270
24,000–26,000	190	240
26,000–28,000	130	130
28,000–30,000	30	50

* * *

Test for goodness of fit any of the frequency distributions in Exercises 16–19 which you have already graduated (according to the wish of your instructor).

16.   Taxation for school support.   (Ex. IV–10.)

17.   Brain-weight of Swedish males.   (Ex. IV–11.)

18.   Intelligence quotients of boys.   (Ex. IV–12.)

19.   Sizes of shoes worn by college girls.   (Ex. IV–13.)

* * *

Discuss, according to the χ^2-test, the significance of the data given in Exercises 20–22.

20.   Inheritance of taste deficiencies (from C. W. Cotterman and L. H. Snyder, "Tests of Simple Mendelian Inheritance in Randomly Collected Data of One and Two Generations," *Journal of the American Statistical Association*, Vol. 34, No. 207.)

Wife \ Husband	Taster	Non-Taster	Total
Taster	43	17	60
Non-Taster	13	5	18
Total	56	22	78

21. Influence of the duration of a certain mental disorder on the intelligence quotient.

Duration IQ	Below 70	70 or above	Total
Less than 10 years.........	62	55	117
More than 10 years........	44	26	70
Total.................	106	81	187

22. Effect of a new treatment on patients afflicted with a certain disease.

	Recovered	Died	Total
Treated.................	73	12	85
Not Treated.............	50	21	71
Total.................	123	33	156

REFERENCES

❖❖|||||||||||❏]||||||||||❏]||||||||||❏]||||||||||❏]||||||||||❏]||||||||||❏]||||||||||❏]||||||||||❏]||||||||||❏]||||||||||❏]||||||||||❏❖❖

GENERAL

1. Camp, Burton H., *The Mathematical Part of Elementary Statistics*, Boston, D. C. Heath, 1931.

2. Croxton, F. E., and Cowden, D. J., *Applied General Statistics*, New York, Prentice-Hall, 1939.

3. Kenney, John F., *Mathematics of Statistics*, New York, Van Nostrand, 1939.

4. Richardson, Clarence H., *An Introduction to Statistical Analysis*, Enlarged Edition, New York, Harcourt, Brace, 1935.

5. Rietz, Henry L., Editor, *Handbook of Mathematical Statistics*, Boston, Houghton Mifflin, 1924.

6. Rietz, Henry L., *Mathematical Statistics*, La Salle, Ill., Open Court, 1927.

7. Yule, G. U., and Kendall, M. G., *An Introduction to the Theory of Statistics*, London, Charles Griffin, 1937.

BIOLOGICAL STATISTICS

8. Davenport, C. B., and Ekas, M. P., *Statistical Methods in Biology, Medicine, and Psychology*, 4th ed., New York, Wiley, 1936.

9. Pearl, Raymond, *Introduction to Medical Biometry and Statistics*, Philadelphia, W. B. Saunders Co., 1930.

10. Snedecor, George W., *Statistical Methods Applied to Experiments in Agriculture and Biology*, Ames, Iowa, Collegiate Press, 1938.

11. Treloar, Alan E., *Elements of Statistical Reasoning*, New York, John Wiley, 1939.

EDUCATIONAL STATISTICS

11a. Enlow, Elmer R., *Statistics in Education and Psychology*, New York, Prentice-Hall, Inc., 1937.

12. Holzinger, Karl, *Statistical Methods for Students in Education*, Boston, Ginn, 1928.

13. Kramer, Edna E., *A First Course in Educational Statistics*, New York, John Wiley, 1935.

14. Sorenson, Herbert, *Statistics for Students of Psychology and Education*, New York, McGraw-Hill, 1936.

ECONOMIC STATISTICS

14a. Croxton, F. E., and Cowden, D. J., *Practical Business Statistics*, New York, Prentice-Hall, Inc., 1938.

15. Crum, W. L., Patton, A. C., and Tebbutt, A. R., *Introduction to Economic Statistics*, New York, McGraw-Hill, 1938.

16. Davis, H. T., and Nelson, W. F. C., *Elements of Statistics with Applications to Economic Data*, Bloomington, Ind., Principia Press, 1935.

17. Day, Edmund E., *Statistical Analysis*, New York, Macmillan, 1925.

18. Fisher, Irving, *The Making of Index Numbers*, Boston, Houghton Mifflin, 1922.

19. Persons, Warren M., *The Construction of Index Numbers*, Boston, Houghton Mifflin, 1928.

MISCELLANEOUS

20. Kurtz, A. K., and Edgerton, Harold A., *Statistical Dictionary of Terms and Symbols*, New York, John Wiley, 1939.

21. Zizek, Franz, *Statistical Averages*, New York, Henry Holt, 1913.

CHARTS, DIAGRAMS, AND GRAPHS

22. Arkin, Herbert, and Colton, Raymond R., *Graphs: How to Make and Use Them*. New York, Harper and Bros., 1936.

23. Haskell, Allan C., *Graphic Charts in Business*, 3rd ed., Norwood, Mass., Codex Book Co., 1928.

23a. Karsten, Karl G., *Charts and Graphs*, New York, Prentice-Hall, Inc., 1925.

24. Modley, Rudolf, *How to Use Pictorial Statistics*, New York, Harper and Bros., 1937.

25. Neurath, Otto, *Modern Man in the Making*, New York, Knopf, 1939.

TABLES

26. *Barlow's Tables*, ed. by L. J. Comrie, 3rd ed., Chemical Publishing Co. of New York, 1930.

27. *Crelle's Tables.* (a) Crelle, A. L., *Tables de Calcul* (photolithographic reprint), United States Geological Survey, Washington, D. C., 1918. (b) Seeliger, Oskar, *Dr. A. L. Crelle's Calculating Tables*, Berlin, Georg Reimer, 1908.

28. Fisher, R. A., and Yates, F., *Statistical Tables for Biological, Agricultural, and Medical Research*, London, Oliver and Boyd, 1938.

29. Glover, James W., *Tables of Applied Mathematics in Finance, Insurance, Statistics*, Ann Arbor, Michigan, George Wahr, 1923.

30. Kelley, Truman L., *The Kelley Statistical Tables*, New York, Macmillan, 1938.

31. Pearson, Karl, *Tables for Statisticians and Biometricians*, Cambridge University Press, 1930–1.

32. Thurstone, L. L., and others, *Computing Diagrams for the Tetrachoric Correlation Coefficient*, University of Chicago, 1933.

JOURNALS

33. *The Annals of Mathematical Statistics, Official Journal of the Institute of Mathematical Statistics.* Secretary-Treasurer, P. R. Rider, Washington University, St. Louis, Mo.

34. *Journal of the American Statistical Association*, 1626 K Street, N. W., Washington, D. C.

STATISTICAL MATERIALS AND SUPPLIES

35. Codex Book Co., Inc., 461 Eighth Avenue, New York, N. Y. Various kinds of chart and graph paper.

36. Keuffel and Esser Co., 127 Fulton Street, New York, N. Y. Slide rules; various kinds of chart and graph paper.

37. Pictorial Statistics, Inc., 142 Lexington Avenue, New York, N. Y. Various kinds of pictorial charts, maps, and ready-made symbols.

INDEX

INDEX